FRACTURE

An Advanced Treatise

Volume IV
Engineering Fracture Design

FRACTURE

An Advanced Treatise

EDITED BY

H. LIEBOWITZ

FRACTURE

An Advanced Treatise

EDITED BY

H. LIEBOWITZ

SCHOOL OF ENGINEERING AND APPLIED SCIENCE
THE GEORGE WASHINGTON UNIVERSITY
WASHINGTON, D.C.

VOLUME IV

Engineering Fracture Design

1969

ACADEMIC PRESS New York and London

ACADEMIC PRESS, INC.
111 Fifth Avenue, New York, New York 10003

United Kingdom Edition published by
ACADEMIC PRESS, INC. (LONDON) LTD.
Berkeley Square House, London W.1

LIBRARY OF CONGRESS CATALOG CARD NUMBER: 68-23499

PRINTED IN THE UNITED STATES OF AMERICA

LIST OF CONTRIBUTORS

Numbers in parentheses indicate the pages on which the authors' contributions begin.

N. R. ADSIT (69), General Dynamics Convair, San Diego, California

FRANK M. ANTHONY (275), Structural Systems Department, Bell Aerosystems Company, Division of Bell Aerospace Corporation, Buffalo, New York

RALPH L. BARNETT (173), Felt Products Mfg. Co., Skokie, Illinois

WILFRED H. DUKES (275), Structural Systems Department, Bell Aerosystems Company, Division of Bell Aerospace Corporation, Buffalo, New York

W. J. HALL (1), Department of Civil Engineering, University of Illinois, Urbana, Illinois

PAUL C. HERMANN (173), Chicago Bridge & Iron, Plainfield, Illinois

H. LIEBOWITZ (113), School of Engineering and Applied Science, The George Washington University, Washington, D.C.

W. H. MUNSE (371), Department of Civil Engineering, University of Illinois, Urbana, Illinois

JOHN E. SRAWLEY (45), National Aeronautics and Space Administration, Lewis Research Center, Cleveland, Ohio

A. A. WELLS (337), Department of Civil Engineering, The Queen's University of Belfast, Belfast, Northern Ireland

W. E. WITZELL (69), General Dynamics Convair, San Diego, California

PREFACE

A. A. Griffith is credited with contributing much of the theoretical foundations for the study of brittle fracture, from a continuum mechanics point of view. This treatise is concerned primarily with the subsequent development and current status of knowledge on sudden, catastrophic failure of structures due to unexpected brittle fracture of component materials. Griffith's two pioneering papers, published in the early 1920's, contained his proposed explanation of fracture phenomena in terms of the energy required for crack propagation. In 1926, Peirce pioneered in the application of probability methods to the study of the strength of fibers; Weibull, in 1939, was the first to apply these statistical methods to brittle fracture.

Building on the work of these pioneers, as well as on that of Theodore von Kármán, a large number of researchers began investigating various aspects of brittle fracture, and, from the 1940's on, a very large body of information on brittle fracture has developed. However, most of the research findings on brittle fracture, to date, have appeared in a somewhat piecemeal, scattered fashion, and no detailed treatment of this subject has considered adequately both the microscopic and the macroscopic viewpoints with regard to research on brittle fracture. With the large quantity of research results published, and the still larger quantity being generated, it seems timely to collect significant information and to present the fundamentals for critical evaluation of the different theories and experimental findings in this field and related ones. These results, together with their design implications, should be made available to professional engineers, students, and researchers in industrial organizations, educational and research institutions, and various governmental agencies. That is the purpose of the present treatise.

Future progress in the understanding of brittle fracture and in application of that knowledge depends largely on the successful integration of continuum mechanics with the scientific disciplines of materials science, physics, mathematics, and chemistry. Since few people have equal experience in all these fields, the text of this treatise has been designed so that the reader may acquire pertinent information by self-study. Most chapters have been written in detail and, insofar as possible, have been made to fill a significant gap by also providing, when appropriate, the details of complicated and involved mathematical derivations in appendixes. Whenever possible, only a level of college calculus on the part of the reader has been assumed. Numerical examples showing the engineering applications have been included; also, photographs and drawings have been greatly utilized for illustrative purposes. Whenever possible and appropriate, reference has been made to both the theoretical and experimental results and also to the interrelationship between the microscopic and macroscopic viewpoints. Of particular importance are the sections near the end of each chapter identifying the technical problems and the specific research areas where efforts are required to fill present and anticipated gaps in our understanding of the subject.

Throughout, an attempt has been made to integrate the atomistic and continuum approaches as much as possible, particularly by inviting many outstanding people in the fields of structures and materials to contribute. In this way, it is hoped that an effective interdisciplinary approach has been achieved.

Seven major areas are covered in this treatise on fracture. They are: (1) microscopic and macroscopic fundamentals of fracture; (2) mathematical fundamentals of fracture; (3) engineering fundamentals of fracture and environmental effects; (4) engineering fracture design (this volume); (5) fracture design of structures; (6) fracture of metals; and (7) fracture of nonmetals and composites.

The first chapter of this volume, by W. J. Hall, deals with the evaluation of fracture tests. He begins by offering observations on the philosophy of testing and continues with descriptions of 11 types of tests commonly employed for steel, with examples of the types of data obtained. For the most part, the discussion centers about the types of tests associated with the transition temperature concept. Factors that play an important role in testing and interpretation are defined; namely, the effects of welding procedures, residual stress, flaws, and instrumentation. The chapter closes with a survey of techniques for interpreting test results.

John E. Srawley's review of plane strain fracture toughness, Chapter 2, outlines, first, the general concept of the K_{Ic} plane strain fracture toughness, and then examines in detail the current (tentative) standard procedure for determination of K_{Ic} with crack-notched bend specimens. The standard procedure constitutes an operational definition of K_{Ic} which is somewhat arbitrary, but no more than is the definition of offset yield strength. Experimental data for high-strength steels, titanium, and aluminum alloys validate the standard procedure for determination of K_{Ic} and confirm that it is reasonable to regard K_{Ic} as an inherent material property which controls fracture under conditions of sufficiently high constraint.

However, the required specimen dimensions increase in proportion to the square of the ratio of K_{Ic} to yield strength, and impractically large specimens may be required for tough, low-strength materials. The chapter ends with guides for adapting the standard test procedure to other types of specimens.

Chapter 3 is an analysis, by W. E. Witzell and N. R. Adsit, of temperature effects on fracture. Their attention is directed primarily to testing at cryogenic temperatures, because fractures tend to be catastrophic in the low temperature ranges. Various specimen configurations are considered for use at cryogenic temperatures: tensile and notched tensile, center notched, single edge notched, surface notched, and slow bend. Problems peculiar to temperature testing are also examined. Strength and toughness values are presented for various engineering alloys tested at cryogenic temperatures. The behavior of several 300-series stainless steels at temperatures between 1200° and −423° F is considered, and several aluminum and titanium alloys are examined at cryogenic temperatures. A compilation of recent work primarily by H. Liebowitz, W. D. Claus, Jr., D. W. Harris, R. J. Sanford, and H. Vanderveldt on the fracture and carrying capacity of long, slender columns and related topics is presented by H. Liebowitz in Chapter 4. These studies were concerned with notched and unnotched columns subjected to concentric and eccentric axial compressive loading. The effects of cracks having different depths and root radii were determined on the maximum load-carrying capacity of long and short columns with notches on one side and on two opposite sides of these columns. Results indicate that the maximum load-carrying capacity of eccentrically loaded columns having slenderness ratios less than 250 may be reduced significantly, particularly when these columns contain fatigue cracks or notches with a root radius smaller than 0.003 inch. Different failure criteria were examined for columns under applied simultaneous compression and bending loads. Four methods are used to analyze the failure data. Results obtained for the specific aluminum columns investigated indicated that the energy required to initiate crack propagation may be stated approximately as an exponential function of crack length, and that stress-intensity factors calculated for the limiting case where $\rho = 0$, and using Neuber's (1937) expressions for maximum stress and appropriate values of the nominal stress, appear to form a basis for a valid fracture toughness analysis.

Prestressing of monolithic and segmented elements in high performance brittle materials gives rise to special problems such as nonlinear response, statistical behavior, and transverse cracking under axial compression. These problems are investigated by Ralph L. Barnett and Paul C. Hermann, in Chapter 5, in connection with beams, columns, and plates, and experimental evidence is offered to support theories proposed for describing the strength and stiffness of these elements. Many examples are included to illuminate the singular characteristics associated with prestressed structures.

In Chapter 6, Wilfred H. Dukes and Frank M. Anthony explore the problem of designing reliable structural joints and attachments for structural components fabricated from nonmetallic refractory materials. Such materials fail mechanically in a completely brittle manner, and successful design with this class of material requires many departures from conventional practices used for metallic materials. These departures are discussed and form the basis for a design philosophy appropriate to the use of brittle materials. It is shown that brittle materials are prone to fail at points of stress concentration, which means that an appropriately refined stress analysis method is required so that peak stresses can be determined. Also inherent in these materials and developing from their brittleness is a wide variability in mechanical properties for nominally identical specimens. This leads to a statistical definition of strength in which stress level is associated with the probability of failure. Special attention must also be given to the definition of loads, particularly those created by internal restraints and by deformation of supporting structures. Other areas where the use of brittle materials requires a different design approach include design criteria, where the conventional safety factors must be replaced by an acceptable failure probability, and the specification of material failure modes, particularly under complex stress systems. The designer must also pay particular attention to material processing and quality control to a degree which is unnecessary with metallic materials. The chapter next considers joining methods and describes potential applications for refractory nonmetallic materials, principally in the high temperature areas of high performance aerospace structures. Specific joining methods appropriate to each application are described. The design problems associated with each of these methods are reviewed; it is shown that these will generally involve (1) eliminating constraints against deformation and, hence, avoiding unknown induced loads and (2) properly defining the areas of peak stress. Another section of the chapter presents the special methods of analysis required. The method of carrying out a failure probability analysis for a brittle component is given, and it is supplemented with charts to facilitate the numerical calculations. The finite element method of stress analysis, which is necessary to obtain a sufficiently detailed analysis of stresses in a brittle component of complex shape, is described, and numerous references are given from which this analytical capability can be established. However, because this technique requires an extensive computer capability which is not available to all agencies, a stress-concentration method of stress analysis is described and, again, supplemented with design charts which facilitate making the numerical calculations. Chapter 6 ends with an accounting of all examples which have been found in the open literature of joints and connections made with brittle materials. In those examples where comparisons between analysis and test can be made, the test results justify surprisingly well the design approach presented in this chapter.

A. A. Wells explores the effects of residual stress on brittle fracture. In his chapter, he notes that the usual definitions of applied stresses and residual stresses, arising from incompatibilities of strain in a body, are considered to depend on arbitrary definition of the boundaries of the body, from which it is argued that the fracture response of the material must be the same for each. Examples of residual stress systems are described, such as bolted, riveted, and welded joints, shrink fits, lack of fit in assembly, and rolled, peened, and differentially hardened surfaces, illustrating the extent to which residual stresses are susceptible to control and are often beneficial. The mechanisms of residual and reaction stress accumulation in welded joints are described in a semiquantitative manner to show, in particular, the influence of the equalization temperature and plastic yielding. The effects of residual stress on brittle fracture in casualties are illustrated in terms of nucleating defects and spontaneous cracking. The Fawley oil storage tank is identified as a model casualty, susceptible to exact analysis, providing the key to laboratory study by notched and welded wide-plate tests. The results of those summarized also contribute to knowledge of the effects of furnace and mechanical stress relief and of multirun welds in thick plates, and show that local damage at the nucleating flaw from thermal strain activated plastic flow is at least as important as elastic residual stress in producing spontaneous or low-stress fractures. The methods of linear fracture mechanics are used to study crack propagation and arrest in low-stress fractures of notched and welded wide plates, such that the applied and residual elastic stress contributions to fracture are quantitatively compared; and the metallurgical nature of the local embrittlement is identified and its influence on toughness estimated. It is shown that critical fracture conditions depend on balance between the static loading toughness in the damaged region and the propagation resistance, as affected by strain rate in the undamaged material beyond. Optimum conditions for furnace, mechanical, and local thermal stress relief are quantitatively described. It is considered that the topic of welding residual stresses is now of waning research interest, having been overtaken by a demand for investigation of the morphology of defect growth and local thermal damage in low-alloy steels of structural quality.

In the concluding chapter, W. H. Munse presents an analysis of the problem of brittle fracture in weldments. Welding, when it was introduced, made possible many improvements in the fabrication of metal structures;

however, it increased also the frequency with which brittle fractures have occurred in such structures. As a result, a great need has existed for a better understanding of the basic factors that determine when a brittle fracture will or will not initiate. Consideration is given primarily to the problem of low-stress fracture and the conditions necessary for such fractures. In brittle fractures of weldments, weld quality, residual welding stresses, and the weld properties are important factors and must be examined in detail. The weld itself, as well as the fusion zone, the heat-affected zone, the thermally affected zone, and the base metal are considered with respect to their toughness. In addition, consideration is given to the various ways in which these regions or zones in a weldment may be embrittled or affected by various welding processes, procedures, and treatments. Finally, the question of designing to protect against brittle fracture is discussed.

November, 1968   H. LIEBOWITZ

CONTENTS

Chapter 4. **Fracture and Carrying Capacity of Notched Columns**

H. Liebowitz

Chapter 5. **Prestressed Brittle Structures**

Ralph L. Barnett and Paul C. Hermann

Chapter 6. **Design of Attachments and Connections with Brittle Materials**

Wilfred H. Dukes and Frank M. Anthony

Chapter 7. **Effects of Residual Stress on Brittle Fracture**

A. A. Wells

Chapter 8. **Brittle Fracture in Weldments**

W. H. Munse

CHAPTER 1

EVALUATION OF FRACTURE TESTS AND SPECIMEN PREPARATION

W. J. Hall

Abstract: Factors affecting the evaluation of fracture tests receive general attention in this chapter. The discussion begins with observations on the philosophy of testing; this is followed by a brief description of 11 types of tests commonly employed for steel, with examples of the types of data obtained. For the most part, the discussion in this chapter centers about those types of tests associated with the transition temperature concept. The topic of fracture mechanics testing, of obvious importance, receives only limited attention because other chapters in this treatise are devoted solely to this complex topic. Brief comments are offered about factors that play an important role in testing and interpretation; namely, the effects of welding procedures, residual stress, flaws, and instrumentation. The last major section discusses techniques for interpreting the test results and factors that must be considered in such interpretation.

1

I. Introduction

One of the keys to successful applied materials technology is knowing when and what to test, for testing is expensive and time consuming and, often, may not supply the information sought. Among the many reasons that can be cited for carrying out a test program are the following:

1. To evaluate the basic behavioral properties of a new material in different environments and loadings, i.e., to obtain the data required for design purposes. As an example, the development of a new steel alloy material generally would include a spectrum of tests of many types to provide the basic engineering data required for design and to demonstrate that the material possesses the desired properties.

2. To rate, through the use of some criterion of design significance, a number of materials relative to each other, or alternatively different batches of a given material as, for example, steel plates from different heats.

3. To maintain quality control, either at the source of the material, as an acceptance-type test, or at the fabricating site. This procedure might involve the testing of samples taken from the fabricated product in a regular or random pattern or, alternatively, involve nondestructive tests.

4. To proof-test (where the word "proof" is associated more with an acceptance criterion) as, for example, the pressure test of a vessel prior to acceptance. Often, such a test serves simultaneously as a form of mechanical stress relief, especially if carried out properly.

5. To examine the material properties of a fabricated piece or structure that has failed, in a search for clues as to the reasons for the failure.

6. For research purposes, in studying various phenomena (effects of crack length, flaw size, residual stress, microstructure variations, etc.), in devising new techniques for evaluation, etc.

One of the major problems associated with conducting any type of test is deciding what to measure, how to measure it, and how to interpret the measurements. Rather obviously, the selected test must involve the item being studied; for example, the fracture properties of a weld zone joining two pieces of plate cannot be inferred from base plate material studies solely. And, in interpreting fracture research results, it is important to remember that the goal is to evaluate the response and environment for situations where the material or detail can be employed successfully, as well as those situations where it cannot be so employed.

Test data alone will rarely provide all the information necessary for successful design. Design, or even the evaluation of a failure, requires use of all available information in addition to any test data as, for example, applicable theoretical considerations, metallurgical considerations, knowledge of the manufacturing controls and inspection techniques employed at the time of fabrication and periodically thereafter, knowledge of the service environment, and knowledge of the maintenance procedures.

The published literature in the field of brittle fracture of metals comprises thousands of articles and many books covering discussions of test data, theoretical considerations, casualty data, etc. Typical of the books available on brittle fracture and general applied fracture concepts are those by Murray (1952), Parker (1957), Shank (1957), Averbach *et al.* (1959), Rühl (1959), Biggs (1960), Tipper (1962), ASME (1964), Szczepanski (1963), Drucker and Gilman (1963), ASTM (1965), and Hall *et al.* (1967). Among the better known references describing failures and followup interpretive studies are those of Shank (1954), Acker (1953), Puzak *et al.* (1958), Pellini and Puzak (1963a), Boyd (1962), Larson and Carr (1964), and the British Engine Boiler Co. (1962). Since 1959, Subcommission D of Commission IX of the International Institute of Welding has compiled summaries of casualty data; these are regularly reported in IIW publications. The references cited provide a review of the available information at the time they were prepared. Such references are especially helpful in tracing the available literature on fracture, for, in view of the immense amount of available literature, without a guide as provided by these books, the interested researcher would be at a loss in trying to trace many valuable studies.

No attempt is made herein to summarize in depth the voluminous fracture test data available in the literature, for there are more than 50 major types of tests or variations of tests that have been used extensively in the applied fracture field. Moreover, almost every paper in this present treatise deals with a topic that is of importance, in terms of interpretation of fracture test results.

With this realization, then, it was decided that this chapter might best provide an introduction to test data interpretation by describing briefly in Sect. II some of the testing methods currently employed, with a few illustrative examples of the types of data obtained. Some of the tests described are those that are employed for quality-control and acceptance-test purposes, while others are of a more basic research type.

Sections III and IV offer brief comment on the role of welding, residual stress flaws, selection of test specimens, and instrumentation. Section V is devoted to a discussion of the interpretation of test results. The chapter concludes with a few comments on recommended studies and a brief summary.

The discussion in subsequent sections centers largely around those tests and data employed in transition-temperature-type approaches. Obviously, in any such presentation, the developing field of fracture mechanics must receive mention, as it does. However, no great detail on fracture mechanics tests is given here, since it is covered in depth elsewhere in this treatise by Srawley, Irwin, Corten, and others, which the reader is urged to consult for a comprehensive overview of the fracture mechanics area.

II. Some Test Methods and Typical Data

In the early decades of the 20th century, when notch brittleness was recognized as a problem of design significance, a number of different types of tests were devised. Generally, these tests involved notched bars tested at various temperatures and loaded in tension or bending by either a slowly or rapidly applied load. When brittle fracture was finally recognized to be a serious strength problem, especially during World War II, a number of different types of tests were developed and employed for material evaluation purposes; many of these have been standardized. Most of the test techniques employed during the past two decades can be traced through the books cited in the introduction to this chapter.

The test methods described below are typical of those that have been employed in practice and research during the last decade and will serve as a basis for later discussion concerning interpretation of test results.

A. CHARPY TEST

Of tests employed for measuring notch sensitivity, the Charpy test is one of the most widely used techniques both in the United States and overseas. The conventional testing machine employs a swinging pendulum which generally has a total available striking energy of 220 ft-lb or less, as requirements dictate. The Charpy test has been so widely adopted that ASTM (1966) Standard E-23 was issued covering preparation and testing of Charpy specimens. The two most common types of specimens employed with the Charpy test in recent years have been the V-notch and keyhole-notch specimens, as shown in Fig. 1. The specimen is machined from the plate or other piece of material for which the test is being made, is cooled to the desired temperature, and is placed in the machine in a manner permitting it to be supported on both sides as a beam. The specimen is broken by a single blow of the pendulum applied to the middle of the specimen and opposite the notch; as the pendulum swings on through, a recording dial indicates the absorbed energy.

Normally, three specimens are tested at a given temperature, and tests are made at selected temperatures. A curve can then be sketched through the mean values at the various temperatures to give a plot of absorbed

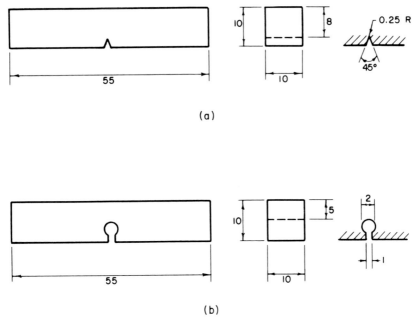

Fig. 1. Charpy specimens. (a) V-notch; (b) keyhole notch. Note: All dimensions in millimeters; not to scale.

energy versus temperature, as shown at the top of Fig. 2 for A-212B firebox-quality steel. The other criteria which are commonly employed for use with a Charpy specimen are also shown in Fig. 2; namely, the lateral expansion, as measured at the compression side of the specimen (or alternatively the lateral contraction at the notch), and the percentage of shear evident from the fractured surface. Also shown in Fig. 2 are typical results for a specimen with its long axis oriented transversely to the major direction of rolling for the plate, i.e., the specimen fracture plane lies in the direction of rolling. For this plate, the energy absorption for the transversely oriented specimen is observed to be less than that for the longitudinally oriented specimen. Thus, the "weak" direction, as given by this criterion, is evident.

Normally, there will be a variation in Charpy data for specimens taken from different regions of a plate, from different plates of a given heat of steel of the same thickness, and even more so from plates of different thicknesses (the thickness reflecting the amount of working of the metal) from a given heat. As an illustration, the median Charpy curves for various thicknesses of plate are shown in Fig. 3, along with two curves for 1-inch-thick plate from different heats, all for A-212B firebox-quality steel.

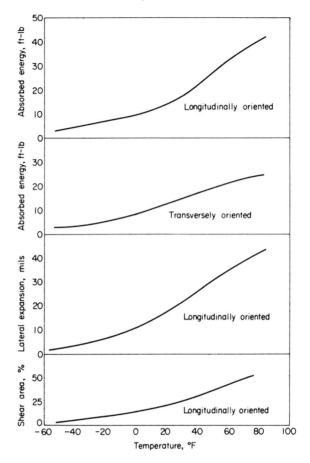

F_{IG}. 2. Charpy V-notch data for A-212B steel (Hall *et al.*, 1962).

The effect of varying the location of the specimen in the plate thickness is also graphically illustrated for $1\frac{5}{8}$-inch-thick specimens.

Occasionally, Charpy tests are employed to obtain an estimate of the embrittlement that occurs in the thermally affected zone around a weld. An example of the trend that may be observed in such cases is shown in Fig. 4. The shaded band represents the variation in Charpy-V data observed for 1-inch plates from two different heats of A-212B steel used on a research program, and is an illustration of the wide variation in Charpy data that can be obtained for a given material. The other curves identified in Fig. 4 illustrate the shift in transition temperature observed for specimens which had been preheated during the welding, thermally stress relieved at 1150° F for 1 hour following welding, and mechanically stress relieved by mechanical straining of 0.6% at room temperature following welding.

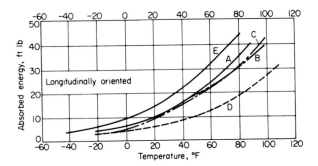

FIG. 3. Charpy V-notch data for plates of varying thickness for A-212B steel (Hall *et al.*, 1965). KEY: A, plate S11, 1 inch thick; B, plate S8, ¾ inch thick; C, plate S15 (mid-thickness), 1⅜ inch thick; D, plate S15 (near plate face), 1⅜ inch thick; E, 1-inch thick plate, from first phase of the program.

The most common interpretation of the Charpy data involves the transition range over which the absorbed energy drops from a high value to a low value, commonly called the transition temperature range. Some acceptance specifications call for a minimum absorbed energy value at a given temperature; for example, at least a 15 ft-lb energy level at 25° F. The top curve in Fig. 2 meets this criterion, while the second from the top (transverse orientation) does not. The specification of fixed energy levels, such as 15 ft-lb, for all types of steels is now recognized to be improper for the simple reason that there are great variations in the transition ranges and in

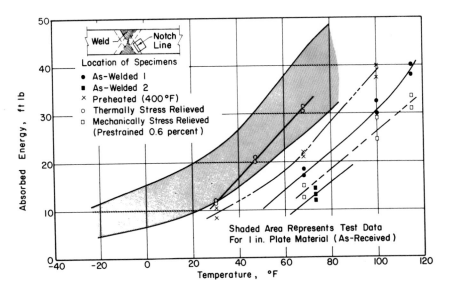

FIG. 4. Charpy V-notch data for plate material near weld (Nordell and Hall, 1965).

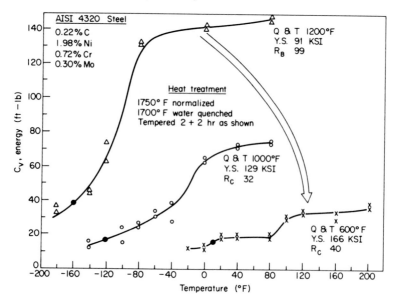

FIG. 5. Change in Charpy V-notch curve with change in strength of Q & T steel (Pellini and Puzak, 1963b).

the shelf values corresponding to both low-temperature (brittle) and high-temperature (ductile) behavior. One of the most graphic illustrations of this trend is shown in Fig. 5, wherein the tremendous change in upper shelf value that occurs for AISI 4320 steel with different heat treatments is demonstrated. These curves also illustrate the variation in temperature range over which the transition can take place or, in other words, the variation in steepness of the transition range that may be observed.

B. SLOW-BEND TESTS

A number of slow-bend tests involving plate specimens have been employed for evaluating the ductility of the specimen prior to fracture. The measurements in these commonly include the fracture appearance (percentage shear), depth of brittle zone, central deflection, load, or area under the load-deflection curve. Each test is run at a constant temperature and the measurements are recorded as a function of temperature. From these data, a temperature-transition plot may be constructed for evaluating brittle-to-ductile behavior.

One of the most widely used bend tests is the van der Veen test (de Graaf and van der Veen, 1953), in which specimens of full plate thickness (*t*) are employed. Generally, in the middle of the specimen, which is about

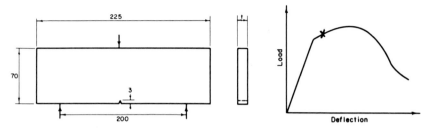

FIG. 6. Van der Veen test specimen and load-deflection diagram (de Graaf and van der Veen, 1953). Note: all dimensions are in millimeters; not to scale.

9 inches long, 2.75 inches deep, and of full plate thickness, a 3-mm sharp groove is made with an angle between the groove walls of 45° (see Fig. 6a). The specimen is normally loaded at the center. A typical load-deflection curve for a ductile specimen appears in Fig. 6b. A brittle specimen might fail after only a small amount of central deflection as, for example, at the point marked by an X on the diagram.

There are many other slow-bend tests, such as the Matton–Sjöberg slow-bend test, the MIT slow-bend test, the Lehigh slow-bend test, and the Kinzel test, for which descriptions can be found in the books referred to in the introduction.

C. Drop-Weight Test

The drop-weight test, developed by Pellini and Puzak (1963a) at the U.S. Naval Research Laboratory, employs special beam specimens in which a material crack is created in the tensile surface at an early time interval during the test. The test piece is generally about 14 inches long, 3.5 inches wide, and between 0.5 and 1 inch thick. A weld deposit is placed at the center of the specimen and notched to provide the initiation source. The drop-weight test is conducted by subjecting each of a series of specimens of a given material to a single impact load at selected temperatures to determine the maximum temperature at which there is a break (go) or no-break (no-go) condition. The impact load is provided by a guided free-falling weight with an energy between 250 and 1200 ft-lb, depending on the yield strength of the steel to be tested and the size of the specimen. The specimens are not allowed to deflect more than a few tenths of an inch before they reach a stop.

The details of the drop-weight test apparatus are shown in Fig. 7. In this figure, D_a represents the distance from the bottom of the unloaded specimen to the anvil stop, T represents the thickness of the specimen, and D_c is representative of the deflection of the specimen at the time cracking

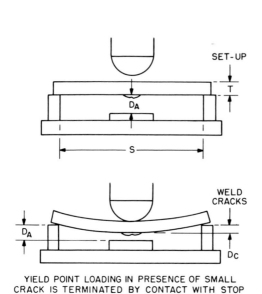

SET-UP

T

D_A

S

WELD
CRACKS

D_A

D_C

YIELD POINT LOADING IN PRESENCE OF SMALL
CRACK IS TERMINATED BY CONTACT WITH STOP

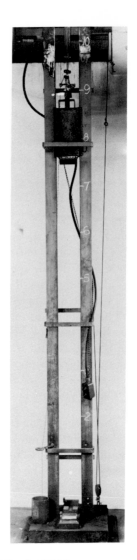

FIG. 7. Drop-weight test apparatus (Pellini and Puzak, 1963a).

normally starts. ASTM (1966) Specification E208-66T describes in detail the provisions for conducting and interpreting such tests. The nil-ductility transition (NDT) temperature is defined as the maximum temperature at which a standard drop-weight specimen breaks when tested in accordance with the provisions of the drop-weight test. A typical drop-weight test series indicating an NDT at 10° F is illustrated in Fig. 8. The sharp transition from "break" to "no break" at the NDT temperature results from

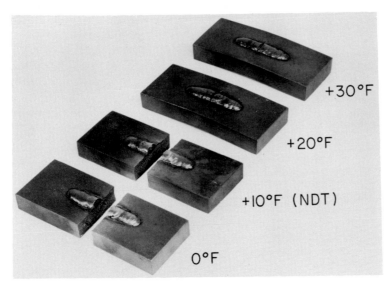

+30°F

+20°F

+10°F (NDT)

0°F

FIG. 8. Typical drop-weight specimens illustrating 10° F NDT (Pellini and Puzak, 1963a).

the increase in the levels of deformation required for fracture initiation and propagation at temperatures above the NDT.

At the present time, the NDT temperature, as determined from the drop-weight test, provides a reference temperature that is much used in certain elements of the steel fabrication industry.

D. EXPLOSION CRACK-STARTER TEST

This test, devised by Pellini and Puzak (1963a) of the U.S. Naval Research Laboratory, was developed to investigate the tendency to brittleness for steels that are to be welded. The test plate, of full thickness and about 14 × 14 inches in plan dimension, has a short crack starter weld bead, which is notched, deposited on one side, just as in the case of the drop-weight test. The plate is then placed over a circular die, as illustrated in Fig. 9, an explosive wafer is detonated a short distance above the plate, and the expanding gas pressure loads the plate. As a result of the explosion, the plate is deformed, permitting the fracture characteristics to be studied. The test is carried out at a number of temperatures.

A dramatic illustration of the effects of such loading on World War II ship plate steel is presented in Fig. 10, which shows pictures of the deformed plates after loading at 20° temperature intervals. The NDT for this particular plate was 20° F. It will be noted that, at this temperature, the plate

Fig. 9. Explosion bulge test apparatus (courtesy P.P. Puzak).

12

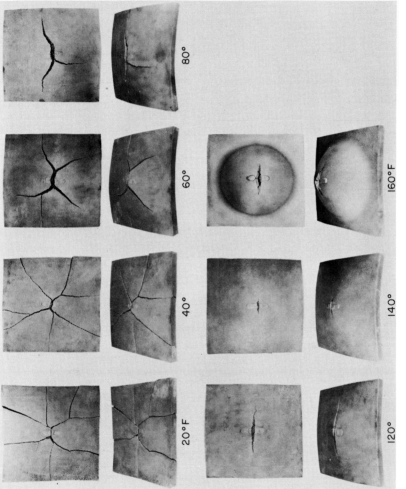

FIG. 10. Explosion crack-starter test series with NDT of 20° F (Pellini and Puzak, 1963a).

breaks in a flat fashion, and, above the NDT temperature, the plates bulge and undergo considerable plastic strain before fracturing or tearing.

An illustration of the relationship between the drop-weight and explosion tests is presented in Fig. 11, along with a conceptual sketch of the relationship of such test data to the crack-arrest temperature (CAT) curve corresponding to the condition in which flaws do not run.

This particular type of test has been especially valuable also in studying the strength of plates containing welds, and fractured specimens illustrating this type of behavior are shown in Fig. 12. The specimen pictured in Fig. 12a depicts a low-energy tear fracture in the heat-affected zone of a quenched and tempered steel weldment, while that in Fig. 12b represents the high fracture toughness characteristic of properly welded HY-80 steel. These two photographs dramatically illustrate the difference in behavior that can be expected with weldments under the conditions noted.

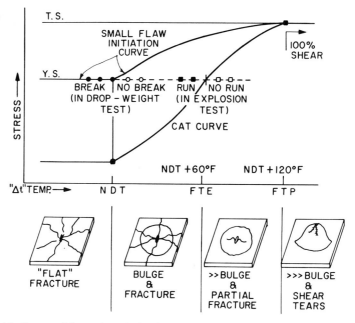

FIG. 11. Drop-weight and explosion crack starter test series related to generalized fracture diagram (Pellini and Puzak, 1963a).

E. DROP-WEIGHT TEAR TEST AND EXPLOSION TEAR TEST

In the last few years, the Naval Research Laboratory group has been developing two new types of tests which should lead to better correlation than is presently possible between laboratory evaluation and service per-

(a)

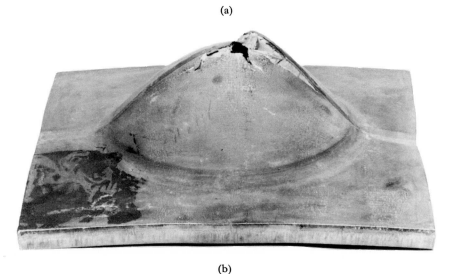

(b)

FIG. 12. Explosion crack-starter test of weldments (Pellini and Puzak, 1963b). (a) Low-energy tear fracture in Q & T steel weldment. (b) High fracture toughness of properly welded HY-80 specimen.

formance. The results of these studies are described in a continuing series of reports as, for example, Pellini *et al.* (1965) and Goode *et al.* (1966).

The initial drop-weight tear test specimen (DWTT), as shown in the top of Fig. 13, employed a notched brittle cast-steel bar that was welded to the bottom of the test specimen. Certain difficulties were experienced with this type of specimen, and the specimen shown in the bottom of Fig. 13 was developed for use with certain steels. The latter DWTT specimen

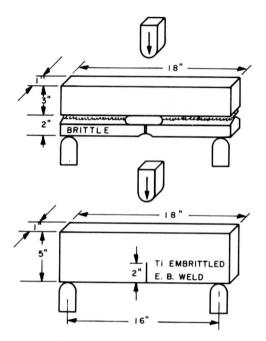

Fɪɢ. 13. Drop-weight tear test (DWTT) specimen design (Pellini *et al.*, 1965).

employs a narrow electron-beam weld which is embrittled through the plate. Subsequently, V-notch side grooves are cut along the embrittled weld to reduce the initiation energy to a low level of approximately 400 ft-lb. Typical fractures of the electron-beam-embrittled weld design DWTT specimen are shown in Fig. 14 for both a fracture-tough steel (top) and a brittle steel (bottom). The data obtained from the DWTT are of the type shown in the bottom three curves of Fig. 15. The two upper curves in that figure represent Charpy-V data in both the strong and weak directions for the particular metal under study, and illustrate the differences in the transition temperature ranges that are commonly observed when different types of tests are employed. Also of interest in Fig. 15 is the position of the NDT temperature, which corresponds quite closely to the lower shelf for the DWTT specimen but falls at high levels on the Charpy curves. This diagram illustrates well the fact that there are no hard and fast rules that can be applied in all cases in correlating findings between the various tests, as will be discussed in Sect. V.

Another new test is the explosion tear test (ETT), which is a variation of the explosion crack-starter test described previously, and is run in essentially the same manner. The plate specimen has saw cuts along one edge,

FIG. 14. Fractures of electron beam embrittled weld design (Pellini *et al.*, 1965).

which reduce the restraint in that direction, leading to more "one-way" deformation. The plate specimen is provided with a through-the-thickness sharp crack of length equal to twice the plate thickness, with embrittling carried out most recently by the electron beam brittle welding technique

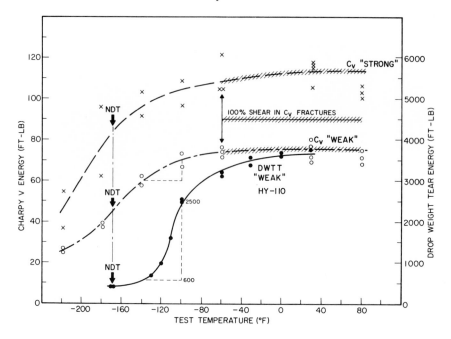

FIG. 15. Comparison of DWTT and Charpy V-notch data for steel heat treated to 110 ksi yield strength (Pellini *et al.*, 1965).

described for the DWTT. The ETT is used to delineate the strain levels at which various types of fracture occur, and thereby permits further correlation or "indexing" with the other test data, such as those obtained with the DWTT.

Three levels of ETT performance for 1-inch-thick plate are illustrated in Fig. 16. The bottom specimen in the figure illustrates "flat break" fracture propagation at low gross strain levels and essentially elastic loading. The middle specimen illustrates a partial fracture for a steel at a strain level of about 3 to 5%. The top specimen of HY-80 steel showed extreme fracture toughness with five blows causing incremental propagation each time and the final deformation being about 10 to 12%.

The tests just described are being employed for a wide variety of materials, including steel, titanium, and aluminum, and are being closely correlated with metallurgical and fracture analysis studies in order to provide better guides for selection and evaluation of materials.

F. ROBERTSON TEST

The Robertson test specimen pictured in Fig. 17 consists of a central test piece with an obtrusion on one end in which a hole is drilled and a small

FIG. 16. Explosion tear test specimens of 1-inch thick plate (Pellini *et al.*, 1965).

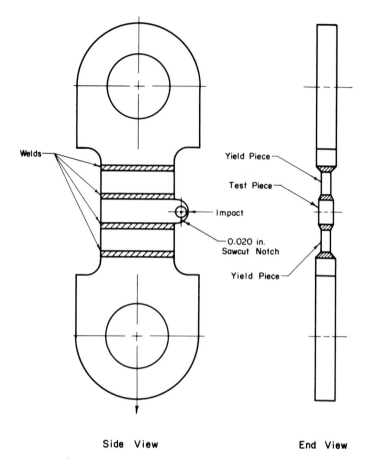

Side View   End View

Fig. 17. Robertson specimen (Cowan and Vaughan, 1962).

saw-cut notch made. The specimen is usually in contact with liquid nitrogen on the initiation edge, where an impact is applied by an explosive bolt gun for fracture initiation. A gas flame or other heat source is applied to the far side, which results in a temperature gradient being set up across the specimen. The specimen is loaded in tension, the gun fired, and the position of fracture arrest of the crack front noted. Results typical of those reported by Robertson and his colleagues are shown in Fig. 18. In general, the data are presented in terms of fracture stress versus temperature at the point of arrest, which results in a go- or no-go-type plot, as shown. In Fig. 18, the data are shown for temperature gradient tests as just described, as well as for isothermal tests. In an isothermal test, a constant temperature is main-

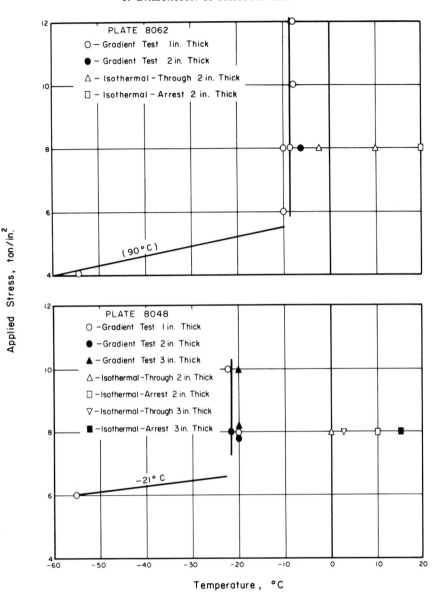

FIG. 18. Robertson crack-arrest data (Cowan and Vaughan, 1962).

tained across the specimen, and the go, no-go data are obtained by successively increasing the stress level to fill out the diagram. The results of these tests, then, provide a temperature value associated with fracture arrest as a function of applied stress level.

G. Esso Test

The Esso test is similar, in many respects, to the Robertson test. After considerable experimentation, the specimen was more or less standardized at about 16 inches wide and 1 inch thick, and has the general form shown in Fig. 19. The specimen is cooled uniformly across the plate, stressed to the desired loading, and the fracture initiated by a wedge driven into a notch cut in the edge of the plate. The data resulting from this type of test are essentially similar in nature to those just described for the Robertson

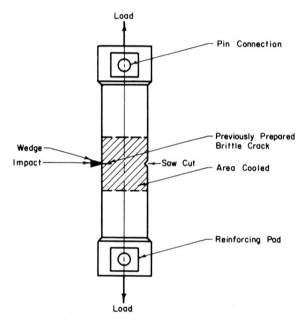

Fig. 19. Early SOD test specimen (Feely *et al.*, 1954).

test. The Esso brittle temperature, or SOD temperature, as it is commonly denoted, refers to the lowest temperature at which a crack does not propagate completely across a plate at a net average stress of 18,000 psi. Again, this is an arrest-type test associated with a go, no-go transition temperature and an applied stress level.

H. Notched and Welded Plate Tests

In the last 15 years, an extensive series of tests of notched and welded plates have been conducted, initially in England by Wells (1956), in Japan by Kihara *et al.* (1959), and, more recently, in the United States by

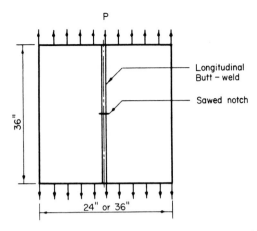

FIG. 20. Notched and welded plate specimen (Hall *et al.*, 1962).

Hall *et al.* (1962). There have been many variations in the type of specimen employed, but, in general, the specimens have followed along the lines
of that shown in Fig. 20, which consists of two plate halves beveled on the
edge, centrally notched, and subsequently welded, resulting in a notch in
the welded specimen of the type shown in Fig. 21. A test of this type of
specimen consists of cooling the specimen to the desired temperature and
then stressing the plate until it fractures; fracture initiation occurs statically
at the notch, and no external energy source is employed. The residual
stress field resulting from the welding plays a significant role in producing
a static-type initiation and subsequent propagation. This type of specimen
has been particularly successful for studying low-stress fractures, that is,
fracture at a low average applied stress, and has been helpful in evaluating
certain problems concerned with fracture of weldments, an area which has
not received as much attention to date as it deserves. What is probably the
most complete description of data resulting from this type of test appears
in Chapter 3 of the book by Hall *et al.* (1967); typical data are presented for

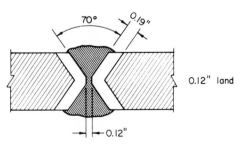

FIG. 21. Notch geometry (Hall and Chamberlain, 1966).

most of the variations of this type of test that have been carried out, both in the United States and abroad. Typical of the data that are obtained from welded wide-plate tests are those presented in Fig. 22; the plot includes some of the Japanese test results from welded plates as well as some data from the Esso test that was mentioned earlier. It will be noted that the stress-temperature transition for the welded plates occurs slightly to the left of that found for the Esso test, a common observation.

In this particular type of specimen, many factors can be studied, including the effects of various welding procedures, different types of stress

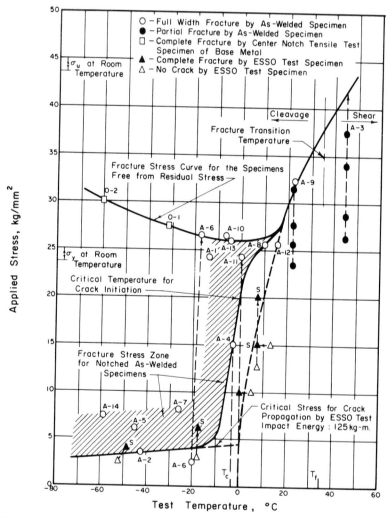

FIG. 22. Tensile tests of centrally notched as-welded specimens (Kihara *et al.*, 1959).

relief (for example, preheat, thermal postheating, and mechanical straining), and, of course, different types of notches. Low-stress brittle fracture has been found to occur in these specimens, generally in conjunction with high residual stresses resulting from welding. The specimens generally undergo a single-stage fracture, meaning that the fracture rapidly propagates completely across both halves of the specimen; in many cases, two-stage fracturing occurs, in which a short arrested crack occurs at a low load and subsequent fracture generally occurs at a later time, at or near a stress level approaching general yield. Typical of two-stage fracturing is that for Specimen A6 in Fig. 22, which shows two test points connected by a dotted line; a low-stress fracture occurred at $-20°$ C at about 2.5 kg/mm^2, and secondary fracture occurred later, with further loading, at about 27 kg/mm^2. Full-width fractures occur in these tests quite often at low applied stress, on the order of 5 to 7 ksi, but, of course, in the presence of higher tensile residual stress systems. One possible design approach often considered for the brittle or frangible regions is to reduce the service stress to so low a value that propagation cannot be sustained. In almost all cases, this is infeasible, economically, and the better approach of upgrading the selected material is adopted.

I. WIDE-PLATE TESTS

Beginning with the World War II casualty investigations, an extensive series of very-wide-plate tests has been carried out to study the effects of notches and plate width, and to study, in some detail, the characteristics of propagating and arresting cracks. These tests are largely of a research nature, aimed at obtaining basic data on fracture speed, strain fields surrounding a propagating crack tip, and (in the case of arrest tests) the possibility of using various types of welded strakes to arrest cracks, or, alternatively, to evaluate crack arrestors made up of riveted strakes. Figure 23 shows a wide-plate test in progress, and Fig. 24 illustrates one type of information obtained from this type of test; namely, the strain versus time history as a fracture propagates across a wide plate. A plot illustrating the major principal strain surrounding a propagating brittle fracture is presented in Fig. 25; these data were obtained from a number of essentially identical wide-plate tests, with the strain data superimposed to obtain the strain pattern. In the wide-plate tests, measurements of crack speed show that the fractures ran at speeds as high as 4000 to 6000 fps; on the other hand, in wide-plate tests involving residual stress fields of both tensile and compressive nature, speeds as low as 50 fps were recorded in some plates, as the crack ran through the initial compressive strain field. A brief summary of the results of such tests is presented in Hall *et al.* (1967).

Fig. 23. Six-foot-wide plate in 3,000,000-lb machine (Rolfe *et al.*, 1959).

J. Prestrain, Temperature, and Ductility Tests of Metals

A more basic study, carried out at Brown University by Mylonas (1964) and his associates over the past decade, as well as by others in Europe and Asia, has provided much useful information concerning the effects of temperature and the amount of prestrain on the fracture strength of steel materials. These tests have been carried out with tensile and bend-type specimens. Typical of such results are the reversed-bend test data on un-aged bars for a rimmed steel shown in Fig. 26. It will be noted that the amount of prestrain has an effect on the tendency to fracture, and is quite

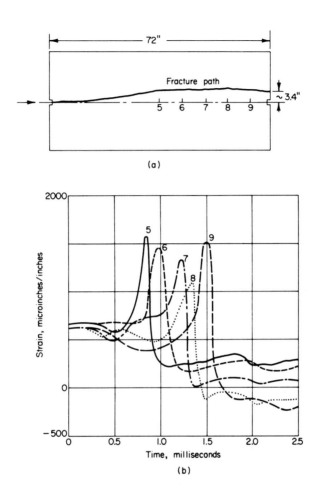

FIG. 24. Strain-time records for 6-foot-wide plain plate (Hall and Barton, 1963). (a) Plate layout and fracture path; (b) strain-time records.

temperature sensitive. Similar data have been obtained for various steels under a number of different types of loading, strain, and temperature conditions. Tests of this type are helpful in explaining some of the observations that arise with fabricated structural elements involving welds, material property changes, and residual stress effects. There is much information of this type available which has not as yet been fully assessed in terms of practical implications. The interested reader is referred to Hall *et al.* (1967) for further discussion of this topic and to enable him to trace the many sources of this type of information.

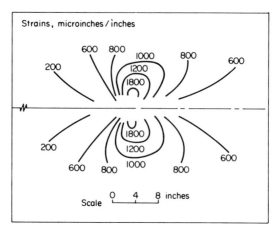

Fig. 25. Maximum principal strain contours for 22- to 50-inch crack in 6-ft-wide plate test (Rolfe and Hall, 1961).

K. Fracture Mechanics Tests

This general survey of test methods and results would be incomplete without mention of the recent developments in the fracture mechanics field. A tremendous amount of literature exists in this field by virtue of its development and application in recent years. No attempt is made to describe the types of specimens employed nor the specific types of results obtained, since this is covered comprehensively in a chapter by J. E. Srawley that appears elsewhere in this treatise. In general summary, the aim of sharp crack fracture testing is to obtain a fracture-toughness index, for example, K or G, where K is defined as a stress-intensity factor related to the stress field surrounding a sharp crack, and G refers to the strain-energy release rate. For fully linear elastic situations, it can be shown that these two quantities are related theoretically.

From a general point of view, the goal of fracture mechanics research has been to provide a basis for evaluating critical flaw size in a structure in terms of its ability to cause failure during the life of the vessel or structure. The studies involve consideration of the type of flaw, the stress field in which it is located, and the role or effects of other environments as, for example, corrosive atmosphere and repeated loading. Associated therewith is the matter of determining which types of flaws might grow to dangerous size and under what conditions they will undergo such growth. Most of the work in past years has been concerned with flaws in base materials, but recent developments by Kies et al. (1965) and others are concerned with applications of this technique to structures with weldments, an encouraging development.

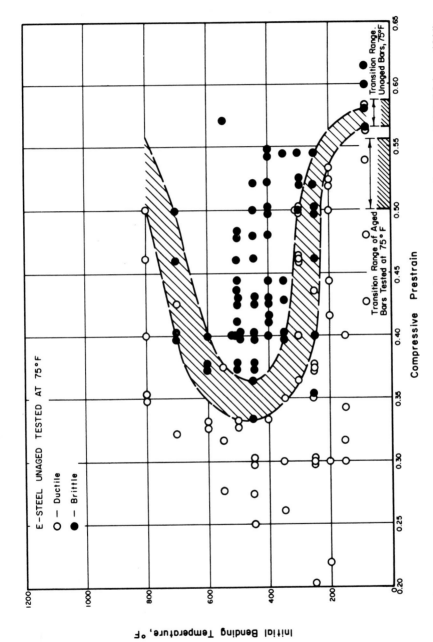

Fig. 26. Reversed-bend tests of unaged bars of E-steel prestrained at various temperatures and tested at 75° F (Mylonas, 1964).

In addition to the presentations given in the chapters by Irwin, Srawley, Corten, and others, one of the most comprehensive recent summaries of the status of fracture mechanics is given in ASTM (1965).

III. Welding Procedures, Residual Stress, and Flaws

There are a host of factors that can affect the interpretation of test results. The environment can have a strong effect on the results, as, for example, the well-known effects of corrosive agents. Examples of other factors having an effect are the type of weld metal employed in joining two pieces of metal, the welding procedure that is employed, the purity of the atmosphere surrounding the metal deposition, and the power levels employed during welding. In addition, the residual stresses set up in a fabricated piece by welding or straining can affect the results of a test, as well as the prototype response. The residual stress distribution in a welded wide plate (Fig. 20) is illustrated in Fig. 27. In Fig. 27a is shown the average residual stress distribution in the longitudinal direction, i.e., parallel to the weld; it will be noted that there is a high tensile residual stress in and near the weld, which drops off to a compressive stress near the plate edge. The transverse value shown is the residual stress measured perpendicular to the weld. The distribution through the thickness of the plate of the residual stress at the weld is shown in Fig. 27b, and it will be observed that a rather large variation can occur. The average residual stress in such specimens, following postheating at 1150° F for 1 hour, is shown in Fig. 27c, and 0.5% strain at room temperature in Fig. 27d. It will be noted that in Figs. 27c and 27d there is a significant reduction in residual stress at the weld, as a result of these treatments.

Residual stress has been much discussed in the literature, especially with regard to its role in initiation, propagation, and arrest of fractures in plates; this topic is covered in detail elsewhere in this treatise by Wells. It suffices to say here that large fields of residual stress can have a significant effect on the observed fracture behavior of specimens and prototype structures, and must be considered fully in any interpretation of tests which contain such stress fields.

Another item of great importance is that of flaws which can exist in the base material as it comes from the mill, or can be introduced as a result of welding, fabricating processes, shearing, or the handling of the material during fabrication. Most service fractures have been found to originate from a flaw source, and, for this reason, flaws have received increased attention in recent years, as their importance is realized, and more so as techniques are developed for evaluating the influence of these flaws on the fracture characteristics. This latter contribution is largely due to the fracture mechanics work that has been carried out, and, at the present time, it is possible to make estimates, in some cases, of the effect of a flaw for a given environment on the margin of safety and service performance of a structural element. Nondestructive test techniques have also opened new possibilities for detecting flaws in fabricated structures and for studying their size and growth in laboratory studies.

IV. Selection of Test Specimen and Instrumentation

To many engineers, and even some researchers, the process of testing appears routine, whereas, in actual fact, it is often anything but straightforward. Routine, standard tests can be employed to determine only a few basic facts about the strength and ductility of materials.

In planning any type of test program, it is necessary to ascertain what one is trying to measure. In other words, there must be an objective for the test, and, in general, this objective is associated with some design criterion or research goal.

Unfortunately, the experimenter is severely limited in what can be measured. In general, he is able to measure load, deformation, strain to some degree, temperature, and, in some cases, energy losses. Through the use of X-ray and ultrasonic techniques, it is possible to detect and measure the size of flaws. Surface flaws can be detected by dye penetrants, magnetic field anomalies, etc. Following a test, one can observe the fracture appearance and the source of the fracture. From a microstructure and metallurgical point of view, it is possible to gain information about the nature and composition of the material under study.

The selection of the type of test to be carried out and the type of specimen to be employed is dictated partly by the type of information that is sought and partly by the type of test and measurements that can be made. The tests described in Sect. II involving largely transition temperature determinations, were evolved after many years of effort, refinement, and expense. In the same manner, the procedures being explored in the fracture mechanics field for evaluation of flaws and notch effects are undergoing the same type of development, and, undoubtedly, in the years ahead, will become more standardized. During the formative stages of such development, great attention to detail and painstaking experimentation are required.

Rarely, if ever, can prototype flaws be duplicated exactly in the laboratory. The laboratory flaw is generally designed to simulate some special and desired condition, yet, at the same time, to be of such a nature that it can be readily duplicated from specimen to specimen. Many special techniques

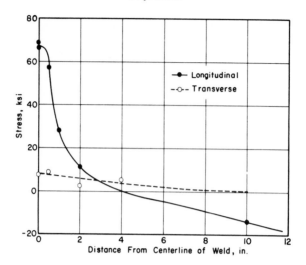

FIG. 27a

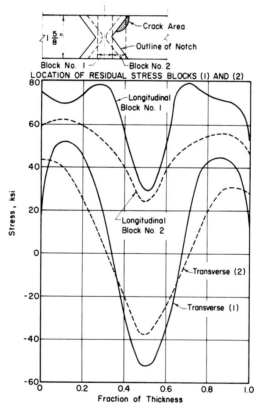

FIG. 27b

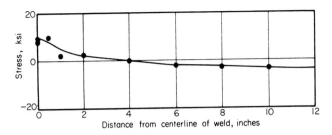

FIG. 27c

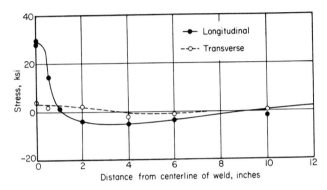

FIG. 27d

FIG. 27. Residual stress in welded wide plates with various welding procedures (Nordell and Hall, 1965). (a) Distribution of average residual stress in a $1\frac{5}{8}$-inch-thick as-welded specimen. (b) Distribution of residual stress through plate thickness in a $1\frac{5}{8}$-inch-thick as-welded plate. (c) Distribution of average longitudinal residual stress in a 1-inch-thick thermally stress-relieved plate. (d) Distribution of average longitudinal residual stress in a 1-inch-thick mechanically stress-relieved specimen.

have been employed to create artificial flaws, including fine saw cuts, pressed notches, nitrided notches, electron-beam processes, and fatigue cracking. Correlation studies have demonstrated that the care taken in preparation of the flaws can have great influence on the test results obtained. Often, much of the scatter in reported data can be traced to variations in flaw preparation. Good workmanship and quality control are just as important in specimen preparation and testing as in design.

In some cases, it is possible to test a full-scale structure or a section thereof. Such a test may be of value in pointing up some defect or critical factor overlooked in design. Or, it may serve to further delineate the behavior believed to have occurred in a failure; unfortunately, such tests often do not confirm behavior during failure. In any event, such tests are expensive and cannot possibly provide all the desired information. From a research standpoint, or even from a quality control standpoint, smaller and cheaper laboratory specimens are desirable. In some cases, if surface finish is a key factor in behavior, the specimen should be of full plate thickness with no surface alteration. In other cases, it is possible to use even smaller specimens if it appears likely that properties do not vary greatly from one point to another and in various directions in the material. In all cases, the selection of the size and type of specimen and of the measurement technique deserves considerable attention prior to fabrication of the specimen.

If a major test program is contemplated, it is good practice to undertake a pilot program before investing large sums of money in a specimen manufacturing program. The pilot program generally would involve several specimens and tests, with instrumentation, to ensure that the desired goal will be attained by use of the planned specimens and measurements.

As technical advances are made in the evaluation of fracture phenomena, the engineer or research director will have to make decisions as to the amount and type of effort to be put into a testing program. In general, it would seem appropriate that the amount of effort and expense associated with testing for any particular design objective should be commensurate with the importance attached to the project. For those types of structures in which the effects of a failure are very great and can have far-reaching consequences, it would seem desirable to have a higher margin of safety, and, appropriately, an investigative program involving both experimental and theoretical aspects in greater depth than might normally be the case. This philosophy seems to be gaining acceptance, although slowly, in some areas.

V. Interpretation of Results

The most interesting aspect of testing is that of evaluating and interpreting the test results. Hopefully, one will find the type of results sought originally; even so, this does not guarantee that the interpretation will be straightforward. Often, the results are not as expected, due to various complications, and may not be subject to clear interpretation. Interpretation requires patience and a certain amount of native ability in perceiving the important facets of the findings.

In most cases, the first step in interpreting test results is to put down on paper the measurements that were made and to plot one variable against another so as to observe trends that might be evident. In many cases, this technique provides the basis for the interpretation. In other cases, it merely constitutes a step in the interpretive process, especially if the experimental findings are to be employed in a theoretical computation. Since the interpretation often cannot be carried out fully because of a lack of theory or understanding for carrying it through at that particular time, it would be most helpful if investigators would record in the literature their basic measurement data in a form which would make it possible for others to go back and reinterpret the data at a later time. There is a great body of data which could be subjected to reevaluation at later dates if the basic data were available, but, unfortunately, in many cases, only the investigator's interpretation of the data is presented, and it is impossible to resurrect the basic measurements from that information presented.

One of the most widely used interpretive techniques is the transition-temperature approach, which also carries through to design, but which is limited to temperature-sensitive and strain-rate-sensitive materials, such as low- and medium-strength structural steels, that exhibit rather sharp behavior transitions for measurements of absorbed energy versus temperature or fracture stress versus temperature. In a most general sense, the definitions of transition temperature, as illustrated by the types of tests cited earlier, fall into the following categories:

1. The temperature or temperature range over which the material's capacity for ductile behavior in the presence of a sharp notch or flaw decreases to a lower value. For example, the transition temperature range for the Charpy-V (weak) data shown in Fig. 15 might be given as $-100°$ to $-220°$ F.

2. The temperature or temperature range over which the mode of crack propagation as reflected in the fracture appearance changes with temperature from a full shear-type failure to flat- or cleavage-type failure.

3. The temperature or temperature range over which a propagating crack is arrested. For example, in Fig. 18, for the Robertson gradient test in the upper plot, the arrest temperature would be $-9°$ C.

4. For certain types of tests involving tensile or bend specimens, the temperature at which the fracture strength of a sharply notched specimen decreases rapidly from values that would customarily be above the yield point to somewhat below the yield point. An illustration of this type of behavior is provided by the welded-plate data in Fig. 22.

One of the principal difficulties in interpreting transition temperature data is the variation in transition temperature or transition-temperature range that is commonly found for various types of tests. For low- and medium-strength steels, any of the commonly employed tests generally rank the steels in the same order. However, the various tests do not give the same transition temperature indication by virtue of differences in the loading and geometry employed. Generally, it is difficult to predict the results for one type of specimen or notch geometry from the test data for another type of specimen or notch geometry, although some progress in this direction has been made recently, as will be discussed next.

Appreciation of this difficulty helps one realize the even greater difficulty in correlating laboratory results with service performance, the rather obvious ultimate objective. Even though the Charpy test has gained wide acceptance as a materials-selection or quality-control test, one need reflect for only a moment to appreciate that it is an impact-type test giving some measure of energy absorption versus temperature. Rarely will a structure in service be subjected to an impact-type loading; instead, the service structure will probably see a series of repeated loadings, possibly of variable magnitude, and, perhaps, some overloading. The conditions for failure in this latter case, which may be associated with the growth of a flaw, likely will bear little resemblance to the Charpy test conditions.

As a result of these perplexing difficulties, there has been a continuing search for test-to-test correlation and test-to-service correlation. The failure of many past correlation attempts can be attributed, at least in part, to a mixing of criteria or a mixing of testing conditions, materials, and specimen geometry. On the other hand, as our understanding of the fracture mechanism has improved, it has become possible to obtain better correlations. Most of the published attempts at data correlation can be found in the books cited in the introduction to this chapter. One of the most comprehensive test-to-test correlation programs undertaken to date was made in Japan, with fair success, and is reported in some detail in Hall *et al.* (1967). One of the most important types of correlation is that between laboratory tests and failed structures, and it is gratifying to see the increased attention recently accorded to this aspect of the fracture problem. Because prototype tests are so expensive and often do not provide the desired information, it is imperative that comprehensive failure examinations be undertaken. Such studies, if publicized, can be of great value to the entire engineering profession.

One of the most useful unifying concepts to be put forth recently is the generalized fracture analysis diagram proposed by Pellini and Puzak, as shown in Fig. 28. The diagram portrays the results of NDT tests, explosion bulge tests, welded-plate tests, wide-plate studies, and some Charpy data, and the authors illustrate applications of the procedure to actual failure cases. In most cases, the trends that are evident in Fig. 28 follow along the lines of the transition-temperature data for mild steels that have been cited and illustrated earlier. This particular diagram is referenced about the NDT, which falls at the lower side of the transition curves. In interpreting the portion of the diagram referenced to the size of the flaws, and especially with reference to the welded-plate specimens, one must appreciate that the stress levels indicated in the diagram refer to the actual stress levels, which must, indeed, include the effects of residual stress. The crack-arrest temperature (CAT) curve, which falls to the right, portrays an upper temperature level at which one would not expect cracks to continue propagation were they to initiate from some source.

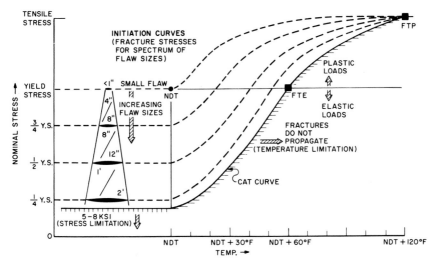

FIG. 28. General fracture analysis diagram as referenced to NDT temperature (Pellini and Puzak, 1963a).

With this type of approach, then, one has the option, in applying test results to actual design conditions, of selecting a material or comparing several materials from laboratory tests or available data to devise a transition-temperature diagram, as, for example, that indicated in Fig. 28. With this information, one can select a stress level and operating temperature at a value to the right of that which would correspond to the CAT curve, or, alternatively, search for a material which would exhibit stress and temperature conditions that were to the left or below the expected stress and service temperature conditions. This technique is extremely simple and easy to understand, and, in some cases, serves quite well the design needs in certain areas of practical application, at least until better techniques are devised.

There are a number of uncertainties and complications associated with the transition-temperature approach. As explained earlier, there are many types of tests that can be employed to obtain the transition data, and few of these will give exactly the same transition temperature or transition-temperature range. Moreover, any extensive test program to obtain such data will be extremely expensive. Judgment must be exercised in deciding which type of test or group of tests can best represent operating conditions, or, alternatively, provide data that can be interpreted as applicable to the real situation.

From the design standpoint, one of the principal problems of the transition-temperature approach is that of deciding what temperature margin should be selected between the lowest service temperature and the CAT or other transition phenomena for the material employed. The conservatism reflected in this decision depends in part on the consequence of failure, and in part on a detailed judgment concerning other factors which could affect the behavior of the structure. The difficulties of greatest concern arise from factors associated with such things as the welds, the welding techniques employed, the properties of the material in the vicinity of the weld, the possibility of flaws and defects other than those for which the design was made, other environments (including corrosive agents), and, possibly, the effects of cyclic loading, as they might affect crack growth or other aspects of design.

For high-strength steels or other materials which do not exhibit a transition effect, other means must be found for evaluation. One of the best-known techniques at present for interpretation of test results and application to practical situations is the fracture mechanics approach, which is discussed in detail elsewhere in this treatise by Srawley, Irwin, and others. Briefly, the fracture mechanics approach may be applied as follows: The fracture toughness of a material, which is considered to be a material parameter, and which is usually described in terms of K_{Ic} [critical stress intensity factor in units of $(lb\sqrt{in.})/in.^2$] or G_{Ic} [critical crack extension force in units of $(in.-lb)/in.^2$], is determined experimentally, employing one of the several types of specimens that have been developed for this purpose. Here the subscript I refers to the opening mode of fracture and c to critical value. The temperature and strain rate employed in the test should be similar to that for the service application. With a knowledge of (a), the fracture toughness, and (b), the actual or expected defect size and shape in the prototype as determined by nondestructive techniques or otherwise, one can evaluate the load-bearing capacity of the prototype by substituting in an appropriate theoretical expression. The expressions are generally functions of the fracture toughness, applied stress, defect size, elastic modulus, and factors accounting for geometry and loading characteristics; the yield stress is also generally required. By substituting in the appropriate relationship, one can compute the critical value of stress at which unstable and possibly catastrophic failure will occur, or, conversely, with the toughness and applied stress specified, one can compute the critical defect size for unstable fracture.

The fracture mechanics approach is being used widely, especially for high-strength metal or frangible material applications. Some of the difficulties associated with its application include the inability to handle elastic-plastic situations, problems associated with applying fracture toughness values obtained under one kind of condition to another kind of condition, and uncertainties as to how to handle residual stress, complicated flaws, and crack growth. The interpretation of fracture mechanics data is no easier nor more difficult than for other approaches, but requires careful insight to be sure that the interpretation has meaning for the particular application. These difficulties are not peculiar to the fracture mechanics approach, for there is no approach that can adequately handle such topics.

Although the fracture mechanics literature is voluminous, articles describing its applications have been rare. Three recent publications, ASTM (1964), Tiffany and Masters (1965), and Wessel *et al.* (1966), provide considerable insight into possible applications and the details that must be considered in the use of this approach.

Other approaches are being developed for handling high-strength materials in the heavy structural range. One of these being developed by Pellini and associates (1965) at the Naval Research Laboratory is illustrated in Fig. 29; it involves the drop-weight tear test, coupled with the explosive tear test data to give some indication of the strain levels for different classes of material. The data presented in Fig. 29 represent tests conducted at $+30°$ F, above the transition range, in all cases. As will be appreciated, this technique involves a tremendous amount of testing under carefully controlled conditions, but, nonetheless, allows one to appraise the upper limits of energy levels and levels of strain that could be expected, corresponding to the failure mode for high-strength materials of various yield strengths.

Other techniques of interpreting experimental data are available, based on such concepts as the local ductility concept advanced by Sachs, the stress concentration factor approach, and critical stress techniques. There are also disadvantages associated with all of these, and they suffer from about the same types of problems as those discussed previously.

The final guide as to whether the interpretation of test results is meaningful, of course, is obtained in terms of evaluation of the service performance of actual structures, hopefully of a satisfactory nature. In those cases in which failure does occur, technical progress will be hastened if steps are taken to ascertain why the failure occurred and to see if it could have been predicted.

VI. Recommended Research

One of the principal drawbacks to most of the testing techniques described thus far in this chapter is that of the cost and time required to make the laboratory studies. As yet, there are still no simple, quick guides by which one can evaluate fracture toughness of materials or fabricated structural elements, and it is expected that this condition will exist for some time. Thus, a continuing search for simplified procedures for evaluation and interpretation in terms of design criteria constitutes a task of

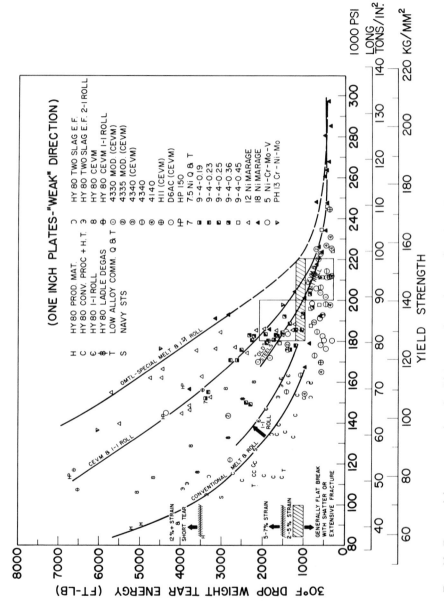

Fig. 29. Drop-weight tear test data for high-strength steels as a function of yield strength and processing practices (Goode *et al.*, 1966).

primary importance. Further research is needed to devise better means of nondestructive inspection and of periodic monitoring to guard against unexpected failure.

The extension of the fracture mechanics approach, or some other rational approach into the low-strength materials area, would be especially helpful if, at the same time, the procedures for carrying out such studies could be simplified.

Another area of major concern is that of cyclic loading and slow crack growth, which is common to many types of structures, including bridges, pressure vessels, and airplanes. More attention needs to be given to this area of research, and it is encouraging to see the large fatigue machines being built around the world which should be able to produce data of significance in this area in the near future. A related topic of importance concerns arresting concepts; further attention needs to be given to arresting mechanisms and their possible incorporation into structures, especially for those types of structures in which small cracks can be tolerated if they are arrested.

And, last, it would seem from a theoretical point of view that random and stochastic processes should eventually play a more important role in the applied materials design field.

VII. Summary

Even though our understanding of the makeup and behavior of constructional materials is continually improving, as yet our understanding, unfortunately, is not to the point where theoretical concepts alone can supply all the necessary design information. For some time to come, it appears there must be recourse to testing to supply much of the required design data and to verify to the extent possible that the procedures employed in design and fabrication will lead to satisfactory service performance. Tests are expensive and time consuming and may not always supply the desired information. A rewarding test program consists of a blend of good planning, careful control over specimen preparation and instrumentation, and intelligent interpretation of the observations. Interpretation, which generally is the most interesting aspect of the program, is also the most difficult. In making the interpretation, one should bring to bear all pertinent information, i.e., the data obtained from the instrumentation and physical examination (which often is quite limited), as well as such other knowledge about the properties of the material as is available. In this sense, this brief chapter can only hope to touch lightly on the subject of interpretation.

Generally, the test program will be undertaken with some fixed objective in mind, as, for example, some service requirement. Obviously, then, the interpretation of the data would be planned to fulfill this goal, as well it should. It would be of great help to the profession if more attention were paid to presentation of the basic information collected in order to enable other researchers at later times to study such data. Through advances in knowledge, new evaluation techniques become available, and it is usually difficult, if not impossible, to reinterpret anything other than the basic data.

In the area of fracture-toughness testing, it is difficult to duplicate exactly the conditions that may lead, or may have led, to failure of a service structure. In an effort to devise means of evaluating fracture toughness, many different types of tests have been devised. Some of these tests and examples of the data obtained therefrom have been presented in the body of this chapter. Most of the examples cited produce data that fall in the transition temperature realm, i.e., as the temperature is increased, the behavior or strength changes from that characterized by the terms "brittle" or "frangible" to "ductile" or "tough." The design approach, then, is to choose the lowest service temperature and an appropriate stress level such that fracture initiation will, hopefully, be precluded or, alternatively, that ductile and tough behavior and crack arrest will occur should a crack originate. This procedure has received wide acceptance for strain-rate-sensitive and temperature-sensitive metals, as, for example, low- and medium-strength steels, and is simple to use when applicable. However, there are many difficulties in its application, with respect to obtaining meaningful data, deciding which transition data are applicable (for the tests do not generally yield comparable data), and assessing the effects of existing flaws, residual stress, welding procedures, etc.

In the last two decades, a new approach, commonly denoted fracture mechanics, has been developing and has been widely adopted, especially in those areas of high-strength metals application or for materials intrinsically possessing frangible behavior characteristics. The fracture mechanics approach has appeal in that it is more rational than previous approaches. It involves consideration of the real flaw, its potential growth, and real material property values, and employs basic theoretical expressions. However, it possesses limitations, in terms of stress analysis restrictions, application of simple test techniques to service conditions, and the usual difficulties involving welding procedures, residual stress, and crack growth. Only limited discussion of this approach was given herein, for the fracture mechanics approach receives detailed attention elsewhere in this treatise.

All of the approaches now available for evaluating fracture toughness are expensive and time consuming. A need still exists for significant refinements in existing techniques or the development of other inexpensive, reliable, and rational material toughness evaluation techniques.

REFERENCES

Acker, H. G. (1953). Report No. SSC-63. Ship Structure Committee, U.S. Coast Guard Hdqtrs. Washington, D.C.

ASME (1964). "A Review of Engineering Approaches to Design against Fracture." ASME, New York.

ASTM (1964). *Mater. Res. Std.* **4** (3), 107.

ASTM (1965). STP 381. ASTM, Philadelphia.

ASTM (1966). ASTM Std., Pt. 30. ASTM, Philadelphia.

Averbach, B. L., Felbeck, D. K., Hahn, G. T., and Thomas, D. Z. (eds.) (1959). " Fracture." Wiley, New York. (Also available from M.I.T. Press, Cambridge, Massachusetts.)

Biggs, W. D. (1960). "The Brittle Fracture of Steel." MacDonald & Evans, London.

Boyd, G. M. (1962). *In* "Brittle Fracture in Steel" (prepared by the Admiralty Advisory Committee on Structural Steel), p. 6. H.M. Stationery Office, London.

British Engine Boiler and Electrical Insurance Co., Ltd. (1962). "Technical Report," Vols. 2 (New series), 3 (New Series), and 4. Manchester, England.

Cowan, A., and Vaughan, H. G. (1962). *Nucl. Eng.* **7** (69), 57.

de Graaf, J. E., and van der Veen, J. H. (1953). *J. Iron Steel Inst. (London)* **173**, 19.

Drucker, D. C., and Gilman, J. J. (eds.) (1963). " Fracture of Solids." Wiley (Interscience), New York. (Also available as *Met. Soc. Conf.* **20**.)

Feely, F. J., Jr., Hrtko, D., Kleppe, S. R., and Northup, M. S. (1954). *Welding J. (N.Y.) Res. Suppl.* **33**, 99s.

Goode, R. J., Huber, R. W., Judy, R. W., Howe, D. G., Puzak, P. P., Lloyd, K. B., Crooker, T. W., Morey, R. E., Lange, E. A., and Freed, C. N. (1966). Report No. 6454. Naval Research Laboratory, Washington, D.C.

Hall, W. J., and Barton, F. W. (1963). Report No. SSC-149. Ship Structure Committee, U.S. Coast Guard Hdqtrs., Washington, D.C.

Hall, W. J., and Chamberlain, A. D. (1966). *Welding J. (N.Y.) Res. Suppl.* **45**, 193s.

Hall, W. J., Nordell, W. J., and Munse, W. H. (1962). *Welding J. (N.Y.) Res. Suppl.* **41**, 505s.

Hall, W. J., Joshi, J. R., and Munse, W. H. (1965). *Welding J. (N.Y.) Res. Suppl.* **44**, 182s.

Hall, W. J., Kihara, H., Soete, W., and Wells, A. A. (1967). "Brittle Fracture of Welded Plate." Prentice-Hall, Englewood Cliffs, New Jersey.

Kies, J. A., Smith, H. L., Romine, H. E., and Bernstein, H. (1965). *In* STP 381, p. 328. ASTM, Philadelphia.

Kihara, H., Masubuchi, K., Iida, K., and Oba, H. (1959). Document No. X-218-59. International Institute of Welding.

Larson, F. R., and Carr, F. L. (1964). *Metal Progr.* **85**, 74, 109.

Murray, W. M. (ed.) (1952). " Fatigue and Fracture of Metals." Wiley, New York. (Also available from M.I.T. Press, Cambridge, Massachusetts.)

Mylonas, C. (1964). Report No. SSC-162. Ship Structure Committee, U.S. Coast Guard Hdqtrs., Washington, D.C.

Nordell, W. J., and Hall, W. J. (1965). *Welding J. (N.Y.) Res. Suppl.* **44**, 124s.

Parker, E. R. (1957). " Brittle Behavior of Engineering Structures." Wiley, New York.

Pellini, W. S., and Puzak, P. P. (1963a). Report No. 5920. Naval Research Laboratory, Washington, D.C. (Also available as Bulletin No. 88, Welding Research Council, New York.)

Pellini, W. S., and Puzak, P. P. (1963b). Report No. 6030. Naval Research Laboratory, Washington, D.C.

Pellini, W. S., Goode, R. J., Puzak, P. P., Lange, E. A., and Huber, R. W. (1965). Report No. 6300. Naval Research Laboratory, Washington D.C.

Puzak, P. P., Babecki, A. J., and Pellini, W. S. (1958). *Welding J. (N. Y.) Res. Suppl.* **37**, 391s.

Rolfe, S. T., and Hall, W. J. (1961). *Proc. Soc. Exptl. Stress. Anal.* **18** (2), 113–119.

Rolfe, S. T., Lynam, T. M., and Hall, W. J. (1959). Report No. SSC-118. Ship Structure Committee, U.S. Coast Guard Hdqtrs., Washington, D.C.

Rühl, K. (1959). "Die Sprödbruchsicherheit von Stahlkonstruktionen." Werner-Verlag, Düsseldorf.

Shank, M. E. (1954). STP 158. ASTM, Philadelphia. (Also available as Report No. SSC-65. Ship Structure Committee, U.S. Coast Guard Hdqtrs., Washington, D.C. Also Bulletin No. 17. Welding Research Council, New York.)

Shank, M. E. (ed.) (1957). "Control of Steel Construction to Avoid Brittle Failure." Welding Research Council, New York.

Szczepanski, M. (1963). "The Brittleness of Steel." Wiley, New York.

Tiffany, C. F., and Masters, J. N. (1965). *In* STP 381, p. 249. ASTM, Philadelphia.

Tipper, C. F (1962). "The Brittle Fracture Story." Cambridge, London.

Wells, A. A. (1956). *Trans. Roy. Inst. Naval Architects* **98**, 296.

Wessel, E. T., Clark, W. G., and Wilson, W. K. (1966). Final Report (Contract No. DA-30-069-AMC-602(T), Department of the Army). Westinghouse Research Laboratories, Pittsburgh.

CHAPTER 2

PLANE STRAIN FRACTURE TOUGHNESS

John E. Srawley

Abstract: The general concept of the K_{Ic} plane strain fracture toughness, due to G. R. Irwin, is reviewed, and the current (tentative) standard procedure for determination of K_{Ic} with crack-notched bend specimens is discussed in detail. The standard procedure constitutes an operational definition of K_{Ic} which is somewhat arbitrary, but no more so than is the definition of offset yield strength. Experimental data for high-strength steels, titanium, and aluminum alloys validate the standard procedure for determination of K_{Ic}, and confirm that it is reasonable to regard K_{Ic} as an inherent material property which controls fracture under conditions of sufficiently high constraint. However, the required specimen dimensions increase in proportion to the square of the ratio of K_{Ic} to yield strength, and impractically large specimens may be required for tough, low-strength materials. The standard test procedure for bend specimens can be adapted to other types of specimens with the aid of information given in an appendix.

I. Introduction: Concept of K_{Ic}

This chapter is concerned with standardized measurement of the K_{Ic} plane strain fracture toughness of materials. The essential concept of K_{Ic} was first described by Irwin *et al.* (1958), but the symbol K was introduced later, for reasons discussed by Irwin (1960a). The concept depends

45

on the stress analysis of cracks in linear-elastic bodies (Irwin, 1957, 1958, 1960a; Williams, 1957), and K_{Ic} is measured in terms of the opening mode stress-intensity factor K_I in units of (stress) $\times$ (length)$^{1/2}$. The important distinction between the mathematical quantity K_I and the material property K_{Ic} is similar to the distinction between stress and strength. The stress analysis of cracks has recently been reviewed in detail by Paris and Sih (1965), and the literature on experimental applications of fracture mechanics has been surveyed thoroughly by Tetelman and McEvily (1967).

In appropriate circumstances, the K_{Ic} toughness of a material can be used to estimate the load that a structural member containing a crack of known dimensions could sustain without fracture. Strength estimates based on K_{Ic} assume a high degree of elastic constraint to plastic flow of the material at the crack tip. This degree of constraint exists when a sufficiently large crack occurs in a sufficiently heavy section in relation to the plastic zone size factor $(K_{Ic}/\sigma_{ys})^2$ (inches), where σ_{ys} is the tensile yield strength. There is a general tendency for K_{Ic} to decrease as the yield strength increases, and the size factor for very high strength steels can be as small as 0.01 inch, or less. On the other hand, it can probably be as large as several inches for very tough materials of relatively low strength.

With less constraint, such as in a sufficiently thin plate, the effective toughness of a material may be substantially greater than K_{Ic}. It is usual to refer to the thickness-dependent toughness of through-cracked plates as K_c, but the measurement and application of K_c is not a simple matter, nor has any standardized procedure for K_c measurement been developed yet (see Srawley and Brown, 1965). For more complicated situations, such as part-through cracks in sections of intermediate thickness, the difficulties are compounded. It is often advisable to depend on a lower-bound strength estimate based on K_{Ic} rather than attempt to take advantage of an expected higher effective toughness, particularly since crack size estimates in engineering components are usually quite uncertain. While it is possible, in principle, for the K_c toughness of extremely thin sections to be less than K_{Ic}, it appears that this has never occurred in practice.

It is appropriate to regard K_{Ic} as a basic material property, since it is the lower limit of effective toughness with increase in the degree of constraint to plastic deformation. In fact, the related quantity $\mathscr{G}_{Ic}$, which is equal to $K_{Ic}^2 (1 - \nu^2)/E$, not $\mathscr{G}_c$, is the appropriate plastic work term for generalization of the Griffith concept (Griffith, 1920; Irwin, 1948; Orowan, 1949). It has been established for a number of materials that K_{Ic} is independent of size and form of specimen when properly measured; which means, among other things, when the specimen dimensions are adequate (Brown and Srawley, 1966).

Up to this point, K_{Ic} has been discussed but not defined. Since K_{Ic} is intended for engineering use, it is appropriate to take the operational viewpoint (Wilson, 1952; Bridgman, 1927) that K_{Ic} should be defined in terms of the operations employed in measuring it. In practice, an operational definition develops out of collective experience and is never complete or entirely unambiguous. Furthermore, the operational definition of a property may be somewhat arbitrary; for example, yield strength (ASTM Standards E8-65T and E9-61). Experience with K_{Ic} measurement has shown that this property has to be defined somewhat arbitrarily in order that it should be applicable to a broad range of engineering materials. An earlier attempt at operational definition of K_{Ic} (Brown and Srawley, 1966) has had to be modified for this reason.

In the 1966 definition, the attempt was made to preserve the aspect of gross abruptness of onset of crack extension (so-called pop-in of the crack front) that had been taken for granted as part of the concept of K_{Ic}. It subsequently became clear that this aspect could only be preserved at the expense of severely restricting the range of materials for which the property could be measured. Crack extension in a K_{Ic} test certainly occurs discontinuously, but, in many materials, the successive increments are so small that it is futile to attempt to specify a minimum size for a single increment as a requirement for determination of K_{Ic}. Nor is it practical to define K_{Ic} in terms of the first increment of crack extension, which is rather like the first increment of plastic deformation in a tension test. The alternative which is now proposed is to define K_{Ic} as the stress intensity at which the crack reaches an effective length 2% greater than at the beginning of the test. This is analogous to definition of yield strength in terms of a specified amount of plastic strain—which is necessary because most materials do not yield abruptly. However, the method given in Sect. II for establishing the value of K_{Ic} from the test record is superficially similar to that for a secant yield strength (Ramberg and Osgood, 1943), rather than an offset yield strength.

It is perhaps somewhat paradoxical at first sight that K_{Ic} can often be measured with specimens that do not fracture completely when the stress intensity reaches the K_{Ic} level. The explanation, however, is quite straightforward. In plate specimens with through-thickness cracks, the effective toughness is higher than K_{Ic} near the plate surfaces where the constraint is relaxed. If the plate is thick enough, the central region of the crack front in the interior of the plate will start to extend when the stress intensity reaches K_{Ic}, but overall advance of the crack front will not occur until a higher value of the stress intensity is reached, sufficient to overcome the higher effective toughness near the plate surfaces. Measurement of K_{Ic}

depends on detection of the advance of the central region of the crack front in the specimen.

The method for determination of K_{Ic}, which is given in Sect. II, has been incorporated into a draft recommended practice for K_{Ic} tests with bend specimens by ASTM Committee E-24 on Fracture Testing of Metals.

II. Procedure for Determination of K_{Ic}

Only the essentials of the procedure are given in this section; the experimental details and recommended specimen dimensions are given in App. A. The procedure is given for a 3-point bend test but could readily be adapted for other types of specimen with the help of the information given in App. B.

The essential feature of the bend specimen shown in Fig. 1 is the notch tipped with a fatigue crack. This crack notch is intended to simulate an ideal plane crack, and it is necessary to control the conditions of fatigue crack production very carefully (App. A). The initial crack length a_0 is approximately one-half the specimen depth W, and the preferred specimen thickness B is also $W/2$. Whichever of a_0 or B is the smaller determines the largest value of K_{Ic} that can be measured with a given specimen, as given below.

The bend test itself is straightforward, but it is necessary to obtain a precise autographic plot of the change in the distance across the open end of the notch ($v = g - g_0$, Fig. 1) as this distance increases with increasing load during the test. This plot is called the load-displacement record of the

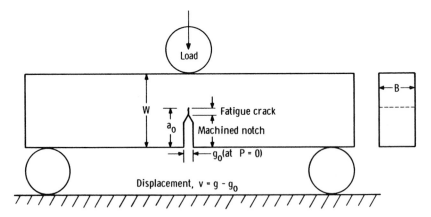

FIG. 1. Essentials of bend specimen for K_{Ic} test.

test, and there are three basic types, as shown in Fig. 2. The procedure for the determination of a K_{Ic} value from such a record is as follows.

First, draw the secant line OP_5 from the origin with slope 5% less than that of the tangent OA to the initial part of the record. (Note that this percentage depends on specimen type and a_0/W; see Sect. II and App. B.) The load P_5 is at the intersection of the secant with the record. Next, draw a horizontal line representing a constant load at 80% of P_5, and measure the distance x_1 along this line from the tangent OA to the record. If x_1 exceeds one-fourth of the corresponding distance at P_5, the test is not considered to be a valid K_{Ic} test. (In practice, tests are rarely rejected by this criterion.)

If the test has not been rejected, determine the load P_Q which will be used to calculate a conditional value of K_{Ic}, called K_Q, as follows: If the load at every point on the record which precedes P_5 is lower than P_5, P_Q is equal to P_5 (Fig. 2, case I); if, however, there is a maximum load preceding P_5 which exceeds it, this maximum load is P_Q (Fig. 2, cases II and III).

Next, calculate the conditional result K_Q from P_Q according to a formula determined by elastic stress analysis and given in App. A. Finally, calculate $2.5(K_Q/\sigma_{ys})^2$, where σ_{ys} is the 0.2% offset tensile yield strength of the material. If this calculated quantity is less than both the thickness B and the crack length a_0 of the specimen, K_Q is the required K_{Ic} result. Other-

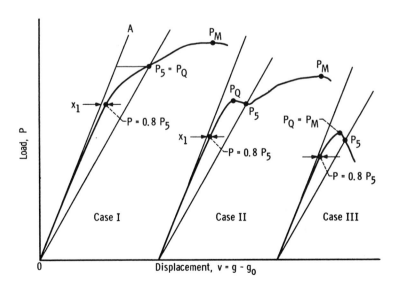

Fig. 2. Types of load displacement curves illustrating procedure for determination of K_{Ic}.

wise, it is necessary to use a larger specimen to determine K_{Ic}, such that both thickness and crack length are greater than $2.5(K_{Ic}/\sigma_{ys})^2$. These dimensions can be estimated on the basis of K_Q; however, for all but the toughest materials, it is possible to predict upper limits for these dimensions from existing data (App. A).

EXPLANATION OF PROCEDURE

Consider first a model K_{Ic} test for a hypothetical linear-elastic material. The crack tip radius is vanishingly small, and the specimen thickness is comparatively large, so that a state of plane strain prevails around the crack tip. The crack length in the model is always uniform throughout the specimen thickness. (In practice, the specimen is not ideal, and the term crack length then means the average over the specimen thickness of the overall length of notch plus fatigue crack.) The path of the load-displacement record for the test, $OP_X P_5 P_M$ in Fig. 3, is linear up to the load P_X at which the crack starts to extend. It is supposed that the crack then extends

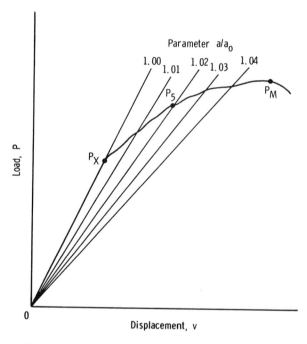

FIG. 3. Load-displacement record for test of hypothetical linear-elastic material with set of parametric straight lines representing different ratios of instantaneous to initial crack length.

somewhat erratically, but increasingly rapidly, as the load increases up to a maximum P_M where the specimen breaks apart. This is essentially what happens in tests of many actual materials.

For a linear-elastic material, the displacement is proportional to the load when the crack length is fixed. Over a small range of crack lengths from a_0 to a, the relation of displacement to load and crack length can be approximated as

$$v = P(c_1 + c_2\, a/a_0) \tag{1}$$

where c_1, c_2, and a_0 are constants of the test. This relation is represented in the load-displacement plane (Fig. 3) by the set of secant lines through the origin with parameter a/a_0. The intersection of each secant with the test record determines the load corresponding to a particular value of the instantaneous crack length. In the procedure for determination of K_{Ic}, the load P_5 is obtained from the secant for a/a_0 equal to 1.02. It is the load at which the crack extension is 2% of the initial length. The necessary quantitative information is given in App. B for several different kinds of specimens.

For real materials which are not linear-elastic, the displacement is not exactly proportional to the load when the crack length is fixed because there is a small component of displacement due to plastic deformation around the crack tip. According to Irwin (1960b), the effect of the crack tip plastic zone (in monotonic loading) can be treated as that of a virtual crack extension of proportionate size. The size of the plastic zone is proportional to the square of the load, and, therefore, the relation of displacement to load and crack length can be approximated as

$$v = P(c_1 + c_2\, a/a_0 + c_3 P^2) \tag{2}$$

where c_1, c_2, c_3, and a_0 are all constants of the test, and the effect of a small change in crack length on plastic zone size has been neglected. This relation is represented in the load-displacement plane (Fig. 4) by the set of curved lines through the origin with parameter a/a_0. The tangents to these curved lines (shown dashed) are the secant lines of Fig. 3.

Clearly, it would be impractical to employ a procedure for determination of K_{Ic} which involved finding the intersection of one of these parametric curves with the test record. Therefore, the effect of plastic deformation is neglected in the proposed procedure for finding the load P_5. This load may then be regarded as corresponding to an *effective* crack extension of 2%; the actual crack extension will be somewhat less than 2% and will differ somewhat from material to material.

There are two safeguards which justify the adoption of this expedient. First, there is a basic requirement which is imposed on specimen dimensions to ensure that the effect of plastic deformation is kept small, namely,

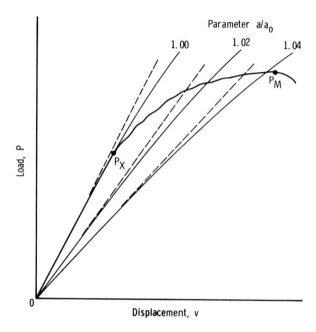

FIG. 4. Load-displacement record for test of material which deforms plastically around crack tip and set of parametric curves representing different ratio of instantaneous to initial crack length.

that neither the crack length nor the specimen thickness shall be less than $2.5(K_{Ic}/\sigma_{ys})^2$—which is a large multiple of the plastic zone size at P_5. Second, there is a check procedure which is designed to determine whether the actual crack extension at P_5 is at least one-half the effective extension; if so, the rate of actual crack extension beyond P_5 will be rapid compared with the rate of growth of the plastic zone.

The ratio of actual crack extension to effective crack extension can be estimated, somewhat indirectly, from the load-displacement record. In Fig. 5, the test record is the curve $OP_1P_X P_5$ and the parametric curve for $a = a_0$ is $OP_1P_X C$. The arc $P_X C$ does not appear on the actual test record, of course, nor is the load P_X for onset of crack extension clearly defined in most cases. However, there is considerable evidence that crack extension ·is negligible at loads less than $0.8P_5$.

Let x_5 [equal to $c_3 P^3$ in Eq. (2)] be the displacement component due to plastic deformation at load P_5, and y_5 the component due to actual crack extension; then

$$\frac{\text{Actual crack extension}}{\text{Effective crack extension}} = R_5 = \frac{y_5}{(x+y)_5} = 1 - \frac{x_5}{(x+y)_5} \qquad (3)$$

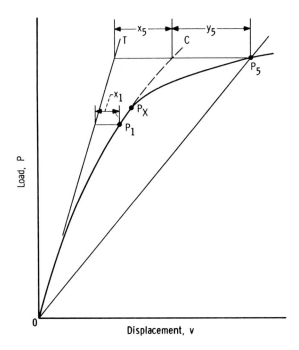

FIG. 5. Load-displacement record for test of material which deforms plastically around crack tip illustrating method of interpretation.

This ratio can be evaluated from the test record because $(x+y)_5$ can be measured (the horizontal distance from the tangent OT to P_5) and x_5 can be calculated from a measurement of x_1 at a load P_1 lower than P_X. Since x is proportional to P^3,

$$x_5 = x_1(P_5/P_1)^3 \tag{4}$$

Hence, from (3) and (4)

$$R_5 = 1 - x_1(P_5/P_1)^3/(x+y)_5 \tag{5}$$

And if P_1 is chosen as $0.8P_5$,

$$R_5 = 1 - 1.95x_1/(x+y)_5 \simeq 1 - 2x_1/(x+y)_5 \tag{6}$$

Finally, if the ratio of actual to effective crack extension R_5 is to be at least one-half, $(x+y)_5$ must be at least $4x_1$, as required in the procedure for determination of K_{Ic}.

III. Some Experimental Results

The results of a large number of K_{Ic} tests on maraging steels at three yield strength levels (285, 259, and 242 ksi) were reported by Brown and Srawley (1966). Three different specimen types were used (center-cracked tension, edge-cracked tension, and bend) with a range of crack lengths from 0.1 to 2.0 inches, and thicknesses from 0.1 to 1.0 inch. The approach to determination of K_{Ic} was more restricted than that of Sect. II, in that a result would then have been considered invalid unless the test record corresponded to either case II or III of Fig. 2. As it happened, all the specimens with sufficient crack length and thickness did produce records of one or other of these types, and all the results are consistent with the present procedure. These results showed that (a) different specimen types were equivalent; (b) the lower limit of both thickness and crack length for a satisfactory K_{Ic} test should be about $2.5(K_{Ic}/\sigma_{ys})^2$ (or approximately an order of magnitude greater than the extent of the mode I plane strain crack tip plastic zone; and (c) the coefficients of variation for the three sets of K_{Ic} values were about 0.05.

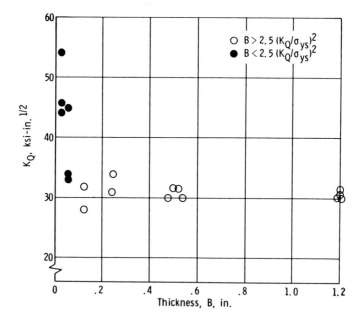

FIG. 6. Results for titanium 6%Al-6%V-2%Sn alloy aged at 1100° F for 4 hours. Yield strength, 174 ksi.

Additional results are shown in Figs. 6–9 from bend tests of a titanium alloy (6%Al-6%V-2%Sn), SAE 4340 steel, and aluminum alloy 7075.T651. The important factor that was varied in these series of bend tests was the specimen thickness. The crack lengths were all greater than $2.5(K_{Ic}/\sigma_{ys})^2$. The thinner specimens in each group were machined from broken halves of the thickest specimens so that heat treatment could be eliminated as a source of variation in the results. The data are presented as K_Q versus specimen thickness, and to distinguish those K_Q values that qualify as K_{Ic} values, according to the procedure of Sect. II, from those that do not, the former are shown as open circles and the latter as filled circles.

The results for the titanium alloy, aged for 4 hours at 1100° F to a yield strength of 174 ksi, are shown in Fig. 6. Type I test records were obtained from all but the thickest specimens, and the ratio of maximum load P_M to P_Q decreases with increasing specimen thickness until the two loads coincided in the type III test records for the thickest specimens. There were no intervening type II records. For this material, K_Q tends to rise considerably when the thickness is reduced below $2.5(K_{Ic}/\sigma_{ys})^2$, which illustrates the importance of this minimum thickness requirement. The results for thicker specimens are independent of thickness, which is a pragmatic justification for the procedure as applied to type I test records.

The results for 4340 steel, when tempered for 1 hour at 600° F (yield strength, 230 ksi), shown in Fig. 7, are similar to those for the titanium alloy, in that the K_Q values from specimens thinner than $2.5(K_Q/\sigma_{ys})^2$ are distinctly higher than the K_{Ic} values from thicker specimens. However, the test records for the thinner specimens of this material were type II, not type I, as in the case of the titanium specimens. These 4340 results show

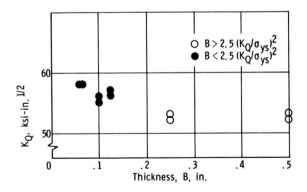

FIG. 7. Results for 4340 steel tempered at 600° F for 1 hour. Yield strength, 230 ksi.

that the occurrence of a marked pop-in of the crack front, indicated by a type II record, is not in itself a reliable criterion of a satisfactory K_{Ic} test result. The maraging steel results of Brown and Srawley (1966) demonstrate the same point.

Figure 8 shows the results for 4340 steel when tempered for 1 hour at 750° F (yield strength, 213 ksi). Here, the K_Q values for specimens thinner than $2.5(K_{Ic}/\sigma_{ys})^2$ are not significantly different from the K_{Ic} values for the thicker specimens. Like the series for the titanium alloy, the test records were type I for all but the thickest specimens, and type III for the thickest specimens. The K_{Ic} test behavior for 4340 steel, when tempered at 750° F, was thus distinctly different from that when tempered at 600° F. Furthermore, there is a substantial increase in K_{Ic} level for a relatively small decrease in yield strength. The increase in $(K_{Ic}/\sigma_{ys})^2$ is from about 0.05 inch to about 0.10 inch.

In the case of the 7075.T651 aluminum alloy (Fig. 9), there is again a tendency for the K_Q values for specimens thinner than $2.5(K_Q/\sigma_{ys})^2$ to be higher than the K_{Ic} values for the thicker specimens. The thinnest specimens (0.03 inch) produced type I records, those of intermediate thickness up to about 0.2 inch produced both type I and type II records, apparently haphazardly, and the thicker specimens produced either well-defined type II or type III records.

Of the four sets of results presented here, there are three in which the K_Q values for specimens thinner than $2.5(K_{Ic}/\sigma_{ys})^2$ are higher than the K_{Ic} values from thicker specimens, and one set where there is no significant difference. These results therefore lend support to the need for the thickness requirement established by Brown and Srawley (1966) which is incorporated in the procedure of Sect. II.

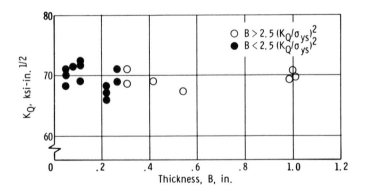

FIG. 8. Results for 4340 steel tempered at 750° F for 1 hour. Yield strength, 213 ksi.

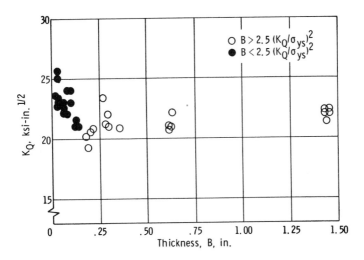

FIG. 9. Results for 7075.T651 aluminum alloy.

IV. Summary and Recommended Research

The results given in Sect. III, together with those in Brown and Srawley (1966), represent a substantial evaluation of the procedure of Sect. II, and thus of the current operational definition of K_{Ic}, covering a quenched and tempered steel at two strength levels, a maraging steel at three strength levels, a high-strength titanium alloy, and a high-strength aluminum alloy. These results confirm that K_{Ic}, as defined, is independent of specimen thickness by comparison with the data scatter for a given thickness. It was also shown in Brown and Srawley (1966) that K_{Ic} is also independent of crack length and specimen type, at least for the maraging steels investigated and for aluminum alloy 7075.T651. Thus, it is reasonable to regard K_{Ic} as an inherent material property which controls fracture under conditions of sufficiently high constraint.

Obviously, there is a need for evaluation of a wider variety of materials, and particularly of lower strength materials. Results are available which are probably valid for materials with yield strengths at least as low as $0.006E$ ksi, but the required specimen thickness for the toughest materials of this strength is probably at least 2.5 inches (see Table A-I, App. A). It would therefore be difficult and expensive to demonstrate independence of thickness for such materials. It is nevertheless of considerable practical interest to establish the upper bound of K_{Ic} as a function of E/σ_{ys} for materials in general (clearly there is no lower bound; brittle materials exist at any yield strength level).

The three-point-loaded bend specimen was chosen for standardization from among a variety of specimen types because of its comparatively low load and material requirements and its general versatility (Brown and Srawley, 1966). It is desirable that a tension-loaded specimen also be standardized, and work is currently proceeding on a compact tension specimen which requires only about one-fourth the material required for the bend specimen. The first compact tension specimen was designed by Manjoine (1965), and the subsequent development and application of such specimens has been comprehensively reviewed by Wessel (1967). Stress-intensity factors for edge-cracked specimens of various shapes have been determined by Srawley and Gross (1967).

One aspect of K_{Ic} testing which has not received sufficient attention is the effect of the characteristics of the fatigue crack on the behavior of the specimen in a subsequent K_{Ic} test. The restrictions on fatigue crack production to avoid unduly "blunt" cracks were prescribed by Brown and Srawley (1966) on the basis of limited available data, and considerably more work would be warranted in this area. Rice (1966) has discussed the mechanics of crack tip deformation and extension by fatigue in considerable detail.

It is to be expected that the application of K_{Ic} testing will be somewhat limited in practice because of the size and cost of specimens of low- and intermediate-strength materials. For this reason, there is considerable interest in correlation with other tests requiring smaller specimens, such as the Charpy-V test. It seems likely, however, that further development of elastic-plastic fracture mechanics (Irwin and McClintock, 1965; Wells, 1965; Rice, 1966) will be required before a satisfactory "small specimen" test can be developed, if then.

A different approach to circumventing the difficulty of specimen size is to attempt to extrapolate from K_{Ic} measurements made at low temperatures and/or high loading rates. Krafft (1964) found that correlation of K_{Ic} with plastic flow properties was a useful basis for such extrapolations. Along somewhat similar lines, Hahn and Rosenfield (1967) have suggested a rationale for relating K_{Ic} to tensile properties.

Appendix A. Details of K_{Ic} Test Practice with Bend Specimens

The essentials of the procedure for determination of K_{Ic} with bend specimens are given in Sect. II. The purpose of this appendix is to provide sufficient additional detail for those readers who wish to conduct tests in accordance with current recommendations of ASTM Committee E-24 (as of early 1967).

SPECIMEN DIMENSIONS

Figure A-1 is a dimensioned drawing of the recommended bend specimen, based on an unspecified thickness B. As stated in Sect. II, for the K_{Ic} test result to be considered valid according to the present operational definition, it is required that both the thickness B and the initial crack length a_0 exceed $2.5(K_{Ic}/\sigma_{ys})^2$ inches (Brown and Srawley, 1966). These required dimensions can be estimated from the ratio of yield strength to Young's modulus of the material, and the estimate will be adequate for all but the toughest materials (see Table A-I). When the form of the available material to be tested is such that the recommended specimen proportions would be impractical, it is permissible to use specimens of any convenient depth W not less than the thickness B, nor greater than $4B$. The crack length a_0 should be between $0.45W$ and $0.55W$, as in the recommended specimen. It should be kept in mind that the K_{Ic} measurement capacity is limited by either thickness or crack length, whichever is the

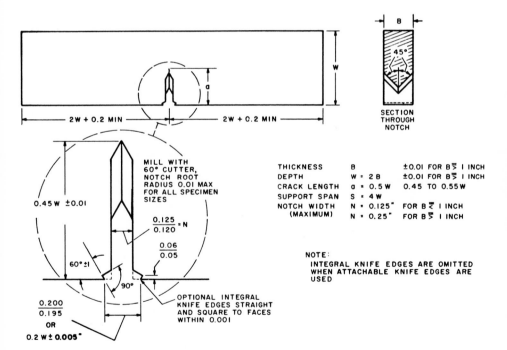

FIG. A-1. Recommended standard bend specimens.

TABLE A-I

σ_{ys}/E			Minimum recommended thickness and crack length (inches)
0.0057	to	0.0062	2.50
0.0062		0.0065	2.00
0.0065		0.0068	1.75
0.0068		0.0071	1.50
0.0071		0.0075	1.25
0.0075		0.0080	1.00
0.0080		0.0085	0.75
0.0085		0.0100	0.50
0.0100	or	greater	0.25

smaller. The chevron notch angle can be increased to accommodate thickness greater than $W/2$, but should not exceed 120°. The ratio of support span to depth should be 4.00, as in the recommended specimen.

Fatigue Crack Production

The fatigue crack should extend at least 0.05 inch from the root of the chevron notch on each side of the specimen. The chevron notch serves to maintain the crack inplane and to ensure that the crack extends well beyond the notch root throughout most of the specimen thickness. This is necessary to avoid undue influence of the notch on the crack tip stress field. If a straight-across notch is used, it is difficult to produce a crack which extends sufficiently from the notch root without deviating substantially from the intended plane. Any convenient method of fatigue cracking can be used, but the maximum load of the fatigue cycle should not exceed that necessary to generate the final 0.050 inch of crack extension in 20,000 cycles, with load range not less than three-fourths of maximum load. A fatigue stress-intensity range of about $5E \times 10^{-7}$ ksi-inch$^{1/2}$, where E is Young's modulus, will usually suffice to produce a crack in reasonable time. Blunt fatigue cracks produced at high stress-intensity levels can significantly affect the results of K_{Ic} tests (Brown and Srawley, 1966). Fatigue cracking should be regarded as a special kind of critical machining operation, and the cost considered accordingly.

Bend Test Fixture (Fig. A-2)

The simple design shown permits the support rolls to rotate and move apart slightly so that rolling contact is maintained and the effect of friction

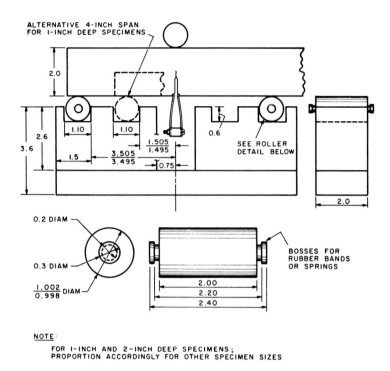

FIG. A-2. Bend test fixture design.

is virtually eliminated. It can be shown that the change in support span is negligible.

DISPLACEMENT MEASUREMENT

It will be appreciated from the discussion of Sect. II that the displacement gage must be sensitive and highly linear, and that there must be no lost motion between the gage and the locating positions on the specimen. Furthermore, the gage must be released without damage when the specimen breaks. Figure A-3 shows the essentials of a recommended form of gage and method of attachment. The linearity of the gage should be proved with an accurate calibrating instrument that is resettable to plus or minus 2×10^{-5} inch, and should be within 1×10^{-4} inch over the working range. Further details of the gage shown in Fig. A-3 are given by Fisher *et al.* (1966). When attachable knife edges are used to locate the gage, they should be accurately made, and the centers of the clamping screws should be no

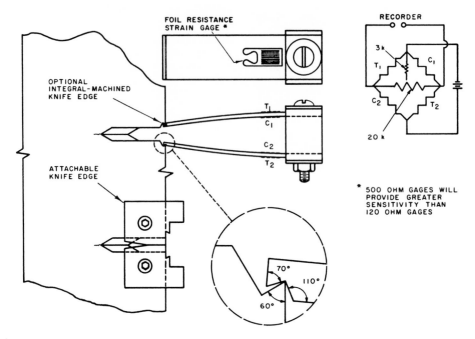

FIG. A-3. Double cantilever clip-in displacement gage and method of mounting.

further than $W/5$ from either the edge of the specimen or the centerline of the notch.

TESTING

The specimen and support fixture should be centered under the loading roll within 0.5%, and alined within 2°. The rate of loading should be such that the rate of increase of stress intensity is between 30 and 150 ksi-inch$^{1/2}$ per minute. The autographic recorder settings should be such that the initial slope of the load-displacement record is not greater than 2 nor less than $\frac{1}{2}$. It is conventional to plot the load along the vertical axis, as in a tension test record.

MEASUREMENTS AND CALCULATIONS

The average thickness and width are measured to within 0.001 inch. The crack length a_0 is measured from the edge of the specimen to the front of the fatigue crack at each surface of the specimen and at the most advanced position on the fracture surface. The average crack length is taken to be one-fourth of the sum of the two surface measurements plus twice the internal measurement. There is no objection, however, to using a more accurate averaging procedure. If the crack front is closer than 0.05 inch to the notch root, or if the crack lengths at any two positions differ by more than 10% of the specimen thickness, the fatigue crack is unsatisfactory. The value of K_Q is calculated from the following expression:

$$K_Q = (P_Q a^{1/2}/BW)[11.6 - 18.4(a_0/W)$$
$$+ 87.2(a_0/W)^2 - 151(a_0/W)^3 + 157(a_0/W)^4]$$

(for three-point bending with $S/W = 4.00$; for other cases, see App. B).

Appendix B. Stress-Intensity Factors and Load-Displacement Slope Factors for Various Specimens

To apply the procedure of Sect. II to other types of specimens, or to bend specimens with a/W substantially different from 0.5, the following additional information is needed:

a. The percentage decrease in secant slope of the load-displacement record for 2% effective crack extension.

This is required in order to find the secant line corresponding to OP_5 of Sect. II. From Eq. (1), this percentage decrease can be expressed as $2c_2/(c_1 + c_2)$ to a sufficient approximation. This factor is tabulated below as a function of relative crack length a/W or $2a/W$ under the heading of each specimen type.

b. An accurate K calibration, that is, a relation for the stress-intensity factor as a function of load and specimen dimensions, particularly relative crack length.

This is given as a polynomial expression under the heading of each specimen type.

Some general comments follow the listings of information by specimen type.

Bend Specimens Three point and four-point loading, $S/W = 4$ or 8

a/W:	0.3	0.4	0.5	0.6	
$2c_2/(c_1 + c_2)$:	3.2	3.9	5.2	7.0	(all types)

Stress-intensity factors are given to within 0.2% for all values of a/W up to 0.6 by

$$K_I BW^2/6Ma^{1/2} = A_0 + A_1(a/W) + A_2(a/W)^2 + A_3(a/W)^3 + A_4(a/W)^4$$

where M is the applied bending moment, and the coefficients have the following values:

	A_0	A_1	A_2	A_3	A_4
Pure bending	$+1.99$	-2.47	$+12.97$	-23.17	$+24.80$
Three-point:					
$S/W = 8$	$+1.96$	-2.75	$+13.66$	-23.98	$+25.22$
$S/W = 4$	$+1.93$	-3.07	$+14.53$	-25.11	$+25.80$

Single-Edge-Crack Tension Specimens (centrally pin loaded with centers not closer than $1.5W$ to the crack)

a/W:	0.3	0.4	0.5	0.6
$2c_2/(c_1 + c_2)$:	3.6	4.2	6.0	9.0

Stress-intensity factors are given to with 0.4% for all values of a/W up to 0.6 by

$$K_I BW/Pa^{1/2} = 1.99 - 0.41(a/W) + 18.70(a/W)^2 - 38.48(a/W)^3$$
$$+ 53.85(a/W)^4$$

Center-Crack Tension Specimens (remotely loaded with pin centers or grips not closer than $1.5W$ to the crack)

$2a/W$:	0.3	0.4	0.5	0.6
$2c_2/(c_1 + c_2)$:	2.0	2.0	3.0	3.3

Stress-intensity factors are given to within 0.5% for all values of $2a/W$ up to 0.7 by

$$K_I BW/Pa^{1/2} = 1.77 + 0.227(2a/W) - 0.510(2a/W)^2 + 2.7(2a/W)^3$$

Also, to within 1% for $2a/W$ up to 0.6:

$$K_I BW/Pa^{1/2} = 1.77[1 - 0.1(2a/W) + (2a/W)^2]$$

Double-Edge-Crack Tension Specimens (remotely loaded with pin centers or grips not closer than $1.5W$ to the crack)

$2a/W$:	0.3	0.4	0.5	0.6
$2c_2/(c_1 + c_2)$:	2.1	2.1	2.1	2.1

Stress-intensity factors are given to within 1% in the range $2a/W$ up to 0.7 by

$$K_I BW/Pa^{1/2} = 1.98 + 0.36(2a/W) - 2.12(2a/W)^2 + 3.42(2a/W)^3$$

Circumferentially Cracked Round Bar Specimens in Tension Stress-intensity factors are given within 1% over the range of d/D between 0.5 and 0.8

$$K_I D^{3/2}/P = 1.72(D/d) - 1.27$$

where D is the major and d the minor diameter.

GENERAL COMMENTS

The preceding expressions for stress-intensity factors were derived from results obtained by mathematical methods of crack stress analysis which are considered to be accurate, in themselves, to within at least 1%. The sources of results are cited in Brown and Srawley (1966). The primary results were fitted by a least-squares-best-fit computer program to obtain the convenient compact polynomial forms which can be readily programmed for computer calculations. The indicated precisions in each case refer to the fit of the primary results to the polynomials.

It should be appreciated that, in a mathematical crack stress analysis, the specimen has to be idealized into a sufficiently simple model. For instance, the complicated stress distribution around a loading pin has to be replaced by a simpler equivalent stress distribution assumed, on the basis of Saint Venant's principle, to have the same effect on the crack stress field. With careful attention to the design of both specimen and mathematical model, and apart from the fact that the model is usually two dimensional, the inaccuracy due to the idealization can be made as small as desired. To achieve high accuracy, however, may entail some sacrifice in compactness of the specimen design. For example, the length of a pin-loaded tension specimen might have to be greater than would otherwise be thought necessary. The accuracy with which any of the K calibrations apply to a specific, detailed specimen design depends, therefore, on the compatibility of the design with the mathematical model on which the K calibration is based.

Apart from the crack-notch round bar, all the specimens considered here are plate specimens with through-thickness cracks. The cracks are assumed to have straight leading edges normal to the plate faces. Because of the difficulty of complete three-dimensional stress analysis, the K calibration procedures that are used, whether mathematical or experimental, treat these plate specimens as essentially two dimensional. Some investigators adjust the two-dimensional K calibrations by multiplying by the factor $(1 - \nu^2)^{-1/2}$, where ν is Poisson's ratio. The magnitude of this adjustment factor is 1.05 when ν is 0.3. The adjustment is intended to improve the accuracy with which a two-dimensional K calibration would apply to a real plane-strain crack-toughness specimen. It is by no means clear, however, that the adjustment factor should be as large as $(1 - \nu^2)^{-1/2}$, although there is general agreement that it should not be less than unity. In view of this uncertainty, we prefer the simpler alternative of using the two-dimensional K calibrations directly, without adjustment. Any error resulting from this practice will be small (probably less than 5%) and conservative in that the K_{Ic} will be underestimated rather than overestimated.

The most commonly used experimental method of K calibration is that due to Irwin and Kies (1954) in which measurements are made of the compliance (reciprocal of the stiffness) of a specimen having a narrow machined slot which is incrementally extended between successive measurements. The machined slot is used to simulate a crack primarily because it is not feasible to produce plane cracks of sufficient size and accuracy. It is apparent, however, that the compliance of a crack of given length will not be exactly the same as that of a finite-width slot of the same length. The experimental data are treated by expressing the specimen compliance as a function of crack length and then obtaining the derivative of this function with respect to crack length. While it is obvious that the compliance of a specimen with a slot will be somewhat greater than that of a specimen with an equally long crack, it does not follow that the derivative of the compliance with respect to the length will always be greater for the slot than for a crack. Since it is not known how to correct for the slot width, it is advisable to take the equivalent crack length as equal to the slot length but uncertain to the extent of the slot width. This uncertainty will be minimal if the specimen is made large and the slot narrow. It is always an advantage to use as large a specimen as possible for compliance measurements, because the displacements will be proportionately large and can be measured with correspondingly good accuracy.

To conduct a compliance calibration with good accuracy, it is necessary to use sensitive, accurate gages, and to pay careful attention to detail. More accurate results can be obtained with compliant specimens, such as bend bars, than with stiff specimens such as notched round bars. It should also be appreciated that the accuracy of the K calibration is likely to be less than that of the compliance measurements themselves because of the differentiation operation required for reducing the experimental data. The error-magnifying effect of differentiation should be less the larger the number of compliance measurements involved for a given range of crack lengths.

The main advantage of the compliance calibration method is that the actual configuration and load distribution of a K_{Ic} test specimen can be closely modeled by the K calibration specimen. In general, mathematical methods are capable of higher precision than experimental methods. Ideally, both methods should be applied to a given specimen so that the results can be compared.

Symbols

a	crack length	K_{Ic}	plane strain crack toughness, as defined in Sect. II
a_0	initial crack length		
$A_0, A_1, \ldots, A_4$	numerical coefficients in polynomial fitting function	K_Q	conditional value of K_{Ic}: see Sect. II
B	specimen thickness	M	bending moment
c_1, c_2, c_3	constants (for a given K_{Ic} test: Sect. II)	N	notch width (Fig. A-1)
		P	load
d	minor diameter of circumferentially cracked round bar	$P_1, P_5, P_Q,$ P_X, P_M	specified load points on a K_{Ic} test record: see Sect. II and Figs. 2–5.
D	major diameter of circumferentially cracked round bar		
		R_5	ratio $y_5/(x+y)_5$: see Sect. II
E	Young's modulus		
g	distance apart of two conjugate gage points (across crack)	S	support span for bend specimen
g_0	initial value of g at zero load	v	relative displacement of two conjugate gage points, equal to $(g - g_0)$
$\mathscr{G}_c$	crack extension force at onset of rapid crack propagation		
$\mathscr{G}_{Ic}$	plane strain fracture toughness in terms of crack extension force	W	specimen depth or width
		x_1, x_5, y_5	measurements made on K_{Ic} test record: see Sect. II and Fig. 5
K	stress-intensity factor	ν	Poisson's ratio
K_c	stress-intensity factor at onset of rapid crack propagation	σ_{ys}	yield strength (0.2% offset)

REFERENCES

Bridgman, P. W. (1927). "The Logic of Modern Physics." Macmillan, New York.

Brown, W. F., Jr., and Srawley, J. E. (1966). "Plane Strain Crack Toughness Testing," SP 410. ASTM, Philadelphia.

Fisher, D. M., Bubsey, R. T., and Srawley, J. E. (1966). NASA TN D-3724.

Griffith, A. A. (1920). *Trans. Roy. Soc. (London)* **221**, 163.

Hahn, G. T., and Rosenfield, A. R. (1967). "Sources of Fracture Toughness: The Relation between K_{Ic} and the Ordinary Tensile Properties of Metals," Report Battelle Memorial Institute, Columbus, Ohio.

Irwin, G. R. (1948). *In* "Fracturing of Metals" (F. Jonassen, W. P. Roop, and R. T. Bayless, eds.), pp. 147–166. ASM, Cleveland.

Irwin, G. R. (1957). *J. Appl. Mech.* **24**, 361.

Irwin, G. R. (1958). *In* "Handbuch der Physik" (S. Flugge, ed.), Vol. 6, pp. 551–590. Springer-Verlag, Berlin.

Irwin, G. R. (1960a). Report No. 5486. U.S. Naval Research Laboratory, Washington, D.C.

Irwin, G. R. (1960b). *In* "Mechanical and Metallurgical Behavior of Sheet Materials: Proceedings of the 7th Sagamore Ordnance Materials Research Conference" (G. Sachs, J. V. Latorre, and A. Jones, eds.), pp. IV-63–IV-78. Syracuse University Research Institute, Syracuse, New York.

Irwin, G. R., and Kies, J. A. (1954). *Welding J. (N.Y.) Res. Suppl.* **33**, 193s.

Irwin, G. R., and McClintock, F. A. (1965). *In* "Symposium on Fracture Toughness Testing and Its Applications," STP 381, pp. 84–113. ASTM, Philadelphia.

Irwin, G. R., Kies, J. A. and Smith, H. L. (1958). *Proc. ASTM* **58**, 640.

Krafft, J. M. (1964). *Appl. Mater. Res.* **3**, 88.

Manjoine, M. J. (1965). *J. Basic Eng.* **87**, 293.

Orowan, E. (1949). *Rept. Progr. Phys.* **12**, 185–232.

Paris, P. C., and Sih, G. (1965). *In* "Symposium on Fracture Toughness Testing and Its Applications," STP 381, pp. 30–81. ASTM, Philadelphia.

Ramburg, W., and Osgood, W. R. (1943). NACA TN 902.

Rice, J. R. (1966). "The Mechanics of Crack Tip Deformation and Extension by Fatigue." Division of Engineering, Brown University, Providence, Rhode Island.

Srawley, J. E., and Brown, W. F., Jr. (1965). *In* "Symposium on Fracture Toughness Testing and Its Applications," STP 381, pp. 133–195. ASTM, Philadelphia.

Srawley, J. E., and Gross, B. (1967). *Mater. Res. Std.* **7**, 155.

Tetelman, A. S., and McEvily, A. J., Jr. (1967). "Fracture of Structural Materials." Wiley, New York.

Wells, A. A. (1965). *Proc. Roy. Soc. (London) Ser. A* **285**, 34.

Wessel, E. T. (1967). "State of the Art of the WOL Specimen for K_{Ic} Fracture Toughness Testing," Scientific Paper No. 67-1D6-BTLRF-R1. Westinghouse Research Laboratories, Pittsburgh.

Williams, M. L. (1957). *J. Appl. Mech.* **24**, 109–114.

Wilson, E. B., Jr. (1952). "An Introduction to Scientific Research." McGraw-Hill, New York.

CHAPTER 3

TEMPERATURE EFFECTS ON FRACTURE

W. E. Witzell   *N. R. Adsit*

Abstract: Some theories of fracture are considered with respect to variations in temperature. Because the fractures tend to be catastrophic at low temperatures, the majority of the discussion concerns testing at cryogenic temperatures. Various specimen configurations are considered for use at cryogenic temperatures, including: tensile and notched tensile, center notched, single edge notched, surface notched, and slow bend. Problems peculiar to temperature testing are examined.

Strength and toughness values are presented for various engineering alloys tested at cryogenic temperatures. The behavior of several 300-series stainless steels at temperatures between 1200° F and −423° F is discussed. In addition, several aluminum and titanium alloys are examined at cryogenic temperatures.

I. Introduction

One is tempted to believe that, as materials get stronger and harder as the temperature is reduced toward absolute zero, they will also become tougher. After all, the physical properties, such as modulus, coefficient of thermal conductivity, etc., show that the electrons and atoms are slowed down and the attractive force between atoms is greatly increased. One factor that we cannot overlook, however, is that these metals are not perfect. They have different structures and a wide variety of defects. Even worse, as we go from pure metals to engineering alloys, these conditions become exaggerated.

The student of metallic fractures is quite aware from the beginning that the catastrophic failure of materials is closely connected to the test or service temperature. The celebrated Boston molasses tank, various ships, and an occasional bridge failed under run-of-the-mill loading conditions, frequently in the wintertime [see Parker (1957), for a comprehensive listing of service failures]. In the early portion of the 20th century, low-temperature problems were usually caused by old man winter. Today, however, the usage of cryogenic fuels and oxidizers for spacecraft have sharply increased the need for an understanding of the low (very low) temperature behavior of many materials (Fig. 1). Worse than that is the very high stress level at which these vehicles operate during their cryogenic exposure. The situation is further complicated by the manner in which the materials are worked during processing and fabrication, and the continual work and thermal cycling designed to increase the ultimate strength by a few more pounds per square inch.

Although the test temperature has an effect on fracture, it is virtually impossible to isolate temperature effects from the effects described in other chapters of this treatise. A complete discussion would necessarily include scores of other effects and related factors. For example, one might discuss the variation of metallographic effects with temperature, or the variation of radiation effects with temperature, and so on. Or a fascinating subject for a paper could be, "The Effects of Radiation on the Fracture of Bones at Elevated and Cryogenic Temperatures."

The very complexity of the subject is well illustrated by the number of chapters in the entire volume.

II. Temperature Dependence

The temperature dependence of a material in general is shown schematically in Fig. 2. The curve labeled σ_{ys} represents the yield strength of the material, and σ_F is the basic cleavage strength of the material. When a

FIG. 1. Fracture of stainless steel pressure vessel at −423° F. This tank was chemically milled prior to welding and surrounded by insulation during burst testing (Convair photo 11778B).

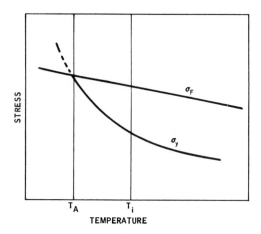

Fig. 2. Schematic of the variation of yield strength and cleavage strength with temperature.

material is stressed at a temperature T_i, it will deform first by plastic yielding, and if it were to strain-harden to the curve σ_F, it would then cleave. If this temperature T_i is below T_A, it is obvious that the material would simply cleave at the weakest point. The σ_{ys} curve is greatly affected by several conditions other than temperature, i.e.

a. The structure of the material
b. The strain rate
c. The state of stress in the part
d. The grain size

The type of lattice structure plays a great role in the shape of the σ_{ys} curve. Body-centered-cubic materials are far more sensitive to temperature than close-packed materials. Therefore, we find that iron will be much more sensitive to temperature than nickel or aluminum. In iron, the yield strength may increase by a factor of 4 to 6 in decreasing from $+18°$ C to $-196°$ C, as shown by Smith and Hendrickson (1962). The yield strength of aluminum, on the other hand, only increases a few percent in the same temperature range, as shown by Byrne et al. (1961).

The reason that the yield strength is more temperature dependent in bcc (body-centered cubic) than in fcc (face-centered cubic) or hcp (hexagonal close-packed) is due to the Peierls–Nabarro stress. This force is the measure of the difficulty in pushing a dislocation through the lattice by moving the bonds of the atoms. Since the bcc structure is not close packed and the bonds are directional, it is more difficult to cause them to shift from one atom to the next atom because of that directionality. This is discussed in more detail by Smith and Hendrickson (1962). The strain rate will tend to increase the yield strength and, therefore, the σ_{ys} curve is displaced upward. This will lead to cleavage or brittle failure at a higher temperature since T_A is now increased.

The third factor, state of stress, causes yield strength to increase as the complexity of the deformation is increased. Again, that is to displace the σ_{ys} curve upward. If a specimen were tested in simple torsion where the maximum shear stress is equal to the maximum normal stress, it could be tested at temperatures down to T_A before it would cleave. For the same material tested in tension, cleavage would occur at the temperature where $\sigma_{ys} = \sigma_F/2$, since the shear stress is half the normal stress. At sharp notches, the stress is increased above the bulk stress and cleavage can occur at even higher temperatures.

The yield strength varies as the inverse square root of grain size. This means that the transition temperature T_A (between cleavage and yielding) is increased as the grain size is increased. This is demonstrated by Tetelman and McEvily (1967).

III. Early Fracture Criteria

A. Nil Ductility Temperature (NDT)

If tensile specimens are tested at lower and lower temperatures, there comes a temperature where the yield strength equals the ultimate strength. This is shown as T_A in Fig. 2, and at that temperature there is no measurable ductility. This point is called the nil ductility temperature, and is affected by several metallurgical variables. It is, therefore, not a materials constant and cannot be defined exactly, but can be defined under a given set of conditions including grain size, etc. If we now introduce a small flaw (stress concentration), the temperature at which there is no apparent ductility will be increased, since we have introduced triaxiality. Therefore, this approach is dependent on the test conditions and specimen configuration. Consequently, the test does not provide a true transition temperature but is quite valuable as a qualitative tool.

B. Charpy Impact Testing

A more useful engineering tool results from the introduction of a given flaw into a specimen and testing that specimen at a high strain rate. Both of these increase the NDT, and the test, therefore, gives an NDT that tends to be conservative. This is the essence of the Charpy impact test. The energy under the stress-strain curve which can be related to the ductility is used as a measure. A low energy is indicative of low ductility, as shown in Fig. 3.

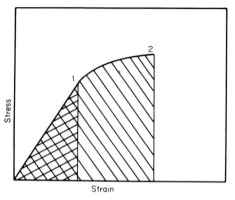

Fɪɢ. 3. Idealized stress-strain curve. A material failing at point 1 would have low ductility and low energy, while a failure at point 2 would indicate large ductility and high energy.

The energy measured is really the amount of energy used in causing yielding or plastic flow. Figure 4 is a schematic for materials tested in impact.

C. Fʀᴀᴄᴛᴜʀᴇ Aᴘᴘᴇᴀʀᴀɴᴄᴇ

A third method that has been used to evaluate a material for brittle behavior is to examine the fracture surface. When one observes that the fracture face is very regular and follows crystal planes, it is apparent that it cleaved. If the crystal size (grain size) is large, one can observe this with the naked eye. This, as previously noted, is indicative of brittle fracture.

In fine-grained materials, it is necessary to increase the resolution to the point that one can examine the surface. But even when one can distinguish the surface, there may be other lines even in a cleavage failure. The

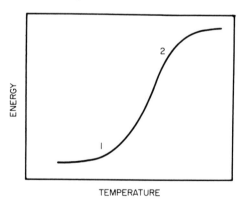

Fɪɢ. 4. Impact energy variation with temperature. Locations 1 and 2 identify the energy associated with the corresponding points in Fig. 3.

lines are tears on a fine scale (sometimes called river lines) that are caused by imperfections within the crystal lattice (i.e., screw dislocation), and are approximately perpendicular to the crack interface.

The opposite extreme of cleavage is the pure shear failure that is typical of ductile single crystals. In this case, there is so much plastic flow that the specimen simply slides apart.

The object of an evaluation of the fracture surface must be to determine what type of fractures occurred and, second, how much of each. If one observes the fractures from a series of specimens tested at decreasing temperature, a transition from ductile shear to brittle cleavage is noted. The temperature is the fracture appearance transition temperature (FATT). This is a very poor method of evaluating materials for design, but it can be used very well for service failures.

IV. Qualitative Evaluations

A. NOTCH-UNNOTCH RATIO

An early and somewhat simple method of evaluating toughness is known as the notched tensile test. The technique involves measurement of the net tensile strength of a bar that contains symmetric edge notches in the center of the reduced section of the flat test specimen (Fig. 5). In the case

FIG. 5. Notched tensile specimen.

of a heavy plate, the tensile specimen takes the shape of a round bar sample with a circumferential notch completely around the center section (Fig. 6). The fracture strength of the sample indicates the strength of the material tested when a notch or imperfection is present. When such a sample is tested at various temperatures, some hint of the toughness is obtained. At the same time, the appearance of the fracture surface provides information as to the ductility or brittleness of the specimen. Such an evaluation was a

FIG. 6. Round notched tensile specimen.

bit too simple and led to some erroneous conclusions. For example, the notch strength of a material could show no degradation of the toughness of the material with a decrease in test temperature. However, when the variation of ultimate tensile strength of the same material is observed, it is conceivable that a tremendous increase in strength with a decrease in temperature occurs. Such a condition suggests a relative decrease in toughness with a decrease in temperature. This apparent discrepancy is quickly cleared up by use of the notched-unnotched tensile ratio. Theoretically, if this ratio exceeds 1.0, the material is tough. The rationale for such a conclusion is that a tough material is one that can redistribute the stresses in the presence of a notch in such a manner as to cause failure at an applied stress greater than the ultimate strength of the material. No attempt is made to determine the principle stresses caused by the interference of normal stresses with the notch and resultant swift reduction in net section area. With a decrease in temperature, the redistribution of stresses may be more difficult, causing a degradation of the toughness of the material. At the same time, the energy causing fracture may be dissipated by the very cold fluid, in which case, a high fracture stress can occur. However, should the load rate be increased to the extent that the heat energy cannot be dissipated, the material can still demonstrate a relatively poor fracture stress.

The prudent investigator should not accept the results of a single test (or type of test) to the exclusion of all others. Particularly, this is true of the notched and unnotched (smooth) tensile tests. Many have felt that high elongation is a perfect indicator of greater toughness. Exceptions can be found to this contention, as will be illustrated later.

While the notched tensile tests are useful for screening purposes, there are several pitfalls of which to be aware. The most critical, perhaps, concerns the "sharpness" of the notch itself. Christian and Hurlich (1963) insist that a "medium" sharp notch is the best predictor of brittleness at cryogenic temperatures. Their claim is that a notched sheet tensile specimen with a K_T of 6.3,

$$K_T = (a/R)^{1/2}$$

where a is one half the distance between the notches and R the root radius of the notch, correlates with the fatigue life of complex welded joints tested at high stress levels. Others disagree, suggesting that only extremely sharp notched specimens can predict embrittlement at low temperatures.

B. Center Notched Tensile Tests

At the same time that experimenters were gleefully obtaining transition temperatures (such as NDT and FATT), others were concerned that the conditions under which these tests were conducted were not very conducive to rigorous stress analysis theories. Worse than that, many illusive materials were providing a transition that was gradual and hard to evaluate. At the same time, the more stringent requirement for high strengths under hostile temperature environments were nibbling away at the boundary conditions of the transition temperature concept. For these reasons (partially), the fracture mechanics concept, as developed by Griffith, Westergaard, Irwin, and others, looked promising for evaluation of materials at various temperatures. Unfortunately, the overwhelming bulk of the investigations have concerned room temperature tests, or a very narrow temperature band surrounding room temperature. Extreme temperature environment tests have been performed only by aerospace companies whose vehicles have had to suffer the outrageous demands from space reentry environments to cryogenic fuels. As in all fascinating scientific endeavors, others, such as those in the academic world, like to jump into the fray and play with superheated materials and exotic (and dangerous) fluids such as liquid oxygen and liquid hydrogen. Nevertheless, the bulk of cryogenic materials studies were performed by those companies whose immediate needs dictated quick (if not prudent) evaluations. [For example, the liquid oxygen usage of General Dynamics/Astronautics (now Convair) was measured in thousand-ton units even before 1960.]

The plane stress fracture toughness approach of Irwin looked useful for the early cryogenic tests. Briefly, this technique requires measurement of the gross stress and crack length at the onset of rapid crack growth. Insertion of these values into the familiar equation (Campbell and Achbach, 1960)

$$K_c = \sigma_G [W \tan(\pi a/W)]^{1/2} \qquad \text{for center notch specimen (Fig. 7)}$$

[where σ_G is the gross stress, a is one half the crack length at onset of rapid growth (critical crack length), and W the specimen width] provides a value for critical crack intensity factor K_c (sometimes called fracture toughness).

Further investigation showed that this value was in error due to the plastic zone that formed at the tip of the crack. Again, Dr. Irwin went to work and deduced that the plastic zone size could be approximated by the equation

$$r_y = (K_c)^2/2\pi(\sigma_{ys})^2$$

where K_c is the first approximation of fracture toughness, σ_{ys} the yield strength of the material, and r_y the plastic zone size.

If the computed plastic zone size is significant (i.e. if K_c is large compared to the yield strength), the value of half crack length must be adjusted to account for this inelastic behavior. From a very simple approach, one

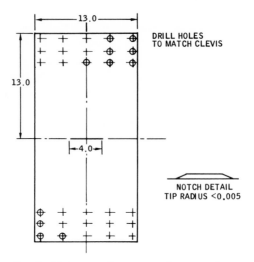

FIG. 7. Plain stress fracture toughness specimen.

could consider the plastic zone as an extension of the actual crack, beyond which is another area of purely elastic behavior. More sophisticated approaches will be found in other chapters of this treatise. See, for example, the chapters by G. Sih and H. Liebowitz, and by G. R. Irwin.

Nevertheless, it would appear that the general technique provides a simple way of obtaining fracture data for materials exposed to various temperature environments. After all, only the yield strength, the gross stress at onset, and the critical crack length are required for the calculations. On second thought, measurement of crack length is not that simple. Admittedly, for thick materials, it is quite possible to determine the critical crack length by observing the fracture appearance after the test. However, for thin sheet materials, such a technique is far more difficult. The difficulty in crack measurement, incidentally, may have provided some impetus for the study of techniques which eliminated the need for crack growth measurement (e.g., some types of plane strain fracture toughness testing).

Initially, it had been proposed to insert a drop of staining fluid into the notch tip prior to loading. During the slow growth period, the fluid follows the crack, but, when fast growth occurs, the fluid is left in the lurch (slow growth portion) and only the slow growth portion is stained. However, it has been reported that staining has altered the crack growth characteristics of various materials. Even if this process did not influence the crack growth, such a technique is impossible at cryogenic temperatures. Logically, it would seem fruitful to develop an instrument to measure crack growth. Such devices would be quite difficult to fabricate if the crack length was to be measured continuously. Various devices were designed to measure the crack opening (similar to compliance) in the direction of the applied load. Unfortunately, such instruments must be calibrated against crack growth which, of course, merely returns us to the original need of measuring crack growth or length. Some use has been made of the so-called crack propagation gage shown in Fig. 8.

As the crack grows, the fine wires in the path of the crack fail progressively and provide a suitable indication on some remote readout device. In addition, strain gages have been manufactured and are available commercially which incorporate these principles. Since the crack length is measured in discrete intervals, absolute crack growth is not actually measured, but can be approached by decreasing the space between crack wires. A disadvantage of such a system is that the crack wire must be carefully selected and/or adjusted to be able to distinguish between cracking and plastic deformation. Furthermore, such bonded instruments are subject to the same difficulties at cryogenic temperatures as are normal strain gages. To be sure, bonded strain gages have been successfully used at General Dynamics Convair, NASA laboratories, and other facilities in liquid hydrogen environments ($-423°$ F) (Fig. 9).

If bonded instrumentation is used for center notched specimens, obviously two installations are needed to track the crack at each notch tip. As early as 1961, Convair was able to observe crack growth in sheet materials immersed in liquid hydrogen and other cryogenic fluids. A very satisfactory method of determining critical crack length in thin sheet material consisted of attaching a scale to the specimen and observing the crack growth with increasing load. At cryogenic temperatures, it is necessary to provide some sort of viewing port and sight through a telescope in order to determine critical crack length (see Figs. 10 and 11). Ironically, the human eyeball seems to be the best instrument available for such observations. While the crack is growing slowly, the length may be measured, but during rapid propagation, the growth is too swift to see. It follows that the last reading taken corresponds to critical crack length—by definition. Obviously, motion pictures can record the same thing, perhaps at greater cost.

In the early investigations, size effects were considered, but were frequently disregarded due to other more immediate problems. For example,

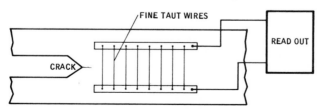

FIG. 8. Crack propagation gage.

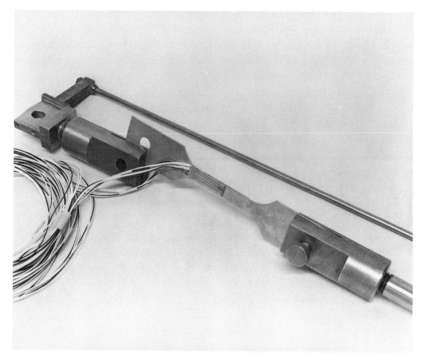

FIG. 9. Strain gaged tensile specimen in clevises used in cryogenic testing. Rod on end of clevis permits quick release of lower clevis for testing in liquid nitrogen (Convair photo 78851B).

engineers who were designing vehicles with a particular material in a very thin gage were not particularly interested in evaluating the material in the heavy plate conditions. Furthermore, the size of existing cryogenic containers restricted the maximum size of fracture specimens. Just as restrictive was the reluctance of engineers to handle large quantities of such dangerous fluids as liquid oxygen and liquid hydrogen. Eventually, the inert liquid nitrogen (boiling point $-320°$ F) was substituted for liquid oxygen (boiling at $-297°$ F) for test purposes. Logically, the placid liquid helium ($-452°$ F) would be a good substitute for the explosive liquid hydrogen ($-423°$ F). However, the extremely high cost of helium and the difficulty in keeping this fluid in the liquid state have minimized such a substitution.

In some cases, the materials in use were less than $\frac{1}{16}$ inch thick (0.063). For example, the Air Force's Atlas ICBM and NASA's Centaur hydrogen-fueled upper stage, both developed by General Dynamics/Astronautics (now Convair), utilize 301 stainless steel in such thicknesses to contain liquid oxygen and liquid hydrogen. If the ASTM recommendations

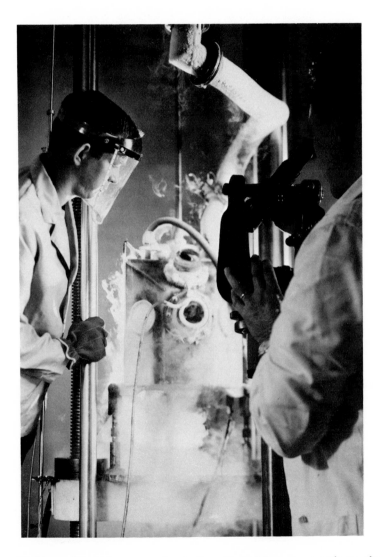

FIG. 10. Cryogenic crack propagation testing. Technician uses transit to observe growth of crack in 4-inch wide center notched specimen that is immersed in cryogenic fluid inside of cryostat. Center viewing port and upper light port on cryostat are machined from clear plexiglass (Convair photo 01678B).

FIG. 11. Cryostat for testing 18-inch wide center notched tensile specimens at cryogenic temperatures. Wide plexiglass window permits direct observation of crack growth by
engineer equipped with transit (Convair photo 01676B).

(ASTM, 1964) are used for a material with a thickness of 0.050 inch, the following limits are obtained:

$16 < W/B < 45$ where $W =$ specimen width and $B =$ thickness

$0.8 < W < 2.25$

$2a = W/3$ where $2a =$ total original crack length

If a specimen width of 0.9 inch were used, $2a = 0.3$ inch, and if $W = 2.25$, $2a = 0.75$ inch.

Intuitively, one would say that the smaller specimen is too small, particularly if slow crack growth is to be measured. In retrospect, the larger specimen may have been too small for some fairly tough materials. If a specimen is too narrow, the net fracture stress will be quite high, conceivably exceeding the yield strength of the material. Another difficulty with the small specimen is the potential percentage of error associated with errors in measurement of the critical crack length.

Nevertheless, from a strict fracture mechanics point of view, many of the specimens used at cryogenic temperatures a few years ago were too small. This is not to say that the data is not useful, but merely that care should be taken in interpretation and presentation of the results.

C. SINGLE EDGE NOTCH (SEN) TESTS

Despite some of the difficulties with the center notched specimens, it appeared that a reasonable plane stress fracture toughness value could be obtained at room temperature. At cryogenic temperatures, crack growth measurement was still a problem. Furthermore, in thicker materials, the failures were frequently mixed modes, i.e., a combination of plane stress and plane strain.

At the Naval Research Laboratory, Krafft and others (ASTM, 1964), were investigating the possibility of utilizing a much smaller, less expensive specimen patterned after the Navy Tear Test Specimen (associated with Kahn). Krafft had hoped to develop a specimen of the size of a Charpy bar that could be easily machined and fatigue notch sharpened in the machine shop. From these tests and from the investigations of others, the single edge notch (SEN) tensile test evolved (Fig. 12).

It was deduced that the specimen of this shape, prior to crack growth, was subject to conditions of plane strain. In addition, if a plot of load variation with compliance were made, a distinctive jog in the curve was observed at about the point that the sharpened notch would reinitiate a crack. This point became known as "pop-in" because of the noises emitting from the specimen at this time. (The measurement of noise emissions has produced

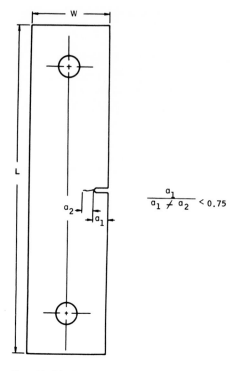

FIG. 12. Single edge notch (SEN) specimen.

some very interesting results lately. Harold Dunegan, of the Lawrence Radiation Laboratory, has measured the continuous noise from a tensile specimen or fracture specimen under load. By suitable presentation of the data, he is able to predict exactly when a specimen or a pressure vessel will fail.)

The pop-in stress is frequently used to calculate the plane strain fracture toughness (K_{Ic}) as follows (see Brown and Srawley, 1966; Campbell and Achbach, 1960):

$$K_{Ic}^2 = \left(\frac{1}{1 - v^2}\right)\left(\frac{P}{B}\right)^2 \frac{1}{W}\left[7.59\,\frac{a}{W} - 32\left(\frac{a}{W}\right)^2 + 117\left(\frac{a}{W}\right)^3\right]$$

where v is Poisson's ratio, P the load at pop-in, B the specimen thickness, W the specimen width, and a the crack length. (The reader is advised to be consistent in use of units. If kips and inches are used, the resulting units for K_{Ic} will be: ksi$\sqrt{\text{inch}}$.)

There is some debate as to whether the K_{Ic} calculated from the pop-in is a true plane strain fracture toughness value. Nevertheless, if the notch starter crack is sharp enough, and if the pop-in is well defined, the value thus obtained will be useful data.

The beauty of such a technique at cryogenic temperature is that the pop-in may be obtained quite readily by use of a compliance gage either fitted into the notch itself, or by attaching the gage across the tip of the crack. A simple compliance gage can be constructed by forming a band of sheet metal in such a way as to permit strain gages to be bonded under a highly and uniformly strained area. For use at $-423°$ F, care must be taken to select the proper adhesive, keep the glue line very thin, provide for contraction of tab wires, and minimize the amount of waterproofing used (Fig. 13).

D. PART-THROUGH CRACK TESTS

The tests already described were designed strictly for purposes of providing notch toughness, and have no relationship to actual cracked structures. A test specimen that simulates an actual crack is the part-through crack specimen. (Sometimes called the shallow crack test specimen.) In this type of test, a semielliptical crack is induced in the surface of the specimen to a depth less than half the thickness of the material, and the specimen is tested in tension. The only measurement made during testing is that of failure load. After fracture, the fracture surface is examined and the critical crack depth is measured. The plane strain fracture toughness is determined by using the ratio of flaw depth to flaw shape parameter (a/Q) in the equation (Tiffany *et al.*, 1966)

$$K_{Ic} = 1.1\sigma(a/Q)^{1/2}\pi^{1/2}$$

The flaw shape parameter Q is determined as follows:

$$Q = \Phi^2 - 0.212(\sigma/\sigma_{ys})^2$$

where σ_{ys} is the yield strength.

The value of Q is frequently found in curves that relate the crack surface length $2c$, crack depth a, and net-stress-to-yield-stress ratios (Tiffany *et al.*, 1966).

Part-through crack tests are most useful for thick plate specimens where the critical crack depth is more readily determined. Again, such tests are useful at cryogenic temperatures, since no crack length measurement is necessary during testing (Fig. 14).

E. BEND TESTS

The notched bend, or slow bend, test has also been used quite extensively for fracture studies. The specimen used for this test resembles that of the single edge notch specimen, except that pinholes are unnecessary. The

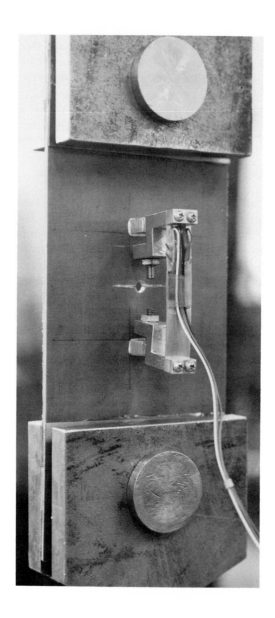

FIG. 13. Strain gaged compliance gage for cryogenic testing of plastic (Convair photo 28921B).

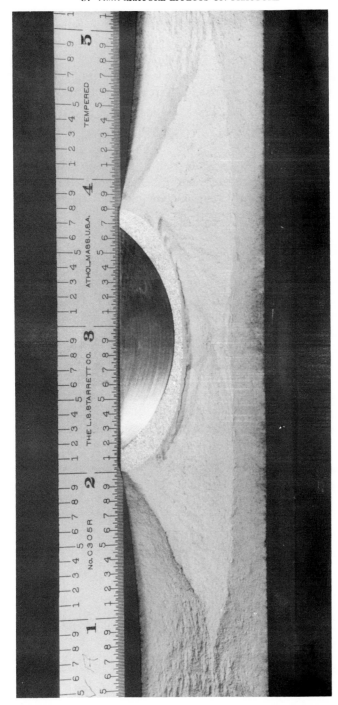

FIG. 14. Fractured 2219-T81 aluminum alloy plate showing machined surface notch, fatigue notch extension and crack growth (GD/Convair photo 84997B).

specimen is loaded in either 3- or 4-point bending. In general, 4-point bending is preferred, since it provides a zone of constant moment that surrounds the notch (on the tension side of the beam). In this case, as in the SEN test, a plot of compliance variation with increasing load is obtained. The plane strain fracture toughness is calculated as follows:

$$K_{Ic}^2 = \frac{1}{1-\nu^2}\left(\frac{P}{B}\right)^2\frac{L^2}{W^3}\left[34.7\,\frac{a}{W} - 55.2\left(\frac{a}{W}\right)^2 + 196\left(\frac{a}{W}\right)^3\right]$$

Again, this type of specimen lends itself to cryogenic testing if the specimen dimensions are not too large. Instrumentation may be a bit of a problem, since normal cryogenic extensometers must be modified somewhat to accommodate the bend specimen (Fig. 15).

F. Time-Dependent Fracture

1. *Fatigue*

Most engineers are familiar with the general concept of fatigue. A specimen is repeatedly cycled between two loads. The failure occurs at stress levels below the strength of the material. The data typically is presented in an *S-N* curve such as is shown in Fig. 16. The surface appearance of a fatigue fracture is much different than a cleavage crack. There are lines parallel to the fatigue crack, because the crack was arrested there for a period of time (Fig. 17). Furthermore, the crack is not necessarily along crystallographic planes. In cleavage, lines on the fracture surface are caused by steps in the surface and result in tears perpendicular to the direction of the crack. The fracture process is divided into three processes: (1) crack initiation, (2) slow crack propagation, and (3) unstable crack growth.

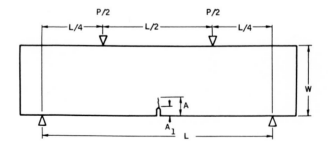

Fig. 15. Slow-bend test specimen configuration. $a_1/a < 0.75$, $L/W \geq 4$, $0.20 < a/W < 0.40$, $1 < W/B < 8$.

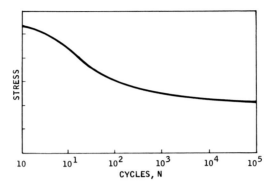

FIG. 16. An idealized fatigue curve.

2. Creep

Materials undergo a transformation in the fracture behavior at temperatures above approximately one-half the absolute melting temperature. The materials that previously deformed by a ductile transcrystalline shear mode now can fracture by intergranular separation. Below this temperature range, the grain boundary was an effective barrier to dislocation motion,

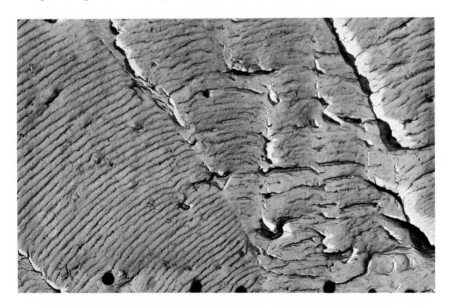

FIG. 17. Electron fractograph of 2021 T8 E31 aluminum alloy tested at −110° F. Fatigue striations were caused by tension-tension cycling at 75° F prior to static testing (Convair photo M2).

but, with the onset of recovery processes, it too is capable of contributing to fracture.

Zener (1948) proposed that the boundary itself was able to shear, and that at points where the shear built up, it did so. The subject of this type of fracture behavior has been reviewed by McLean (1963), Grant (1959), and Gifkins (1959), and Dr. Grant is to bring the subject up to date in another chapter of this book.

V. Some Noteworthy Results

The authors decided against calling this portion "typical" results, due to the problems in obtaining valid data at various temperatures. Furthermore, the favorite fracture mechanics alloy, 7075 aluminum, has not been investigated nearly as thoroughly at cryogenic temperatures as at other temperatures. It is unfortunate that comparison is difficult, due to the fact that there is a minimum of duplication by various laboratories in evaluating the same material at cryogenic temperatures either by the same or different techniques.

The types of materials that will be discussed here will be the medium to high-strength materials generally used in the aerospace industry. Included will be steel, aluminum, and titanium alloys, primarily in sheet thicknesses.

A. Stainless Steels

As has already been mentioned, both the Atlas ICBM (and space launch vehicle) and the Centaur hydrogen-fueled upper stage are manufactured from rather thin-gage 301 stainless steel in various degrees of cold work. This material is purchased under a company specification which places reasonably tight controls on the room temperature properties of the material. Properties specified include yield strength (minimum), elongation (minimum), but no good toughness indicators. Properties pertaining to strength are designated for each temper. This material responds to cold-working, so temper designations refer to the amount of cold reduction; e.g., $\frac{1}{2}$ hard, $\frac{3}{4}$ hard, full hard. The upper strength bound is found in the material known as extra hard (XH) or extra full hard (XFH). Unfortunately, the XFH condition requires a minimum yield strength of 180 ksi, but no maximum is specified. It is only natural for the material supplier to try to work this material to the point that absolutely assures him of meeting the minimum yield strength without wasting time in costly inspection and testing technique. This specification then could conceivably accept material that has been overworked to the point of causing severe embrittlement. To add to the dilemma, the supplier is not interested in a requirement that causes him to perform "fancy" fracture toughness testing in order to establish toughness values—particularly when the particular material under consideration has a rather low tonnage requirement. It goes without saying that virtually any supplier will fabricate any material and supply any data—if the price is high enough.

For cryogenic usage, the buyer faces a larger, seemingly hopeless dilemma. Most suppliers will not and cannot provide material with guaranteed properties at cryogenic temperatures. The problem is compounded if the material is to be used at liquid hydrogen temperatures, since facilities for hydrogen testing are extremely limited throughout the country. To face the specific problem of evaluating the 301 stainless steel for liquid oxygen and liquid hydrogen tankage, Convair actually uses *two* sets of specifications. The first set (already mentioned) is provided to the supplier and is the document to which the material is accepted or rejected, as far as the supplier is concerned. The second set of specifications actually establishes the requirements for acceptance of the material with respect to the specific end product usage. That is, if the 301 stainless steel is to be used as a liquid hydrogen fuel tank for the Centaur vehicle, the specification requires certain notch tensile test results at liquid hydrogen temperature. In addition, there are requirements that evaluate the material after it has been subjected to some fabrication processes (such as welding and spot welding).

Obviously, with experience, a clever engineer can relate room temperature characteristics to low-temperature properties for some applications. To a certain degree, this has been done in preparation of the first specification. At the same time, the most critical property of the material appeared to be fatigue of the standard welded joint at $-423°$ F. As soon as this was established, engineers immediately began to search for a material property or simple test at room temperature that would be a good indicator of the fatigue resistance in the joint at $-423°$ F. For some time, it was thought that the notch-unnotch ratio of the material could be used satisfactorily. The notch that was selected had a K_T of 6.3 (Christian and Hurlich, 1963). However, when sufficient data was generated to supply a good history of the material, it was found that there was sufficient variation from heat to heat of the material to cast doubt on the predictive powers of the notched tensile test at room temperature.

The variation of yield strength with temperature for a single heat of 301 (XFH, $T = 0.025$ inch) is shown in Fig. 18 along with some highly cold-worked 304 and 310 stainless steels. Properties were examined in the direction of rolling (longitudinal) and perpendicular to the direction of rolling. The general shape of all the curves within this family of stainless

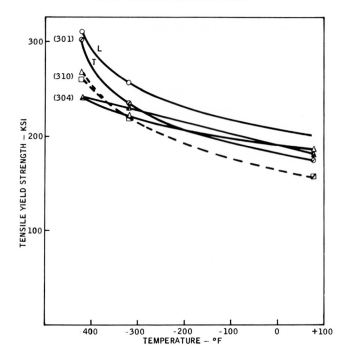

FIG. 18. Variation of yield strength with temperature for stainless steel.

steels is similar, although the 301 appears to gain more strength despite slightly less cold rolling (60% versus 70 or 75%). There is no question that the tensile strengths of the material increase with a lowering of the test temperature, and, in the case of 301 and 310, there is a greater rate of increase in yield strength below −320° F. The strength of 301 (XFH) in the longitudinal direction is always greater than that in the transverse direction, although this difference diminishes as absolute zero is approached. This effect is not apparent in 304 or 310, again, despite the rather large amount of cold work induced. A possible explanation may involve the fact that austenitic 301 transforms quite readily into martensite under strain at reduced temperatures. In fact, both Arde Portland Co. and Convair have been able to obtain rather interesting results by working of annealed 301 stainless at −320° F. In both cases, however, the toughness of the material was lowered significantly at −423° F.

Before proceeding on to a study of the toughness of stainless steels at low temperature, one might consider the effect of cold-work on the properties of 301. For instance, if 301 (annealed) is cold reduced by about 60%, the yield strength at room temperature will be in the neighborhood of 200 ksi. A brief study at Convair (Witzell, 1962a) showed that the toughness of the longitudinal material, obtained through center notched tests, increased with an addition of cold-work until a peak was reached at a yield strength of approximately 150 ksi (Fig. 19). At that point, additional cold-work embrittles the material at a rapid rate. The toughness characteristics shown here are for room temperature only. Further, more recent unpublished work has shown that, at lower temperatures, the peak toughness does not correspond with the peak at room temperature, but is at some higher yield strength level. More research is needed in this area to establish a more acceptable explanation of the relationship between toughness and yield strength.

There was little concern about the fact that the longitudinal material was stronger than the transverse. Actually, the material that is formed into pressure vessel tanks is oriented in such a way as to permit the longitudinal grain direction to resist the larger stresses, i.e., the hoop stresses in the right circular cylindrical tanks. Eventually, center notched specimens were tested at several test temperatures to establish fracture toughness. Original specimens were 4 inches wide and 12 inches long, containing a slot cut by use of an electrical discharge machine that produced a crack tip radius of less than 0.001 inch. These specimens were pulled statically to failure (without fatigue crack extension), while the crack growth was observed visually and recorded. The results obtained were slightly unconservative at some temperatures due to the lack of fatigue crack extension. However, the plastic zone correction was omitted, causing an error in the opposite direction. Nevertheless, some definite trends were observed.

The variation of G_c (where $G_c = K_c^2/E$) with temperature is shown in Fig. 20. If one were to evaluate this material in the longitudinal grain direction at room temperature, the results could be misleading. The G_c at this point exceeds 1500 in.-lb./in.^{2}, which is laudably high. At the same time, the transverse material has a G_c of only 750, even though the yield strengths of the longitudinal and transverse material are quite similar. At $-320°$ F, the longitudinal G_c is slightly lower, due, primarily, to a change in modulus. At the same time, the transverse material has suffered a larger loss in toughness. Careful evaluation at this point can demonstrate a dangerous trend. Recall that, for use in a cylindrical pressure vessel, the longitudinal grain direction is oriented in such a way as to resist the large hoop stresses. Assume that the axial stress σ_A is half the hoop stress σ_H; that is, $\sigma_H = 2\sigma_A$.

The uncorrected G_c values for the material are:

	Longitudinal	Transverse
75° F	1642	747
$-320°$ F	1500	395

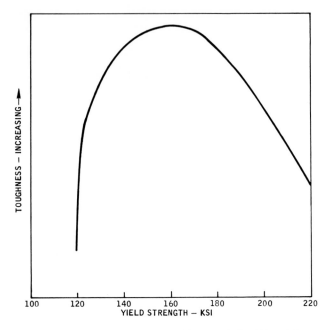

FIG. 19. Variation of toughness with yield strength for 301 stainless steel.

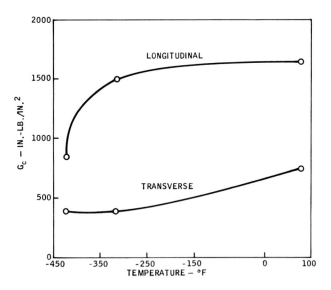

FIG. 20. Variation of G_c with temperature for 301 XFH stainless steel.

Using the Irwin tangent formula,

$$G_c = [\sigma^2 W \tan(\pi a/W)]/E$$

Substituting $2\sigma_A$ for σ

$$G_c = [(2\sigma_A)^2 \tan(\pi a/W)]/E = [4\sigma_A^2 \tan(\pi a/W)]/E$$

It follows that, for a given material in a cylindrical pressure vessel, if the G_c for the longitudinal grain direction is four times the G_c in the transverse grain direction, the resistance to brittle fracture is equivalent in both directions. In this case, the ratio of G_c (transverse) to G_c (longitudinal) is 45.5% at room temperature, but drops rapidly to 26% at $-320°$ F. Had this ratio been less than 25%, the critical design criteria would have to be reconsidered and the transverse fracture properties would have dictated the selection of material size.

This particular case serves to illustrate another very important point. Assume, for the moment, that the investigators had run tests at room temperature and $-320°$ F, only. From the preceding discussion, and by a simple extrapolation, it might be concluded that, at $-423°$ F, the transverse G_c would drop below 25% of the longitudinal G_c. The experimental results show clearly that such a conclusion would have been erroneous. Furthermore, an extrapolation of the longitudinal G_c to $-423°$ F would have projected a G_c substantially greater than the experimental value obtained.

It is clear, then, that anticipating results at cryogenic temperatures is both risky and dangerous. If possible, perform an experiment at the expected temperature!

While there may be some question as to the acceptance of the fracture values with regard to specimen configuration, net-stress-to-yield-strength ratio, and so on, it would appear that such data can be used for design, particularly if the final form of the material is the same as that investigated (e.g., sheet thickness). Variations of crack length and stress with temperature are shown in Fig. 21. In general, these curves reflect the same trends seen in the G_c curves.

Another pitfall that awaits the innocent engineer is the assumption that materials in the same family (or number series) have the same properties. These three 300 series stainless steels (301, 304, and 310) make a good illustration. All three work-harden nicely into reasonably high-strength alloys. The chemical compositions vary somewhat in the following elements (% by weight):

Element	301	304	310
Chromium	17	18	25
Nickel	7	10	20

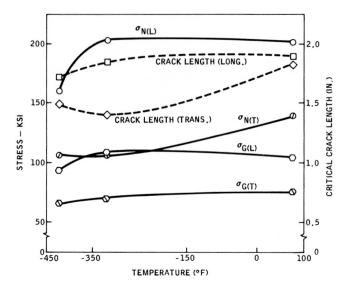

FIG. 21. Ultimate stress, gross stress, and critical crack length for 301 XFH.

The 304 alloy can be improved somewhat by reducing the percentage of carbon (a familiar grade is ELC, extra low carbon). The 301 transforms readily into martensite, while the other two alloys do not.

Nevertheless, an imprudent engineer may be lulled into the belief that the three alloys have similar low-temperature characteristics. As a matter of fact, the yield strength curves previously displayed indicate that strength behavior of the alloys is quite similar. Now, we observe the toughness of 304 and 310, tested in the same manner and at the same temperatures as the 301 (Figs. 22 and 23). The 304 has a rather marginal G_c of 685 in.-lb/in.[2] in the longitudinal direction at room temperature (and 260 in the transverse direction). If we had predicted that the behavior of 304 would be similar to 301 at lower temperature, we would have rejected this material for cryogenic usage. However, the results show that the G_c increases at $-320°$ F in both directions. In similar manner, 310 shows mediocre room temperature toughness, but good G_c at $-320°$ F. The transverse 310 sheet shows a continuous increase of toughness with a decrease in temperature.

The one outstanding similarity between the three materials is the consistent loss of toughness of the longitudinal sheet between $-320°$ and $-423°$ F. The percentage of loss in each case is as follows:

$$301 \quad 43\%; \quad 310 \quad 41\%; \quad 304 \quad 41\%$$

The exact reason for this similarity is unknown. Since the transverse sheet displays no such similarity, it may well be that the phenomenon is

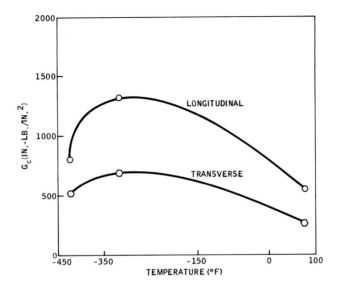

FIG. 22. Variation of G_c with temperature for 304 stainless steel.

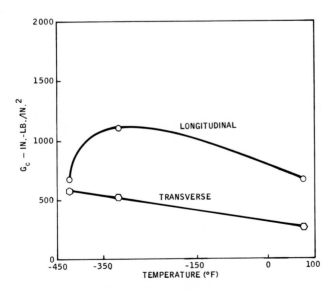

FIG. 23. Variation of G_c with temperature for 310 stainless steel.

due to mathematical chance and has nothing to do with the physical properties of the material.

All data presented to date concerns the properties of the materials in the parent metal condition. Unfortunately, most materials must be joined into efficient structures. One of the most common joining techniques and the one that can cause the most havoc with clean-cut theories is welding. The Atlas and Centaur vehicles utilize thousands of butt welds, overlap welds, and spot welds in the 301 stainless steel in varying degrees of cold work. Obviously, the cold-work properties of the material are affected by welding. In fact, one might consider the 60% cold-worked material to be islands, surrounded by dead annealed weldments. To increase the efficiency of the joint, Convair engineers have designed doublers that help distribute the load from one sheet to the next across the welded joint. This load "helper" is attached to the skin with a series of spot welds which, of course, distort the stress field surrounding the joint. A fracture evaluation of such a joint is virtually impossible. Nevertheless, attempts have been made to determine the toughness of the weldments themselves by running a seam weld through the center of specimen perpendicular to the direction of the load. The center notch was cut into the center of the weld metal and tested in the manner prescribed.

As one might suspect, the properties of the cold-rolled materials are changed when the sheet is welded. The fracture toughness values are surprisingly consistent with a variation in temperature. At room temperature and at $-320°$ F, welding lowers the K_c value by about 25%, but at $-423°$ F the G_c is essentially unchanged. Although the *gross* stress decreases substantially at $-423°$ F, critical crack length increases considerably with a corresponding slight increase in net stress.

Due to the uncertainty of locating the most critical (brittle) area of the weld, notches were cut in various areas of the weld and in the heat-affected zone of the 301 stainless steel. At room temperature, variation of the location of the notch caused no appreciable change in the fracture toughness. However, at $-320°$ F, the critical crack length increased in the heat-affected zone, resulting in an increased net stress. For all practical purposes, the fracture toughness in the heat-affected zone at $-320°$ F is equal to the base metal value at that temperature.

Welding of the 304 sheet lowered the fracture toughness at all temperatures. In addition, the welded sheet at room temperature had a tendency to elongate, causing the load on the testing machine to decrease. Even though the material sustained a large crack length (1.83 inches), the critical load was low and the K_c was low. Calculations were performed to determine if the crack intensity force at the maximum load was greater than the critical crack intensity force (K_c). Despite the larger load, and because of the shorter crack length at that load, the crack intensity force was roughly equivalent at both loads.

Characteristics of 301 Stainless Steel at Elevated Temperatures

By and large, the investigation of materials at elevated temperatures is restricted to short-time tensile properties and creep properties at the expected operating temperatures. Although the Atlas and Centaur vehicles were cryogenic pressure vessels, they were subjected to moderately elevated temperature exposures in two areas. At the back end of the vehicle, exhaust gases from the propulsion and steering rockets caused some elevated temperature problems that were minimized by careful use of thermal protection systems. At the other end of the vehicle, aerodynamic heating played some part. Nevertheless, neither of these problems put much of a burden on the capacity of the vehicle to perform its functions, primarily due to the rather short time of exposure (less than 5 minutes).

Sometime after Atlas became operational as an ICBM (Intercontinental Ballistic Missile), and while it was being used as a space launch vehicle, the requirement for trajectory angle was changed. Because of this more severe flight, the temperature environment changed quite drastically. As a consequence, it became necessary to evaluate the existing material under different load and environmental conditions. The time-temperature profile requirement is shown in Fig. 24.

The engineers involved in verification of the design anticipated other similar profiles for future vehicles. In order to make maximum use of test data, a temperature profile was used, as shown in Fig. 25. Where the original profile showed temperatures increasing up to a certain point

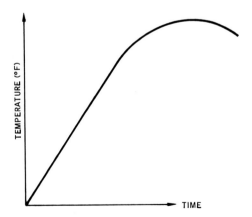

FIG. 24. Required temperature profile.

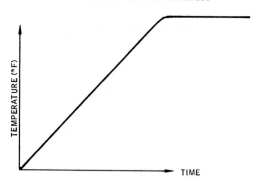

FIG. 25. General temperature exposure.

(several minutes) and then tapering off, the applied temperature profile required an increasing temperature to a prescribed maximum, which was then held constant until failure occurred. For practical reasons, the lower maximum temperature tests were limited to 30 minutes duration. One slight variation with actual flight conditions was that a given stress was applied to the test specimens prior to the increase of temperature and held constant throughout the test (dead loading). Various combinations of stress level and maximum temperature were utilized. Later, the material was tested in a welded condition at similar temperature-stress conditions (Kerr, 1967b), and, finally, pressure vessels were exposed to the same environments (Kerr, 1967a). Some of the results of the uniaxial testing are shown in Fig. 26. The only measurement required was time to failure

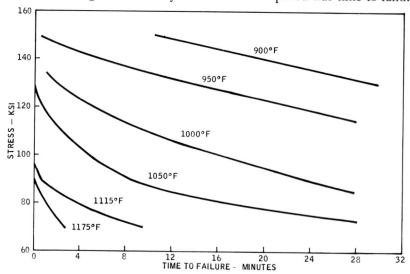

FIG. 26. Elevated temperature behavior of 301 XFH stainless steel.

after stress level and temperature were established. The results are about what one would predict; that is, with an increase in temperature, the time to failure decreases at a given stress level. Such a family of curves is quite useful to the design engineer who contemplates the maximum stress level permissible with a given flight time. Again, one should beware of extrapolation of data. The data presented was for one particular heat of 301 XFH stainless steel with an ultimate room temperature tensile strength of 213 ksi. Other heats of this material tested by Convair produced results that were not predictable on a straight ultimate room temperature, strength-ratio basis.

B. ALUMINUM ALLOYS

Data obtained on several aluminum alloys will be presented without trying to establish the best alloy from a fracture point of view. Material suppliers of aluminum are quite cooperative in presenting as much test data as possible to materials users. At least one company, Alcoa Research Laboratory, provides data on its alloys not only in the form of useful fracture information, but also at cryogenic temperatures.

As has been mentioned previously, the fracture mechanics' favorite alloy, 7075, has not received the tremendous attention at cryogenic temperature that it has at room temperature. Although the object of this treatise is not to recommend specific alloys, some mention will be made of useful materials at cryogenic temperatures, but will not necessarily be limited to all acceptable alloys. In passing, it should be noted that various aluminum suppliers have made a specific effort to formulate and develop alloys for use at cryogenic temperatures, for which they should be applauded.

At this point, strength variation with temperature has been presented at cryogenic temperatures only. While it is not suggested that this is a typical case, it is still interesting to note the variation of the aluminum alloy 7039 with temperature from $-423°$ F to $+400°$ F, as shown in Fig. 27. The trends of the tensile yield and ultimate strength curves are what one would expect; that is, a decrease in strength with an increase in temperature. What is intriguing, however, is the relationship of yield strength to ultimate strength as the test temperature changes. From a quite large difference in yield and ultimate at $-423°$ F, the difference decreases, until they are virtually identical at $+400°$ F.

A similar relationship is reported by Christian et al. (1964), who examined 7039-T6 sheet ($T = 0.063$ inch), at temperatures from $75°$ F to $-423°$ F. The notched tensile strength of the material exceeded the ultimate tensile strength at $75°$ F, but was only 80% of the ultimate at $-423°$ F (for a specimen with a K_T of 6.3). When a sharper notched specimen was used

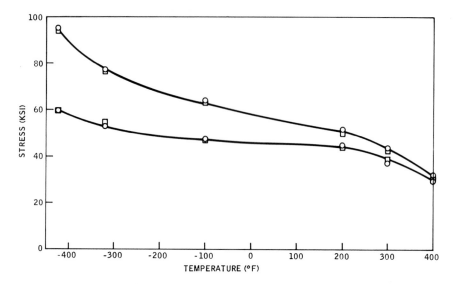

F<small>IG</small>. 27. Ultimate strength and yield strength as a function of temperature for 7039 aluminum.

($K_T = 19$), the notch strength actually *decreased* with a decrease in test temperature. All the while, the elongation exceeded 10%. When tested in the form of a center notched crack propagation specimen, this material showed a marked decrease in toughness as the temperature was lowered from room temperature.

Several 2000 series aluminum alloys have had some usage at cryogenic temperatures. At present, the 2021 alloy, in an experimental temper (T8-E31), has been designed specifically for cryogenic usage. Because of its fine weldability (Witzell *et al.*, 1967), 2219 has been considered in both its T81 and T87 tempers. Some alloys, such as 2024, have been selected for toughness, only to be plagued with weld cracking problems. Tiffany and co-workers (1966), at Boeing have investigated the plane strain fracture toughness of 2219-T87 in various thicknesses and in the form of cryogenic pressure vessels. The material was examined in thicknesses of 0.60 inch and 1.25 inch plate, under static and fatigue loading, using part-through crack tensile specimens. Static fracture toughness for the material was relatively independent of the test temperature from room to cryogenic temperatures (approximately 35 ksi $\sqrt{\text{inch}}$). They concluded that the cyclic lives, flaw growth rates, and critical flaw (crack depth) sizes were approximately the same for uniaxial and biaxial test specimens. Flaw shapes were reported to have assumed a classic semielliptical shape during both static and fatigue tests at all test temperatures. (Such growth makes calculation of K_{Ic} quite easy, since the basic equation reduces to a simple case when the maximum crack depth is on the minor axis of the ellipse, 0°.) Presentation of data took two forms for fatigue tests, namely: (1) K_I versus flaw growth rate, and (2) K_{Ii}/K_{Ic} versus cycles to failure, where K_{Ii} is the maximum initial stress-intensity factor.

This program, which was sponsored by the NASA Lewis Research Center, has been extended to include 2219-T81 weldments and repair welds in a contract with General Dynamics Convair. The final summary report was published in late 1967 (Witzell and Kropp, 1967), including static and fatigue testing of 2219-T87 in two thicknesses (0.063 and 1.0 inch) at room temperature, at −320° F, and at −423° F.

At the same time that the Boeing study was underway, a companion program was being conducted at Douglas (Eitman and Rowe, 1966). The Douglas study also examined uniaxial and biaxial properties of 2219-T87 sheet ($B = 0.060$ inch), and titanium 5Al–2.5Sn (ELI) sheet ($B = 0.020$ inch). However, due to the fact that much thinner material was used, the tests were confined to conditions of plane stress obtained through center cracked tensile specimens. The static test results indicated that the K_c at −320° F was about 20% higher at −320° than at 70° F, which decreased somewhat (about 14% higher than 70° F) at −423° F. These results are more or less verified by Christian et al. (1964), who tested 4-inch-wide center notched specimens, even though the net fracture stress exceeded 80% of yield strength for some cases.

Some rather interesting results were published in late 1967 on the 2021-T8E31 aluminum alloy sheet statically tested at 75°, −110°, −320°, and −423° F in rather small-sized center-notch and single edge notched specimen configurations (Witzell, 1967).

C. TITANIUM ALLOYS

A great deal of interest has been shown in the use of titanium alloys for various applications under various temperature environments. The need for higher strength-to-density alloys has elevated these alloys to the class of "promising" materials. The most celebrated of these alloys is the so-called "8-1-1" titanium (8Al-1Mo-1V) that figured prominently in the competition for award of the supersonic transport. Apparently, 8-1-1 has an Achilles heel called "hot salt cracking" that has reduced some of the interest in this material. Nevertheless, 8-1-1 is listed in the Cryogenic Materials Data Handbook, (Schwartzberg et al., 1966) as a cryogenic alloy. Although the data is scanty, some generalizations can be made. The tensile strength of 8-1-1 increases with a decrease in temperature, the elongation drops off precipitously between −320° and −423° F, and the notch strength varies widely, depending on the notch acuity.

The overwhelming amount of data in the cryogenic handbook is devoted to titanium 5Al-2.5Sn and titanium 6Al-4V. Results of tests on these two alloys can be misleading, since there are two grades of materials for each of the alloys. These are (1) the "commercial" grade or garden variety of the material, and (2) extra-low-interstitial (ELI) grade which has somewhat better chemistry control with respect to several "impurities."

A great deal of the titanium alloys are used in the annealed condition. However, one must use some caution in results obtained from such materials until the true condition is determined. Apparently, the material obtained from some suppliers is in the "mill annealed" condition, which is occasionally different from the "dead annealed condition." It is rumored that the suppliers will sometimes work the annealed material a slight amount in order to obtain the required flatness in the sheet. This slight working can cause differences in both strength and toughness of the materials.

Carman, Forney, and Katlin of Frankford Arsenal evaluated the 5Al-2.5Sn ELI material at room and cryogenic temperatures by using both single edge notch and slow notched bend specimens (Carman *et al.*, 1966). This NASA Lewis Research Center sponsored program evaluated both ¼- and ½-inch thick plate material. A rather unique method of measuring pop-in was used that consisted of bonding of a high elongation strain gage on the bend specimen near the crack tip. In this program, the K_{Ic} steadily decreased from about 120 ksi $\sqrt{\text{inch}}$ at room temperature to about 50 ksi $\sqrt{\text{inch}}$ at $-423°$ F. These values agree quite well with the results obtained by Tiffany and co-workers (1966), who tested surface-flawed specimens of 0.188 inch thickness. Similar trends are reported by Eitman and Rawe (1966) using plane stress techniques.

Center notched tests on Ti6Al-4V (ELI) sheet ($B = 0.025$ inch) performed by Christian *et al.* (1964) show similar degradation of toughness with a decrease in temperature.

At the same time, C. J. Kropp of General Dynamics Convair was attempting to develop a superior titanium alloy under contract to the Air Force Materials Laboratory (Kropp, 1966). The object of the program was to fabricate an alloy with a minimum room temperature yield strength of 120 ksi and a notch-unnotched tensile ratio of 0.90 or greater at $-423°$ F. An alloy was developed (Ti-5Al-2.5Sn-2.5V-1.3Cb-1.3Ta) with a room temperature yield strength range of 119 to 129 ksi, and notch-unnotched tensile ratios of 0.90 to 0.96 at $-423°$ F. (The K_T for the notched specimens was approximately 6.3). No fracture data was required under this contract, but the initial results are quite promising. A thorough fracture toughness program should be planned to evaluate this material at various temperatures.

VI. Recommended Research

It becomes more and more apparent that a wide gap exists between the theoreticians who expound dislocation parables and the practical engineers who test engineering materials. Actually, a good deal of information exists at both ends of this spectrum. Unfortunately, the theoretical man is unable to experimentally prove his mathematics, and the practical man is unable to apply the theory to his test data. The field of fracture variation with temperature faces the same dilemma. The middle ground needs a great deal more attention. It is probable that those agencies who have a definite immediate need for answers will not be willing to pay for research that will not provide instantaneous answers. If money were no object, a systematic program such as the following would be interesting

I. Theoretical
    A. Establish a theory of fracture for a single metal system
        1. Build a mathematical model for a simple tension field
        2. Massage the model to account for a growing microcrack
        3. Extend the model to include the presence of a macro-crack or notch
        4. Apply the knowledge gained in (1), (2) and (3) to a system whose temperature varies.

II. Experimental
    A. Apply the tensile load to the selected material
        1. Stop the test (a) below the proportional limit for one specimen, (b) above the proportional limit for another, (c) at fracture for a third
        2. Examine the internal structure of the material with existing tools; e.g., electron fractography, field ion microscopy, electron diffraction, etc.
        3. Induce a crack into the material that simulates the macrocrack of the theoretical model. Repeat 1 and 2 on these specimens
        4. Repeat 1, 2, and 3 at the required temperature.

If such a program produced reliable results, the program could be extended to include various strain rates, fatigue cycling, and sustained load conditions at the same temperatures.

VII. Summary

The study of fracture variation with temperature is a very complex subject. To date, the area has hardly been touched. Some theories have been expounded, but experimental verification of such theories has been minimal. Not the least impediment to progress is the extreme difficulty and expense in performance of sufficient tests for experimental accuracy. While experimentation has been conducted for many years at elevated temperatures, the subject of fracture at these temperatures has been neglected. Perhaps this neglect has been justified, since fracture (by definition) is a somewhat nebulous (and noncritical) characteristic as temperature increases. At the other end of the scale, experimentation has exploded in recent years due to the widespread usage of cryogenic fluids as rocket fuels and oxidizers. At these temperatures, fracture and fracture toughness become extremely important. When the operating temperature of the structure is below some transition temperature (e.g., NDT or FATT), catastrophic failure results. A more tenuous problem arises when the engineering material selected or developed has a poorly defined transition. Added to the hazard of cryogenic application is the innocent fact that most materials become much stronger as the temperature approaches absolute zero.

The influence of temperature on brittleness is not a new concept, of course. Fracture of storage tanks, bridges, and pipelines under moderately cold temperatures have been recorded for nearly 100 years. What is new is the concentrated effort in the evaluation of material at low temperatures. In the past few years, notched tensile tests, center notched tests, single edge notched tests and slow-bend tests have been added to tensile and impact tests in a frantic effort to evaluate materials. All of the tests mentioned have some utility for some application. The ASTM Committee on Fracture Testing has made a continuing effort to develop standards for tests that provide legitimate fracture toughness data. Unfortunately, virtually all of the studies were performed at laboratory ambient temperatures, and tentative recommendations reflect these studies. This is not to say that the recommendations are not valid at cryogenic and elevated temperatures, but only that the techniques have not been thoroughly evaluated at these temperatures. The foremost criteria for acceptance of fracture data concerns the relationship of the net fracture stress (or net stress at crack instability) to the yield strength of the material. Virtually all other requirements for valid data are simply predetermined specimen geometries, sizes, and test techniques. Verification of such requirements is frequently quite difficult at extreme temperatures. Furthermore, the final utilization of some engineering materials dictates that the alloy be evaluated in thicknesses that are not acceptable sizes for fracture specimens.

In general, valid fracture data is obtained from rather large specimens that are quite difficult to test at elevated and cryogenic temperatures. Nevertheless, the test techniques prescribed are adaptable to cryogenic testing, provided that such equipment as cryostats, cryogenic extensometers, and cryogenic compliance gages are available (Figs. 28 and 29).

For testing of tensile and notched tensile specimens, the technique is virtually the same as for room temperature testing. Obviously, the specimen must be cooled, and the instrumentation used must not be unduly influenced by the variation in temperature. At liquid hydrogen temperatures, greater care must be taken to minimize the safety hazards that accompany the use of this dangerous fluid.

For those tests where crack length must be measured during testing, the procedures become much more severe. Convair has successfully measured crack growth optically at cryogenic temperatures by providing a viewing port through the side of the cryostat. Most of the plane strain fracture tests do not require measurement of crack growth, which makes testing much simpler. Pop-in can be readily measured by cryogenic compliance gages (assuming that a pop-in occurs, or that a suitable procedure can be designed that identifies the initial mode of cracking).

In general, elevated temperature testing does not attempt to evaluate brittle fracture, since such a phenomenon is associated with lower rather than higher temperatures. Such testing is directed toward short-time tensile properties and long-time creep properties of the material.

Furthermore, the fracture appearance of a metal that failed at cryogenic temperatures is not distinguishable from other fractures of the same type (cleavage, etc.).

The thing that does characterize cryogenic failures is the unpredictable behavior of the alloy that is being examined. Generally, metallic materials become stronger as the temperature decreases. No such generalization can be made for the toughness of engineering materials. In the discussion in this treatise of some common aerospace materials, some demonstrate increasing toughness with a decrease in temperature, some show the opposite trend, while others vary, depending on the conditions of testing, grain direction, or notch acuity.

Finally, the prudent engineer will always remember that fracture behavior is the result of a combination of things including temperature, strain rate, geometry of the structure, the presence of discontinuities, and the manner in which the load is applied.

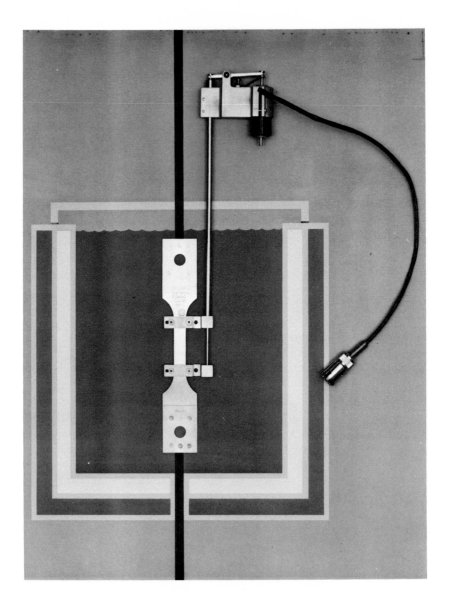

FIG. 28. Schematic of tensile test specimen in cryogenic fluid showing attachment of remote cryoextensometer (Convair photo M1).

FIG. 29. Simple Mylar cryogenic container for liquid nitrogen tensile tests (Convair photo 16790B).

Symbols

a	half crack length for center notched specimens	L	length between supports for bend specimen
a	crack length for single edge notched specimens and slow bend specimens	N	cycles
		P	load
a	crack depth for surface crack specimens	Q	flaw shape parameter (part-through crack)
a	half the distance between notches in a notched tensile specimen	R	root radius of notch
		r_y	plastic zone correction
B	specimen thickness	T	temperature (°F unless otherwise noted)
e	elongation		
E	modulus of elasticity	T_A	temperature where yield strength equals cleavage stress
F	Fahrenheit		
G_c	crack extension force	T_i	intermediate temperature
K_c	plane stress fracture toughness	W	specimen width
K_I	stress-intensity factor	ν	Poisson's ratio
K_{Ii}	initial stress-intensity factor	σ_F	cleavage stress
K_{Ic}	plane strain fracture toughness	σ_G	gross stress
K_T	notch acuity for notched tensile specimen	σ_N	net stress
		σ_{ys}	yield strength

REFERENCES

ASTM (1960). "Fracture Testing of High-Strength Sheet Materials." *ASTM Bull.*, January. ASTM, Philadelphia.

ASTM (1964). "Symposium on Fracture Toughness Testing and Its Applications," STP 381. ASTM, Philadelphia.

ASTM (1966). "Behavior of Materials at Cryogenic Temperatures," STP 387. ASTM, Philadelphia.

Bell, J. H., Jr. (1963). "Cryogenic Engineering." Prentice-Hall, Englewood Cliffs, New Jersey.

Brown, W. F., Jr., and Srawley, J. E. (1966). "Plane Strain Crack Toughness Testing of High Strength Metallic Materials," STP 410. ASTM, Philadelphia.

Byrne, J. G., Fine, M. E., and Kelly, A. (1961). *Phil. Mag.* **6**, 1119–1145.

Campbell, J. E., and Achbach, W. P. (1960). "Current Tests for Evaluating Fracture Toughness of Sheet Metals at High Strength Levels," Report No. 124. Defense Materials Information Center, Battelle Memorial Institute, Columbus, Ohio.

Carman, C. M., Forney, J. W., and Katlin, J. M. (1966). "Plane Strain Fracture Toughness and Mechanical Properties of 5Al-2.5Sn ELI Titanium at Room and Cryogenic Temperatures," NASA CR-54296.

Christensen, R. H., and Denke, P. H. (1961). "Crack Strength and Crack Propagation Characteristics of High Strength Materials," ASD-TR-61-207. Aeronautic Systems Division, Dayton, Ohio.

Christian, J. L. (1962). "Physical and Mechanical Properties of Pressure Vessel Materials for Application in a Cryogenic Environment," ASD-TDR-62-258. Aeronautic Systems Division, Dayton, Ohio.

Christian, J. L., and Hurlich, A. (1963). "Physical and Mechanical Properties of Pressure Vessel Materials for Application in a Cryogenic Environment," Pt. 2, ASD-DTR-62-258. Aeronautic Systems Division, Dayton, Ohio.

Christian, J. L., Yang, C. T., and Witzell, W. E. (1964). "Physical and Mechanical Properties of Pressure Vessel Materials for Application in a Cryogenic Environment," Pt. 3, ASD-TDR-62-258. Aeronautic Systems Division, Dayton, Ohio.

Edelglass, S. M. (1966). "Engineering Materials Science." Ronald Press, New York.

Eitman, D. A., and Rawe, R. A. (1966). "Plane Stress Cyclic Flaw Growth of 2219-T87 Aluminum and 5Al-2.5Sn ELI Titanium Alloys at Room and Cryogenic Temperatures," NASA CR-54956.

Gifkins, R. C. (1959). "Mechanism of Intergranular Fracture at Elevated Temperatures." In "Fracture," pp. 579–627. M.I.T. Press, Cambridge, Massachusetts.

Grant, N. J. (1959). "Intercrystalline Failure at High Temperatures." In "Fracture," pp. 562–578. M.I.T. Press, Cambridge, Massachusetts.

Jones, R. L., and Mikus, E. G. (1961). "The Elevated Temperature Properties of Type 301 EFH Stainless Steel," Report No. MRG 247. Materials Research Group, General Dynamics Convair, San Diego, California.

Kerr, J. R. (1967a). "A Comparison of Uniaxial and Biaxial Creep Rupture Properties of Type 301 EFH Stainless Steel at Temperatures near 1000° F," Report No. ZZL-66-023. General Dynamics Convair, San Diego, California.

Kerr, J. R. (1967b). "Creep Life of Cold Rolled Type 301 Stainless Steel Sheet in the Temperature Range 1200° F to 1600° F," Report No. ZZL-67-045. General Dynamics Convair, San Diego, California.

Kropp, C. J. (1966). "The Development of a Superior Titanium-Base Alloy for Cryogenic Applications," Vol. 2, AFML-TR-65-308. Air Force Materials Laboratory, Wright-Patterson Air Force Base, Dayton, Ohio.

McClintock, M. (1964). "Cryogenics." Reinhold, New York.

McLean, D. (1963). J. Australian Inst. Metals 8 (1), 45–51.

Parker, E. R. (1957). "Brittle Behavior of Engineering Structures." Wiley, New York.

Schwartzberg, F. R., Osgood, S. H., Keys, R. D., and Kiefer, T. F. (1966). "Cryogenic Materials Data Handbook," Revised, Technical Documentary Report No. ML-TDR-64-280. Materials Laboratory, Air Force Materials Laboratory, Wright-Patterson Air Force Base, Dayton, Ohio.

Scott, R. B. (1959). "Cryogenic Engineering." Van Nostrand, Princeton, New Jersey.

Sittig, M. (1963). "Cryogenics: Research and Applications." Van Nostrand, Princeton, New Jersey.

Smith, R. L., and Hendrickson, A. A. (1962). In "Ultra-High Purity Metals," pp. 85–114. ASM, Metals Park, Ohio.

Tetelman, A. S., and McEvily, A. J., Jr. (1967). "Fracture of Structural Materials," p. 268. Wiley, New York.

Tiffany, C. F., Lorenz, P. M., and Hall, L. R. (1966). "Investigation of Plane-Strain Flaw Growth in Thick Walled Tanks." NASA CR-54837.

Timmerhaus, K. D. (ed.) (1954-1965). "Advances in Cryogenic Engineering," Vols. 1–11. Plenum, New York.

Vance, R. W., and Dukes, W. H. (1962). "Applied Cryogenic Engineering." Wiley, New York.

Witzell, W. E. (1962a). "An Introduction to Crack Propagation in High Strength Sheet Materials," Report No. MRG-286. Materials Research Group, General Dynamics Convair, San Diego, California.

Witzell, W. E. (1962b). " Crack Propagation Characteristics of Stainless Steels at Cryogenic Temperatures," Report No. GDC-ERR-AN-138. General Dynamics Convair, San Diego, California.

Witzell, W. E. (1962c). " Fracture Toughness of Stainless Steel Sheet at Cryogenic Temperatures," Paper No. 2418-62. American Rocket Society, Phoenix, Arizona.

Witzell, W. E. (1965a). " Creep Life of Type 301 XFH Stainless Steel Subjected to Various Stress Levels and Elevated Temperature Environments," Report No. ZZL-65-009. General Dynamics Convair, San Diego, California.

Witzell, W. E. (1965b). "Mechanical Properties of 7039-T61 Aluminum Alloy at Temperatures from −423° F to +400° F," Report No. ZZL-65-001 (not releasable). General Dynamics Convair, San Diego, California.

Witzell, W. E. (1967). " Fracture Data for Materials at Cryogenic Temperatures," Report No. GDC-ZZL-67-017. General Dynamics Convair, San Diego, California. (Also published as AFML Rept. AFML-TR-67-257. Air Force Materials Laboratory, Wright-Patterson Air Force Base, Dayton, Ohio.)

Witzell, W. E., and Kropp, C. J. (1967). "Weldment Flaw Growth Characteristics of 2219-T81 Aluminum Alloy," NASA CR-72288.

Witzell, W. E., Hersh, M. S., and Anderson, R. T. (1967). "A Survey of Welding and Inspection Techniques for 2219-T81 Aluminum Alloy," NASA CR-72097.

Zener, C. (1948). "Elasticity and Anelasticity of Metals," p. 158. University of Chicago Press, Chicago.

CHAPTER 4

FRACTURE AND CARRYING CAPACITY OF NOTCHED COLUMNS

H. Liebowitz

Abstract: A compilation of the recent work by Liebowitz *et al.* (1967a,b,c), Liebowitz and Claus (1968), on the fracture and carrying capacity of long, slender columns is presented in this chapter. These studies were concerned with notched and unnotched columns subjected to concentric and eccentric axial compressive loading. The effects of cracks having different depths and root radii were determined on the maximum load-carrying capacity of long and short columns with notches on one side and on two opposite sides of these columns. Results indicate that the maximum load-carrying capacity of eccentrically loaded columns having slenderness ratios less than 250 may be reduced significantly, particularly when these columns contain fatigue cracks or notches with a root radius smaller than 0.003 inch.

Different failure criteria were examined for columns under applied simultaneous compression and bending loads. Four methods are used to analyze the failure data. Results obtained for the specific aluminum columns investigated indicated that the energy required to initiate crack propagation may be stated approximately as an exponential function of crack length, and that stress-intensity factors calculated for the limiting case where $\rho = 0$, and using Neuber's (1937) expressions for maximum stress and appropriate values of the nominal stress, appear to form a basis for a valid fracture toughness analysis.

During the course of this investigation, the stress-concentration formulas, for the case of bending (plane stress condition), developed by Neuber (1937), Kikukawa (1957), and Paprino (1962) were examined in detail. It became advantageous to develop a photoelastic technique to determine accurately the fringe order of a sharp notch in a sheet subjected to tension loading. It is felt that this technique may be useful for other similar studies; this method may be extended to apply to a variety of sections under different loading conditions. For the purpose of this chapter, the experimental results on very sharply notched thin sheets under tensile loading, which appear to be the only data available, are discussed and compared to values obtained from some existing theoretical solutions.

I. Introduction

Advances in metallurgical and structural technologies have led to the development of new high-strength engineering materials. Along with the additional strength obtainable with these alloys of aluminum, steel, and other advanced structural materials, there may be an increase in sensitivity to cracks and other defects. Beginning with work by Inglis (1913) and

Griffith (1920, 1925) to the present time, a large number of studies, both theoretical and experimental, have been conducted in this area. Most of these, however, have dealt with failure of precracked members in tension or in pure bending. Apparently, the effect of flaws on the buckling or critical load was not treated until recently (Liebowitz *et al.*, 1967a,b,c). For research on buckling of unnotched columns, see Hoff (1956), Timoshenko and Gere (1961), Langhaar (1962), and Donnell (1966).

Studies have been made by Dr. Liebowitz and his students on columns subjected simultaneously to axial compression and bending. Experiments conducted exploit the combined effects of notch depth, root radius, column length, single and double notches, and eccentricity of loading. The data from these experiments are compared to results obtained from similar columns without notches to determine the effects of notches on the load-carrying ability and/or the failure loads. Fatigue cracks and notches of root radii equal to 0.003 inch or smaller have a significant effect on reducing the load-carrying capacity of eccentrically loaded aluminum columns.

In this chapter, four methods of analyses are used in examining failure criteria for members subjected to axial compressive bending. The first method (energy method) required the determination of the energy to cause crack propagation. The second method (stress concentration method) utilized the unnotched beam analysis with appropriate stress-concentration relationships by Neuber (1937) for the limiting case where the radius of the notch approaches zero. The third method (equivalent beam analysis) was an attempt to relate, in an approximate manner, the experimental failure data to the experimental failure criteria developed for beams in pure bending. The fourth method (slender column analysis) utilized the slender unnotched column analysis with the appropriate stress-concentration relationships developed by Neuber (1937) and stress-intensity factors for the limiting case where the radius of the notch approaches zero.

In addition to the above, the stress-concentration formulas for plane stress which were developed by Neuber (1937) and others are examined, and the results are compared to those obtained from photoelastic tests. For this purpose, a photoelastic technique employing a microscope was developed in order to determine accurately the fringe order of a sharp notch; i.e., as small as 0.0019 inch in radius, to within $\pm$ 0.0004 inch of the boundary. The stress was frozen into the specimen, enabling careful study of the specimen. Experimental results are discussed and compared to values obtained from some existing theoretical solutions for tension-loaded specimens.

The results presented in sharply notched components treated in this chapter may be of significance in many areas of engineering, particularly where slender columns are employed to achieve high-strength-to-weight performance. For example, the results are applicable to the aeronautical and aerospace industries, since aircraft and missiles have slender column construction in wing and fuselage sections. Flaws may develop in these structures from mechanical vibrations, aerodynamic loads, rocket fuel exhaust, leakage of rocket fuel, or acoustical fatigue.

II. Test Equipment and Procedure for Testing of Columns

The columns (Fig. 1) were loaded in a fixture (Fig. 2) having knife edges (Fig. 3) at the ends with adjustments to enable concentric and eccentric loading. This assembly was mounted in a Tinius Olsen 120,000-lb-capacity universal testing machine. The movement of the loading head of the testing machine was maintained at a constant rate. The applied load versus vertical displacement of the loading head was plotted automatically on a chart recorder. The transverse deflection of the column was also measured. The columns were loaded to failure or, in case of no failure, well beyond the point of maximum load.

For these investigations, $\frac{1}{2}$- x $\frac{1}{2}$-inch rolled bars made of 7075-T6511

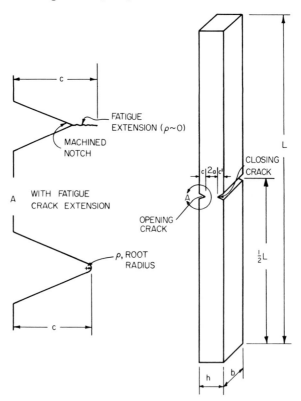

FIG. 1. Test specimen.

FIG. 2a

aluminum were selected. The column specimens were made by cutting the bars to the desired lengths and facing off the ends. The columns containing cracks had notches on one side or on two opposite sides, as required. In some cases, shallow notches were machined into the two sides adjacent to the prepared "crack." These notches were intended to (a) control the direction of the fatigue cracks, (b) attempt to control the direction of failure, and (c) minimize possible surface effects caused by the rolling operations of the manufacturing process.

Some columns were tested having machined notches of root radius of approximately 0.003 inch. Other columns were fatigued (ASTM, 1960, 1961a,b, 1962, 1964) at the notch to produce a very small crack by mounting one end in a fixture held eccentrically in the chuck of a 16-inch Hendley lathe and holding the other end rigidly by the tool post.

The columns were subjected to a simultaneous compressive load and a bending moment. The specimens were clamped in a special loading

FIG. 2b

FIG. 2. (a) Specimen and (b) test equipment.

fixture designed so that the compressive load was eccentrically applied and transmitted through a knife edge to produce a bending moment in the column.

This assembly was then mounted into the testing machine (Fig. 2) equipped with special pedestals to ensure vertical alinement of the knife

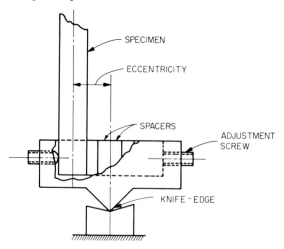

FIG. 3. Knife-edge assembly.

edges (Fig. 3). The specimen was loaded by lowering the heads at a constant rate, with the vertical displacement of the head versus the applied load being recorded on an X-Y plotter. The horizontal displacement of the center of the column and the load were recorded at predetermined intervals. The tests were continued until failure occurred, or well beyond the point where the load began to decrease. In the tests where failure did occur, the failure load and maximum horizontal displacement were also recorded. The depths of the cracks were measured with an optical comparator after failure. Where cracks contained a fatigue extension, 10 readings were taken across the width of the specimen. The rms value of these readings was recorded as the crack depth. A typical failure surface, where fatigue crack extension was present, is shown in Fig. 4. It was observed that columns having machined notches of radius of approximately 0.003 inch behaved similarly to fatigued notched specimens.

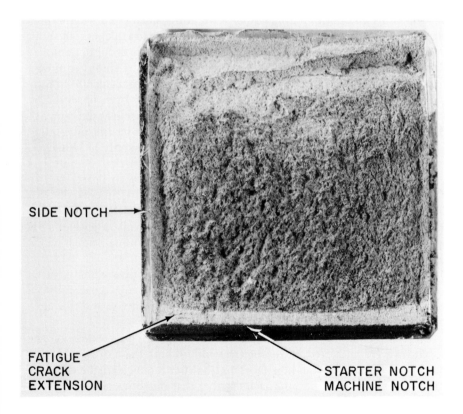

SIDE NOTCH⟶

FATIGUE
CRACK
EXTENSION

STARTER NOTCH
MACHINE NOTCH

FIG. 4. Typical fracture surface of a fatigue-cracked specimen.

III. Test Equipment for Photoelastic Investigation of Stress-Concentration Factors

Photoelastic tests were made to determine the validity of the accepted stress-concentration formulas when applied to notches having very small radii; i.e., $\rho = 0.003$ inch. However, for this investigation, experiments were performed only on thin sheets subjected to uniform tensile loading. While the main part of the work described in this chapter is concerned with long slender columns, it was felt that the information obtained for thin sheets could shed some light on the problem of notches under study. Also, since the cracks were apt to propagate under tensile loading, further insight was needed on the buildup of stresses near the boundary of a sharp notch. In addition, the thin sheet test under tensile loading yields some useful information and is simpler to perform than one in bending.

For these studies, a photoelastic model (Fig. 5) was fabricated from epoxy resin Hysol 4290. This material was chosen for its photoelastic properties as well as its ease of machining. Models were machined from $\frac{1}{4}$-inch-thick stress-free sheets. These sheets were machined ground to a thickness of about 0.025 inch, because a state of plane stress was desirable in order to minimize dimples at the root of the notches. Furthermore, since the study required a microscope (Fig. 6), it was desirable to minimize the integrating effect of the light as it passed through the model. This has already been observed by Hiltscher (1938, 1944), who minimized its effect by focusing at the center of the slice under examination. In the present investigation, the integrating effect is considerably smaller than that obtained in the study of Hiltscher, where slices about 0.12 inch thick were used.

A hole from as small as 0.003 inch in diameter up to 0.056 inch in diameter was drilled perpendicular to the plane of the specimen and about 0.1 inch from the edge using precision microdrilling techniques. A fine wire was then placed through the hole to protect it, while a jeweler's file was used to cut a slot from the edge to the hole, thus forming a notch with a uniform radius.

The specimen was loaded in tension, using loading pins which assured very good axial load application. The specimens were then subjected to a conventional stress freezing cycle to increase their sensitivity and to enable more freedom in handling.

On completion of the stress freezing cycle, the dimensions of the specimen were measured, including the width of both the narrow and wide portions of the shank, the hole location, the root radius, and the depth of the notches (Fig. 5). This approach ensured that the dimensions would be effective notch dimensions so that any blunting effect, or the like, would not pass unnoticed. Also, the specimen was calibrated using its self-calibrating characteristics.

Just prior to determining the stress-concentration effect due to the notches, the specimen was thoroughly cleaned, paying particular attention to the bottom of the notches.

A Reichert microscope (Fig. 6) model MeF, adapted for use as a transmission-type polariscope, was used to determine the fringe order at the

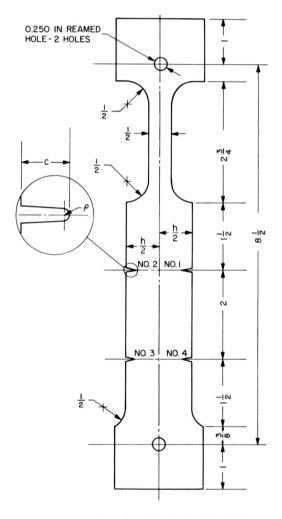

FIG. 5. Specimen configuration. Material: Hysol 4290; thickness: 0.025 inch.

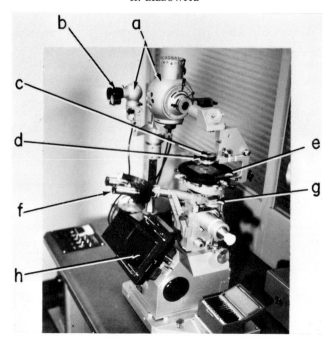

Fig. 6. Apparatus for photoelastic studies of notches with small root radii. Key: a, light sources; b, diaphragm; c, polarizing element; d, diaphragm; e, specimen; f, binocular tube; g, analyzer; h, camera.

bottom of the notch (Fig. 7). It was found necessary to use the well-known oil immersion technique at the root of the notch. The oil immersion was achieved by putting a drop of oil with the same index of refraction as Hysol 4290 at the notch and placing a round microscope cover plate at each side of the specimen. Consequently, any surface roughness from the grinding was eliminated and any dimpling effect, although small, would not obstruct the light path through the specimen. Using the above procedure and the appropriate magnification (from $70\times$ to about $300\times$), the number of fringes produced at the boundary was sufficient to obtain an accurate measure of the stress at the bottom of the notch. The focusing was done on an imaginary plane approximately halfway between the outside faces of the specimen. Both a xenon lamp and a sodium vapor lamp were used. The above procedure enabled the observer to locate the boundary to within ± 0.0004 inch. To increase the depth of field and to minimize the integrating effect due to the nonparallelism of the light, the diaphragm on the light source was closed down as far as possible, as was the diaphragm on the condensing lens. This was felt to give a minimal integrating effect, because there was no shift in the fringe location as the focus point was varied.

The fringe order at the root of the notch is really the most important

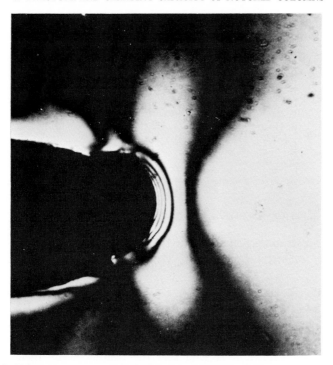

FIG. 7. Fringe pattern at a typical notch (approximately 0.0035-inch root radius).

variable. Extreme care was therefore taken to determine it. First, an estimate was made of the fringe order at the boundary. Both monochromatic
and white light were used. By adjusting the focus while observing the notch
in the microscope and by changing from light field to dark field, and vice
versa, the fringe order was found. Second, a Polaroid photograph was
made (Fig. 7). For this, high-contrast film (ASA 10,000) and a 5460-Å
filter were used. Using this photograph, the fringe order was plotted versus
the distance from the boundary point. The previously estimated fringe
order was included as a data point. A curve was then drawn as closely
through the plotted points as possible. Using these curves, the stress-
concentration factor was computed using as nominal fringe order that for
the gross cross section without the notches. This was determined from the
fringe order in the narrow uniform shank.

IV. Theoretical Considerations

A. EULER BUCKLING LOAD

The Euler buckling load P_E, for elastic unnotched columns (Fig. 8)
with pinned ends, is well known (Euler, 1744) as

$$P_E = \pi^2 E I / L^2 \tag{1}$$

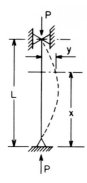

Fig. 8. Elastic unnotched column subjected to concentric load.

B. Euler Critical Stress

The Euler stress corresponding to the above load is

$$\sigma_E = \pi^2 E/(L/R)^2 \tag{2}$$

where, in the above Eqs. (1) and (2), E is Young's modulus, I is the moment of inertia, of the section of the column about its neutral axis, L is the effective length of the column, and R is the radius of gyration of the section as is defined as equal to $(I/A)^{1/2}$, where A is the cross-sectional area of the column. From Fig. 9, it is seen that the results of the theoretical and experimental findings for the straight columns agree quite well. Buckling tests on various lengths of columns, with and without initial eccentricities, were performed; in particular, extensive tests were conducted on 12-inch columns. It should be noted that the Euler buckling load, which is for an idealized column, may be obtained from experiments on straight columns. In order to maintain a straight column during the test with increasing load, it is necessary to adjust the column horizontally at the ends of the column so that there is no bowing effect of the column. This straightening may be achieved by adjusting the screw in the rig, as shown in Fig. 3. Finally, a load will be reached at which it is no longer possible to straighten the column; at this time the critical load may be determined (Fig. 9). The derivation of the critical load is given in App. A.

C. Equation of Stress for Unnotched Columns Loaded Eccentrically

1. Beam Analysis

It is possible to determine the approximate stress in columns (Fig. 10a) subjected to an eccentric compressive load. Within the linear range, this stress is equal to the sum of the compressive stress and the stress due to

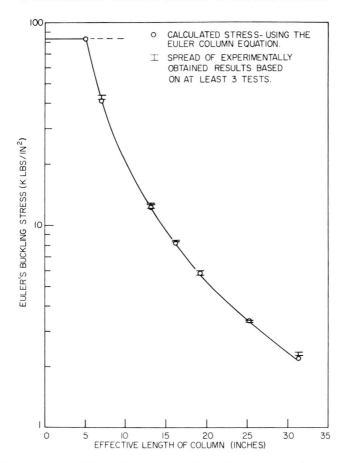

FIG. 9. Comparison of theoretically predicted Euler load with experimental results.

bending. The tensile stress due to bending could be used in the following equations, since the opening mode of the crack is of interest. Using beam column assumptions, the approximate stresses become

$$\sigma = \sigma_C + \sigma_B \tag{3}$$

where

$$\sigma_C = -P/bh \tag{3a}$$

$$\sigma_B = \frac{12P(e + \delta)d}{bh^3} \tag{3b}$$

in which P is the applied load, $d = h/2$ is the distance from the neutral axis to the outer fiber, e is the eccentricity of loading, and δ is the horizontal

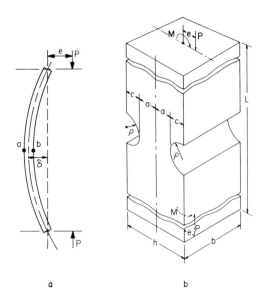

FIG. 10. (a) Unnotched specimen and (b) notched specimen loaded eccentrically.

deflection at the midpoint of the column. Finally, substituting Eqs. (3a) and (3b) into Eq. (3) results in

$$\sigma = \frac{P}{bh}\left[-1 + \frac{6(e+\delta)}{h}\right] \tag{4}$$

Equation (4) is valid for a uniform column, of rectangular cross section, without notches.

2. Slender Column Analysis

The maximum combined stress σ_{max}, for an unnotched column loaded eccentrically (Fig. 10a), can be written as

$$\sigma_{max}\big|_{L/2} = \mp e(P/Z)\sec[(\pi/2)(P/P_E)^{1/2}] - (P/A) \tag{5}$$

where e is the eccentricity of loading, P is the failure load, Z is the section modulus, and A is the area of the cross section. In order to determine the maximum stress at the outer fiber at b in Fig. 10a, on the compression side of the column, both minus signs should be used in Eq. (5), while the maximum stress at a will require the use of the plus sign of the first term and the minus sign of the second term of Eq. (5). This equation is derived in App. B.

D. Equation of Stress for Notched Columns Loaded Eccentrically

1. Beam Analysis

The approximate maximum stress could be determined by employing stress-concentration formulas developed by Neuber (1937).

For example, he considered the effect of deep and shallow hyperbolic external notches (Fig. 10b) for cases of pure tension and bending. The maximum stress at the root of the notch may be determined for tension as

$$\sigma_{\max} = \frac{P}{2ab} \frac{[(a/\rho)+1](a/\rho)^{1/2}}{[(a/\rho)+1]\arctan(a/\rho)^{1/2}+(a/\rho)^{1/2}} \tag{6}$$

where $P/2ab$ is the nominal stress, and for pure bending, as

$$\sigma_{\max} = \frac{2P(e+\delta)(a/\rho)(a/\rho)^{1/2}}{a^2 b[(a/\rho)^{1/2}+[(a/\rho)-1]\arctan(a/\rho)^{1/2}]} \tag{7}$$

where $2P(e+\delta)/a^2 b$ is the nominal stress, ρ is the radius of curvature of the root of the notch, and a is half the width of the net cross section at the root of the notch. Equations (6) and (7) may be combined with appropriate signs to give the resulting stress at a notch in a column subjected to an axial compressive load and a bending load. The superposition of Eqs. (6) and (7) is valid within the limits of the linear theory of elasticity.

One difficulty in using Eqs. (6) and (7) is that the dimensions of the net section area are required to obtain the maximum stress for each incremental load. Obviously, errors are introduced in using Eqs. (4), (6), and (7) for determining the maximum stress in notched columns. Furthermore, as discussed later, Neuber's expression for stress concentration is not valid for fatigued crack specimens where ρ approaches zero.

2. Slender Column Analysis

It is also possible to determine the approximate stress in columns subjected to eccentric compression loads, by using the nominal stress calculated from the beam column formula in Eq. (6) and substituting this value for stress into the approximate Neuber's stress-concentration expressions, as for example those given in Eqs. (6) and (7). Therefore, the maximum stress of the notched column is

$$\sigma_{\max} = e\frac{P}{Z}\sec\left[\frac{\pi}{2}\left(\frac{P}{P_E}\right)^{1/2}\right]\frac{4(a/\rho)(a/\rho)^{1/2}}{3[(a/\rho)^{1/2}+[(a/\rho)-1]\arctan(a/\rho)^{1/2}]}$$
$$-\frac{P}{A}\frac{2[(a/\rho)+1](a/\rho)^{1/2}}{[(a/\rho)+1]\arctan(a/\rho)^{1/2}+(a/\rho)^{1/2}} \tag{8}$$

It should be noted that Eq. (8) is similar to the algebraic difference of Eqs. (6) and (7), except for the values of the nominal stresses.

V. Discussion of Results for Critical Load

Tests were conducted on columns having lengths of 6, 9, 12, 15, 18, 24, and 30 inches. The majority of the tests were performed on columns 12 inches long, but an adequate number of other lengths were also studied.

The results for unnotched columns subjected to a concentric axial load are shown in Fig. 8. In these tests, with the eccentricity equal to zero, the columns were continually adjusted, during the loading, to ensure straightness. The required adjustments were always very small. Some tests were also conducted using double notched columns. For the case of zero eccentricity, no appreciable difference for the Euler buckling load was observed for notched and unnotched columns. This result is apparently correct, since the column is subjected solely to an axial load and not permitted to bend. Consequently, the cracks close under compressive load and have virtually no effect on straight columns which are made to remain straight until buckling. A series of tests was also run on 12-inch-long unnotched columns at various eccentricities of loading (Table I). In these tests, the columns were loaded well beyond the inflection point on the load deflection curve.

The same eccentricities were used for the unnotched and notched columns. The depth of notch (or crack) was varied. The deflection in the horizontal direction was measured at approximately the center of the column. Load deflection curves obtained for various crack depths are shown in

TABLE I

Maximum Loads of the 12-Inch-Long
Unnotched Columns Having Different
Eccentricities

Eccentricity (inches)	Experimentally determined maximum load (lb)
0	3045[a]
0	3150
0.090	2440
0.250	2050
0.500	1590
1.000	1200
1.250	1020

[a] Euler buckling load which was calculated using a length of column, plus the added length due to the knife edges.

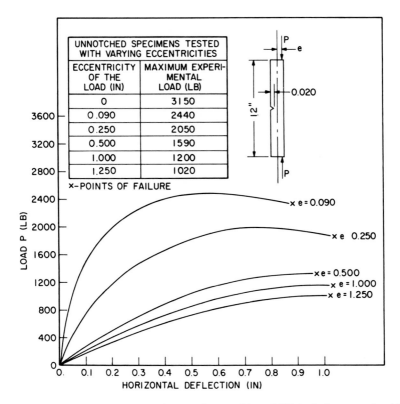

FIG. 11. Load-deflection curve for a column with a 0.020-inch-deep notch with a fatigue crack extension.

Figs. 11–17. Although experiments were conducted on columns with one and two notches, Figs. 11–17 show only the results of columns with a single notch; the results for the double notch are discussed later. The notch was on the side of the column farthest from the axis of the applied load.

The failure load was measured using seven crack depths at five eccentricities. A comparison between the response of the notched bars at various eccentricities with those of the unnotched bars is tabulated in Figs. 11–17. The comparison shows that a fatigue crack in a column under axial load reduces its load-carrying ability. The load-carrying capacity of the column is further reduced as the depth of the crack is increased. Furthermore, increasing the eccentricity of the applied load decreases the load-carrying ability. Finally, it appears that the horizontal deflection is approximately constant for a given crack depth. This can be seen from Fig. 18, where failure load has been plotted versus the corresponding maximum horizontal

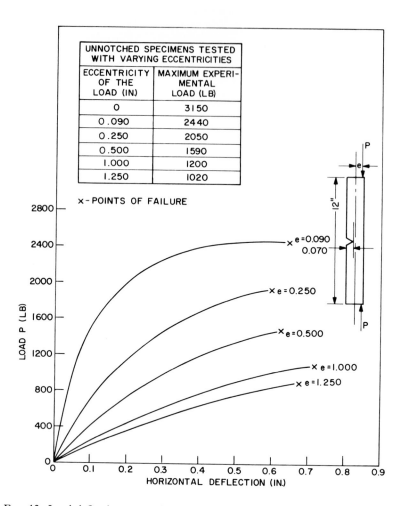

FIG. 12. Load-deflection curve for a column with a 0.070-inch-deep notch with a fatigue crack extension.

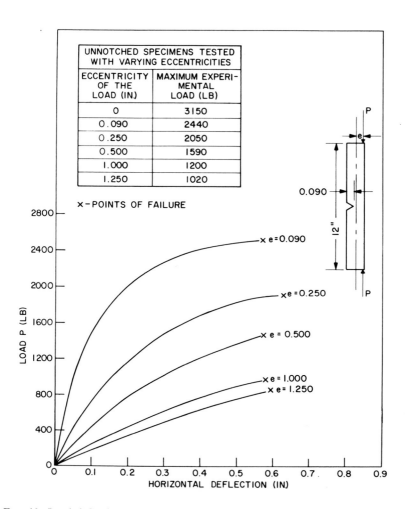

FIG. 13. Load-deflection curve for a column with a 0.090-inch-deep notch with a fatigue crack extension.

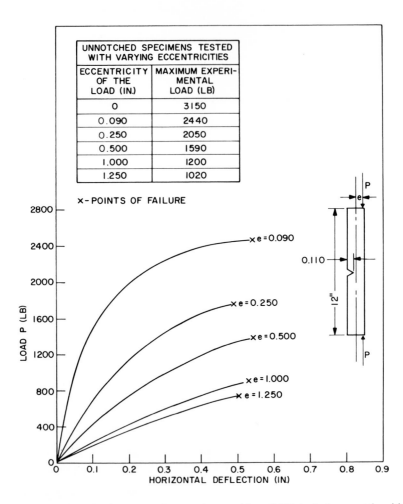

FIG. 14. Load-deflection curve for a column with a 0.110-inch-deep notch with a fatigue crack extension.

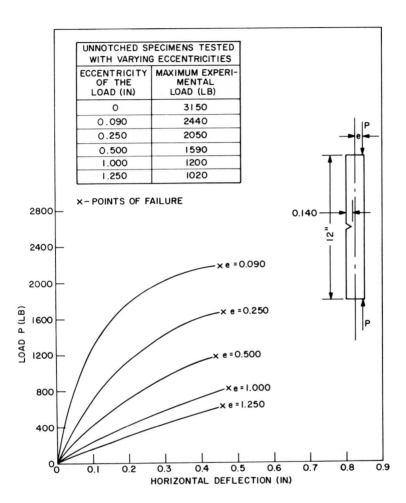

FIG. 15. Load-deflection curve for a column with a 0.140-inch-deep notch with a fatigue crack extension.

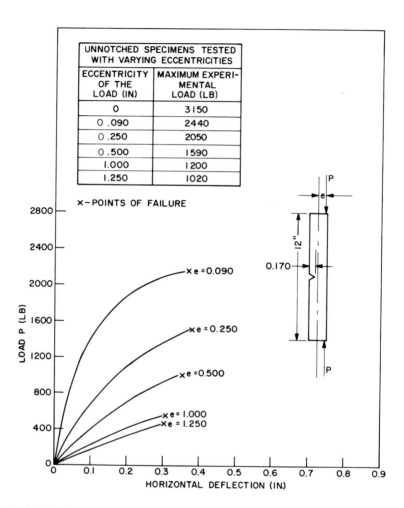

FIG. 16. Load-deflection curve for a column with a 0.170-inch-deep notch with a fatigue crack extension.

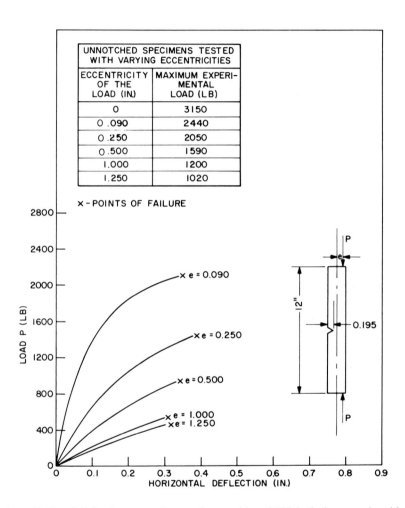

FIG. 17. Load-deflection curve for a column with a 0.195-inch-deep notch with a fatigue crack extension.

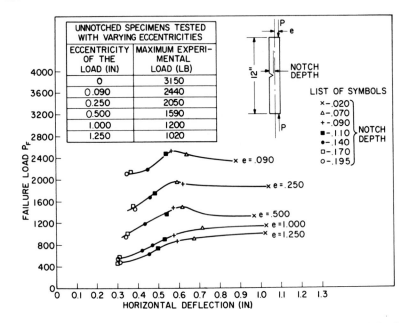

FIG. 18. Effect of notch depth on failure load and maximum horizontal deflection of the column (all notches have a fatigue crack extension).

deflection. The largest decrease in load-carrying ability from the notched to the unnotched column was 55%, which occurred for a notch depth of 0.195 inch and an eccentricity of 1.250 inches. The failure loads were plotted versus the notch depths at various eccentricities (Fig. 19). The values presented at zero notch depth are the maximum loads obtained for the tests on the unnotched columns for the eccentricities indicated.

The effect of the root radius of the crack was also studied (Fig. 20). The majority of the results were obtained using a notch with a fatigue crack extension. In Fig. 20, results have also been given for 0.003- and 0.0625-inch root radii; the large root radius resulted in higher failure loads than those for small root radius for the tests conducted in this research. No appreciable difference was found between the fatigue crack and the 0.003-inch-radius crack. However, the 0.0625-inch root radius appears to have no effect on preventing the load from reaching a maximum value before failure, because the corresponding load deflection curves have approximately zero slope at failure.

The results of the effect of putting a notch on both sides of the column are shown in Fig. 21. Note that the total notch depth for the double V-notch indicated in the table on this figure is equal to the sum of the length of the crack on each side of the column. These tests indicate that a double

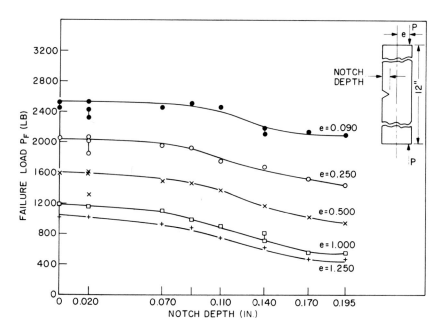

FIG. 19. Effect of depth of notch with a fatigue crack extension on failure load.

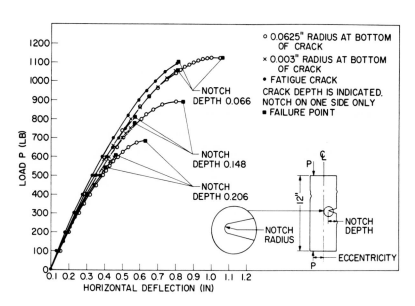

FIG. 20. Effect of notch depth and root radii on load-carrying ability of columns (eccentricity = 1.0 inch).

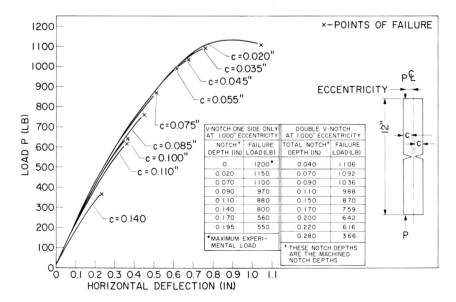

V-NOTCH ONE SIDE ONLY AT 1.000" ECCENTRICITY		DOUBLE V-NOTCH AT 1.000" ECCENTRICITY	
NOTCH[+] DEPTH (IN)	FAILURE LOAD(LB)	TOTAL NOTCH[+] DEPTH (IN)	FAILURE LOAD(LB)
0	1200*	0.040	1106
0.020	1150	0.070	1092
0.070	1100	0.090	1036
0.090	970	0.110	988
0.110	880	0.150	870
0.140	800	0.170	759
0.170	560	0.200	642
0.195	550	0.220	616
		0.280	366

*MAXIMUM EXPERIMENTAL LOAD

[+] THESE NOTCH DEPTHS ARE THE MACHINED NOTCH DEPTHS

FIG. 21. Load deflection for a column with two V-notches on opposite sides and of varying depth (eccentricity = 1.0 inch).

notch is less disastrous than a single notch with a crack depth equal to the total crack depth of the double notch. Symmetry appears to be maintained for a double notch but is not maintained for a single notch.

The results of a series of tests on the effects of slenderness ratio, depth of notch, and eccentricity on the maximum load-carrying capacity of the column are shown in Figs. 22 and 23. Two eccentricities were considered, namely, 1.000 inch in Fig. 22 and 0.090 inch in Fig. 23. A variety of notches were considered, namely, a single 0.110-inch-deep notch and double notches 0.020 and 0.110 inch deep. From Figs. 22 and 23, it appears that the load-carrying ability of 7075-T6511 aluminum columns having slenderness ratios larger than 250, and for eccentricities of 0.090 and 1.000 inch, is not noticeably affected by notches. However, as the slenderness ratio decreases from a value of 250, the effect of notches on the load-carrying capacity of the column increases. For small slenderness ratios, the weakening effect of the notches is most pronounced, especially for the 1.000-inch eccentricity.

To determine whether a preferred orientation caused by manufacturing processes existed in the rolled bar, four columns taken from the same bar were tested. A single identical notch was put into each of these columns but placed on their four different sides for the four tests. Differences in the load-carrying capacity and transverse deflection were less than the experimental accuracy.

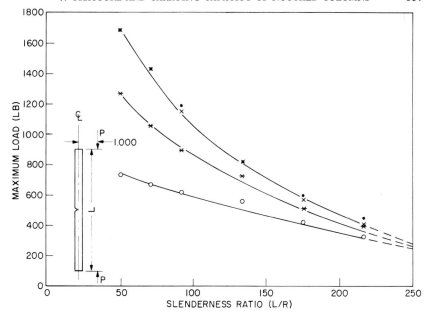

FIG. 22. Effect of notches and slenderness ratio on the maximum carrying capacity of columns (eccentricity = 1.0 inch).

KEY: ×, double 0.020-inch-deep notches; O, double 0.110-inch-deep notches;
*, single 0.110-inch notch; ●, unnotched column.

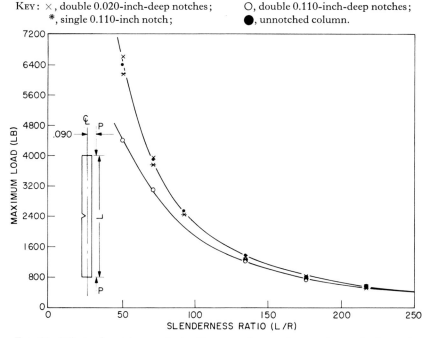

FIG. 23. Effect of notches and slenderness ratio on the maximum load-carrying capacity of columns (eccentricity = 0.090 inch). (For KEY, see Fig. 22.)

VI. Fracture of Columns

A. Energy Method

In the energy method of analysis, the total energy input to the specimen, the external energy, was determined by measuring the area under the load vertical deflection curve. The energy required to deform the specimen was made up chiefly of two parts: the energy of bending, and the energy of compression. Neglecting any losses through the knife edges, the energy available to cause crack propagation is

$$U_{cr} = U_A - (U_B + U_C) \tag{9}$$

The energy of bending is known to be

$$U_B = \int_0^L (M^2/2EI)\, dx \tag{10}$$

The moment in terms of load, eccentricity of loading, and the horizontal deflection of the column is

$$M = P(e + y)$$

Thus

$$M^2 = P^2(e^2 + 2ey + y^2)$$

If the deformed shape of the column is assumed to be that of a half sine wave, then the deflection at any point x on the column can be determined from the expression

$$y = y_M \sin(\pi x/L)$$

where y_M is the transverse deflection of the midpoint of the column at failure. Thus, the energy of bending can be rewritten as

$$U_B = (P^2/2EI)\left[e^2 \int_0^L dx + 2ey_M \int_0^L \sin(\pi x/L)\, dx + y_M^2 \int_0^L \sin^2(\pi x/L)\, dx \right]$$

After integration and simplification, the expression becomes

$$U_B = (P^2L/2EI)[e^2 + (4e/\pi)y_M + \tfrac{1}{2}y_M^2] \tag{11}$$

The energy of compression U_C was determined from the expression

$$U_C = P^2L/2abE \tag{12}$$

B. Stress-Concentration Method

The stress-concentration method of analysis uses the stress concentration caused by the presence of notches in members subjected to tensile loading and to pure bending. The following equations for stress intensity for cracks were developed from Neuber's stress-concentration equations for deep notches (Neuber, 1937).

For a double notched member under tension, the stress concentration is given in Eq. (6). The stress-intensity factor is defined by

$$K = \lim_{\rho \to 0} \frac{\sigma_{max}(\pi\rho)^{1/2}}{2} \tag{13}$$

After substituting Eq. (6) into Eq. (13) and allowing the notch radius to go to zero, the stress-intensity expression (App. C) becomes

$$K_T = (P/b)(a\pi)^{-1/2} \tag{14}$$

For a double notched member under pure bending, the stress concentration is given in Eq. (7). Again, the stress-intensity factor is defined by Eq. (14). After combining Eqs. (7) and (13) and allowing the notch radius to go to zero, the stress-intensity expression (App. C) of bending becomes

$$K_B = 2M/a^{3/2}b\pi^{1/2} \tag{15}$$

For columns subjected to axial compressive loading and bending moments, it may be assumed that the stress-intensity expression then can be obtained from superposition and written (App. C) as

$$K = -K_T \pm K_B \tag{16}$$

The point of interest in this case is the root of the opening crack; therefore, the positive value of K_B is taken, and the final expression becomes

$$K = \frac{P}{b(a\pi)^{1/2}} \left[\frac{2(e + \delta)}{a} - 1 \right] \tag{17}$$

Neuber's stress-concentration equations for members with double (shallow) notches under tensile loads and in pure bending are, respectively,

$$\sigma_{max}/(P/2ab) = 3(c/2\rho)^{1/2} - 1 + 4[2 + (c/2\rho)^{1/2}] \tag{18}$$

and

$$\sigma_{max}/[3M/(2a)^2b] = 3(c/2\rho)^{1/2} - 1 + 4[2 + (c/2\rho)^{1/2}] \tag{19}$$

By a development similar to that used for deep notches, the final expression for the stress intensity, where shallow notches are present, becomes

$$K = \frac{3P}{4ab}(\pi c)^{1/2} \left[\frac{6(e + \delta)}{a} - 1 \right] \tag{20}$$

C. Equivalent Beam Analysis

The equivalent beam analysis required the development of an expression of the stress at the midpoint of the column. The approximate stress in a column subjected to axial compressive load and bending, within the linear range, is equal to the sum of the stress due to compression and the stress due to bending:

$$\sigma_T = \sigma_C + \sigma_B \tag{21}$$

where

$$\sigma_C = \frac{-P}{A} = \frac{-P}{2ab} \tag{21a}$$

$$\sigma_B = \frac{Md}{I} = \frac{P(e+\delta)d}{b(2a)^3 \, 12} \tag{21b}$$

If linear stress distribution is assumed, $\sigma_B = \sigma_{max}$ when $d = a$. By substituting Eqs. (21a) and (21b) into Eq. (21) and simplifying, it becomes

$$\sigma_{max} = \frac{P}{2ab}\left[\pm\frac{3(e+\delta)}{a} - 1\right] \tag{22}$$

The point of interest is the tip of the opening crack. Therefore, the positive value of stress due to bending will be used. The expressions for stress intensity in the opening mode for a single edge precracked notch specimen under tensile loading given by Gross, Srawley, and Bowie and Neal (Universal Technology Company, 1967), are

TABLE II

Functions Given by Gross and Bowie for
Determining the Stress Intensity for the
Opening Mode

c/h	$f_G\,(c/h)$	$f_B\,(c/h)$
0.05	1.14	1.14
0.10	1.19	1.15
0.15	1.29	1.18
0.20	1.37	1.22
0.25	1.50	1.31
0.30	1.66	1.46
0.35	1.87	1.67
0.40	2.12	1.95
0.45	2.44	2.25
0.50	2.82	2.58

Gross,

$$K_{\mathrm{I}} = \sigma_N (\pi c)^{1/2} f_{\mathrm{G}} (c/h) \tag{23}$$

Bowie and Neal,

$$K_{\mathrm{I}} = \sigma_N (\pi c)^{1/2} f_B (c/h) \tag{24}$$

where σ_N is the nominal stress, c is the crack length, and $f(c/h)$ is given in Table II from the 4th Annual Workshop (Universal Technology Company, 1967). (The subscript G refers to Gross and B refers to Bowie.) The expression for stress intensity in the opening mode for a precracked notch bend specimen shown in the publication of the Workshop on Fracture Mechanics is

$$K_{\mathrm{I}} = \sigma_N (h - c)^{1/2} f(c/h) \tag{25}$$

where values of $f(c/h)$ are given by Paris and Sih (1964) and Bueckner (1960). There are many other expressions for the stress intensity of beams subjected to various loading conditions. Some of these are given by Paris and Sih (1965), and Brown and Srawley (1967).

TABLE III

FUNCTIONS GIVEN BY PARIS AND BUECKNER
FOR DETERMINING THE STRESS INTENSITY FOR
THE OPENING MODE

	$f(c/h)$	
c/h	Paris	Bueckner
0.05	0.36	0.25
0.10	0.49	0.48
0.20	0.60	0.60
0.30	0.66	0.66
0.40	0.69	0.70
0.50	0.72	0.72
0.60	0.73	0.72

D. SLENDER COLUMN ANALYSIS

The slender column analysis is essentially the same as the stress-concentration method which, however, requires in its present form the use of the horizontal deflection obtained from experiment. On the other hand, the slender column analysis utilizes the analytical expression for the stress at the midpoint of the column subjected to a concentrated force loaded eccentrically. Of course, the horizontal deflection δ could also have been derived theoretically and then used in Eq. (17), but there was some interest in determining the stress-intensity factor by using long slender column specimens; there is some novelty in using these specimens since deflection measurements are utilized, while conventional tests usually require compliance and other type measurements.

As in the above methods, the approximate stress in a column subjected to axial compression and bending, within the linear range, is equal to the sum of the stresses due to compression and the stresses due to bending. Consequently, using Eqs. (6) and (7) and the stress-intensity relationships for the sharp crack [Eqs. (14) and (15)] results in the following:

$$K = K_{tot} = K_B + K_C = \tfrac{4}{3}(a/\pi)^{1/2}\sigma_{NB} - 2(a/\pi)^{1/2}\sigma_{NT} \qquad (26)$$

where K_{tot} is the total stress-intensity factor, K_B is the stress intensity for bending, K_C is the stress intensity for compression which is equal to $-K_T$ (stress intensity for tension), σ_{NB} is the nominal bending stress at one-half the length of the column, and σ_{NT} is the nominal tensile stress at one-half the length of the column. Therefore, by using Eq. (5) and $\sigma_{NT} = P/A$, the total stress intensity becomes

$$K = \left[\frac{4}{3}\left(\frac{a}{\pi}\right)^{1/2}\right]\frac{Pe}{(I/d)\cos{(kL/2)}} - 2\left(\frac{a}{\pi}\right)^{1/2}\frac{P}{A} \qquad (27)$$

Since $d = a$, $A = 2ab$, and $I = \tfrac{1}{12}(b)(2a)^3$, the total stress-intensity factor becomes

$$K = K_{tot} = \frac{4}{3}\left(\frac{a}{\pi}\right)^{1/2}\frac{Pea}{(2ba^3/3)\cos(kL/2)} - 2\left(\frac{a}{\pi}\right)^{1/2}\frac{P}{2ab} \qquad (28)$$

Rearranging terms gives the following for the stress intensity:

$$K = \frac{2Pe}{b\pi^{1/2}}\frac{1}{a^{3/2}}\frac{1}{\cos(kL/2)} - \frac{P}{\pi^{1/2}a^{1/2}b} \qquad (28a)$$

$$= \frac{P}{(\pi a)^{1/2}b}\left[\frac{2e}{a}\sec\left(\frac{kL}{2}\right) - 1\right] \qquad (29)$$

where

$$k^2 = P/EI \qquad (29a)$$

The stress-intensity value in Eq. (29) may also be expressed as a function of the Euler load, P_E. Since

$$kL/2 = (L/2)(P/EI)^{1/2} \qquad (30)$$

and

$$EI = P_E L^2/\pi^2 \qquad (31)$$

the following is obtained for

$$kL/2 = (\pi/2)(P/P_E)^{1/2} \tag{32}$$

Using Eqs. (29), (30), and (32), the stress intensity becomes

$$K = \frac{P}{(\pi a)^{1/2}b}\left[\frac{2e}{a\cos[(\pi/2)(P/P_E)^{1/2}]} - 1\right] \tag{33}$$

or

$$K = \frac{P}{(\pi a)^{1/2}b}\left[\frac{2e}{a}\sec\left(\frac{\pi}{a}(P/P_E)^{1/2}\right) - 1\right] \tag{34}$$

For some of the tests performed by Liebowitz et al. (1967b), the following values were used:

$$K = 38,000 \quad \text{lb-inch}^{-3/2}, \qquad b = h = 0.5 \quad \text{inch} \qquad \text{and} \qquad P_E = 2930 \quad \text{lb}$$

Therefore, the stress intensity, for these particular tests, is

$$K = 38,000 = (1.13)\frac{P}{a^{1/2}}\left[\frac{2e}{a\cos(0.029P^{1/2})} - 1\right] \tag{35}$$

Equation (35) appears to be sensitive in determining, by trial-and-error process, the maximum load P.

VII. Discussion of Fracture Results

The results presented in this paper were obtained from a group of experiments in which the effects of notch depth, root radii, column length, single notches, double notches, and eccentricity of loading were determined. The range of single crack depths studied was 0.018 to 0.214 inch. The range of double crack depths was 0.016 to 0.154 inch. The root radii were fatigue cracks ($\rho \approx 0$) and machined notches with radii of 0.003 and 0.0625 inch. The column lengths were 6.00, 9.00, 12.00, and 18.00 inches. The eccentricities of loading were 0.090, 0.25, 1.00, and 1.25 inches.

The effect of the notch depth on the failure load is shown in Fig. 19 and is discussed in detail (Liebowitz et al., 1967a). Tests conducted on specimens with notch root radii of 0.003 inch and fatigue cracks do not indicate significant difference between the two in their load-carrying capacity or failure load. Tests conducted on specimens with larger notch root radii (0.0625 inch) indicated that notches or defects with large root radii are less critical than those with small root radii (Liebowitz et al., 1967a). The effects of notch depth and root radius on the various failure criteria will be discussed later in this chapter.

A. Energy Method

In the analysis of test data by the energy method, the energy input was determined from the area under the load displacement curve. Any slippage of the specimen in the end adapters (Fig. 3) would cause error in this curve; therefore, (a) extra care was taken at that point in the experimental setup, and (b) before reading any curve, it was inspected for discontinuities. Of about 80 data points taken, 10 were omitted because it was felt that they gave invalid results because of the above-mentioned slippage and also because of the sticking of the plunger from the extensiometer. The values of energy input are plotted in Fig. 24. The data exhibit a fairly large amount of scatter. However, points representing single notched specimens which were studied may be fitted to an empirical function of the form $y = e^{b+mx}$ (solid line in Fig. 24). The data points representing specimens with small

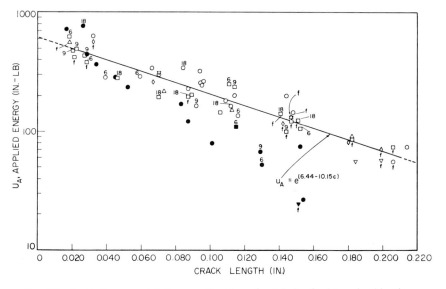

FIG. 24. Applied energy at failure as a function of notch depth, determined by the area under the load—vertical displacement curve.

KEY:

1. □, 0.090 in. eccentricity.
2. △, 0.250 in. eccentricity.
3. ◇, 0.500 in. eccentricity.
4. ○, 1.000 in. eccentricity.
5. ▽, 1.250 in. eccentricity.
6. Solid symbols denote double notched specimens.
7. Open symbols denote single notched specimens.

8. Superscripts denote specimen length in inches.
9. No superscript denotes specimen 12 inches long.
10. Subscript f denotes fatigue crack extension.
11. No subscript denotes machined notch, $\rho < 0.003$ in.

double notches, where notch lengths are for opening notches only, are in good agreement with those having small single notches. This indicates that the small notches in compression had little effect on the failure of the columns. This is supported by the observation of actual failures; i.e., in several extreme cases (notches less than 0.030 inch) the fracture did not pass through the closing notch. Closing cracks of greater depth (0.040 inch and above) do affect the failure of the specimen. This was also indicated by the reduction in load-carrying capacity with increasing notch depth (Liebowitz *et al.*, 1967a).

The energy of deformation ($U_B + U_C$) was determined from data which are subject to experimental error. In addition, both the expression for U_B, Eq. (11), and U_C, Eq. (12), apply only in the range of linear elasticity. If, as indicated earlier, the specimens with small notches did exhibit plastic deformation before failure, then both of these values would be in error to that extent. The values of $U_B + U_C$ are plotted in Fig. 25. With the exception of a few points, these data exhibit a slightly smaller scatter range than do the values of U_A. Again, an empirical function of the form $y = e^{b+mx}$ may be fitted to those points representing single notched specimens (solid line in Fig. 25).

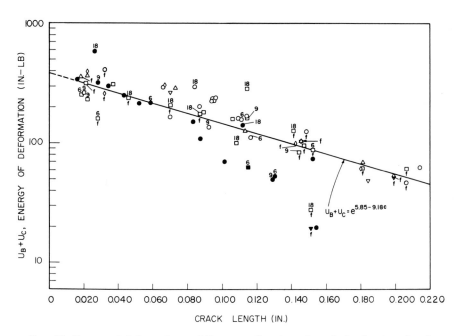

FIG. 25. Energy of deformation at failure as a function of notch depth, given by the sum of Eqs. (2a) and (3). (For KEY, see Fig. 24.)

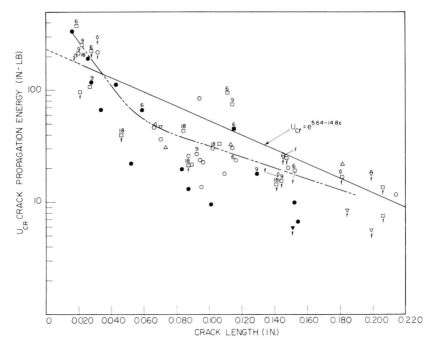

FIG. 26. Crack-propagation energy as a function of notch length (applied energy minus energy of deformation). (For KEY, see Fig. 24.)

The values for energy available to cause crack propagation (U_{cr}) are plotted in Fig. 26. The scatter of these points is somewhat larger than that for U_A and $U_B + U_C$. This would be expected, since they represent the difference between two large values and are affected to a larger extent by the error of each. However, if one attempts to draw a straight line through the points, then $U_{cr} = e^{5.64 - 14.8c}$ results. This relationship only approximately represents all the data, as can be readily seen in Fig. 26.

B. STRESS-CONCENTRATION METHOD

Of the methods described in this chapter, with the exception of the "slender column analysis," to relate possible failure criteria for structural members subjected simultaneously to axial compression and bending, the stress-concentration results, using the stress-intensity factor for $\rho \to 0$, gives better agreement in spite of being valid only for linear elasticity (Neuber, 1937). These conditions may have been violated only in the case of very small notch depths where some plastic deformation of the specimen may have occurred only before fracture. The values of stress intensity for

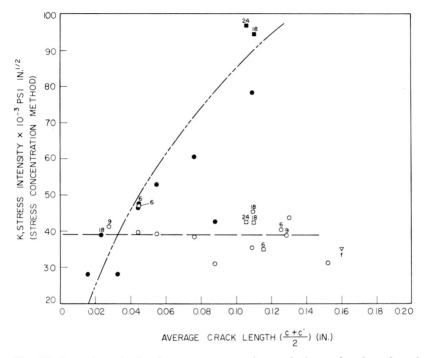

FIG. 27. Stress intensity by the stress-concentration method as a function of notch depth determined, from Eqs. (9a) and (12).

KEY:

1. □, 0.090 in. eccentricity.
2. ○, 1.000 in. eccentricity.
3. ▽, 1.250 in. eccentricity.
4. Solid symbols denote values obtained by shallow notch analysis.

5. Open symbols denote values obtained by deep notch analysis.
6. Superscript denotes specimen length in inches.
7. No superscript denotes specimen length of 12 inches.

double notched specimens obtained from this method are plotted in Fig. 27. The points denoted by the open symbols were obtained using the equation for the deep notch analysis, Eq. (17). The values denoted by solid symbols were obtained using the same experimental data as above by using the equation for the shallow notch analysis, Eq. (20). The values denoted by the open symbols may be fitted to a function of the form $y = $ constant, and most of these values determined by Liebowitz et al. (1967b) are within the range of stress-intensity values (32 to 40×10^3 psi-inch$^{1/2}$) found for the 7075-T6511 aluminum alloy by other test methods (Kaufman and Hunsicker, 1965; Heyer, 1965). The number of test results shown are too small to be conclusive, but the data appear to be independent of column length and eccentricity of loading. Therefore, this method of testing may be considered to give a valid failure criteria for a high-strength aluminum alloy.

The points denoted by the solid symbols in Fig. 27 appear to be higher than the above for the stress-intensity values obtained by other test methods. Apparently, this method of analysis for double notched specimens is not as useful as other procedures for determining failure for the specimens under consideration.

Attempts were made to apply similar stress-concentration analyses to columns with single opening notches. Both the deep and shallow notch relations gave extremely inconsistent results. Therefore, no attempt was made to establish a failure criteria for that configuration.

C. Equivalent Beam Analysis

The method of equivalent beam analysis was employed to relate approximately the results, obtained from a new type of specimen under a different loading condition, to other experimental values of fracture toughness (32 to 40×10^3 psi-inch$^{1/2}$) for the 7075 aluminum alloy (Kaufman and Hunsicker, 1965; Heyer, 1965). The results of this analysis are given in Fig. 28. With the exception of seven high values, these results exhibit a

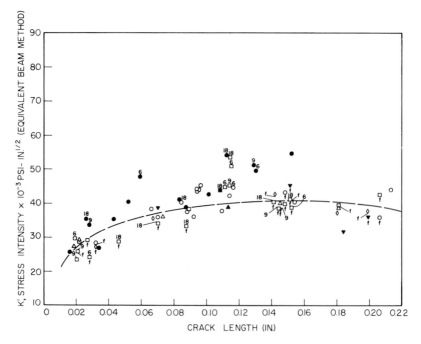

Fig. 28. Stress intensity by the equivalent beam method as a function of notch depth. (For Key, see Fig. 24.)

moderate amount of scatter over the entire range of notch length tested. From these seven values, four were from specimens in which the opening notch was at least 10% deeper than the closing notch. Close examination of the other three specimens gave no apparent reason for the high stress-intensity values. For notch lengths greater than 0.060 inch, the results are in fair agreement with those determined from tensile and beam fracture tests. For notch lengths less than 0.060 inch, the results are not in agreement with values from other fracture tests. This would be expected, since both methods are limited to cases where the nominal stress is less than about 0.6 of the yield strength (Paris and Sih, 1965; Payne, 1964).

Failure criteria obtained by the energy method (Fig. 26) and by the equivalent beam analysis (Fig. 28) include both notches with fatigue extension and machined notches with root radii less than 0.003 inch. Values for each type of notch exhibit similar scatter over the range of crack lengths tested. Thus, the use of the 0.003-inch root radii is justified in these fracture tests.

D. SLENDER COLUMN ANALYSIS

Equations (33) and (34) are very useful in obtaining the maximum load-carrying capacity that a notched column can withstand when subjected to a load applied eccentrically. Table IV indicates the experimental values obtained by Liebowitz et al. (1967a) for the maximum load on a column and also the values obtained by using Eq. (35). It is interesting to note that, for crack lengths from 0.02 inch to about 0.15 inch, the prediction of the maximum load from Eq. (35) is quite good while, for larger values of crack length, the results are not as favorable.

In determining the load from Eq. (35), a value of $K = 38,000$ lb-inch$^{-3/2}$ was used. Undoubtedly, there is some error in using this value, since the stress-intensity value has been shown, in Fig. 28, by using the equivalent beam analysis, to vary from 30,000 to 40,000. In a recent report by Davis et al. (1967), the stress-intensity value varied from $K = 22,000$ to $K = 35,000$ and was a function of the type of test and direction of the sample material studied. Some investigators have been using a value of $K = 32,000$. The new test procedures recommended by Brown and Srawley (1967) should lead to more consistent results for determining the stress intensity. These test procedures could also be applied to the specimens investigated by Liebowitz et al. (1967a,b,c) and Liebowitz and Claus (1968). Failure criteria obtained by use of the "slender column analysis," however, appear in general to give better correlation with experimental results than the three other methods described in this chapter. This engineering analysis may also be used in determining the stress-intensity values. The validity of using the other methods has been indicated in the preceding sections.

TABLE IV

Comparison of Experimental with Theoretical Values of Maximum Load

Notch depth (c)	Eccentricity (e)	Theoretical maximum load (P_{cr})	Experimental maximum load (P_{cr})
0.020	0.090	2548	2340
0.020	0.250	2074	1850
0.020	0.500	1613	1300
0.020	1.000	1121	1100
0.020	1.250	973	980
0.070	0.090	2417	2500
0.070	0.250	1848	1900
0.070	0.500	1355	1420
0.070	1.000	887	1050
0.070	1.250	756	980
0.090	0.090	2342	2550
0.090	0.250	1731	1920
0.090	0.500	1234	1460
0.090	1.000	784	980
0.090	1.250	633	900
0.110	0.090	2248	2470
0.110	0.250	1594	1760
0.110	0.500	1098	1400
0.110	1.000	677	950
0.110	1.250	568	720
0.170	0.090	1751	2130
0.170	0.250	1016	1530
0.170	0.500	611	1020
0.170	1.000	340	550
0.170	1.250	278	480
0.195	0.090	1359	2150
0.195	0.250	685	1460
0.195	0.500	384	960
0.195	1.000	204	540
0.195	1.250	165	470

VIII. Some Stress-Concentration Factors

Many researchers in experimental and theoretical stress analysis have been concerned with the effect of stress-concentration factors in structures and their components. (Neuber (1937), Kikukawa (1957), Wigglesworth (1957), Irwin (1958), Savin (1961), Paprino (1962), Gerberich (1962), Liebowitz et al. (1967a,b,c), Creager and Paris (1967), and Liebowitz and Claus (1968).) Significant work has been accomplished in the proximity of notches and cracks by such workers as Post (1954), Wells and Post (1957),

Dixon (1960, 1962), Oppel and Hill (1964), Bowie (1964), Kobayashi *et al.* (1965), and Dixon and Strannigan (1964).

In most of these experimental studies, the exact stress-concentration effect or the distribution of the stress-strain field around the notch or crack was found to within several thousandths of an inch of the boundary. Specific mention is made of the photoelastic work of Paprino (1962), who reported that his results were valid to within 0.003 inch from the boundary by using extrapolation. Furthermore, the smallest root diameter of a notch (other than a crack) used in photoelastic studies was given in his paper as 0.0280 inch.

The results to be presented in this chapter are primarily concerned with notched sheets subjected to tensile loading and the determination of stresses very close to the exact boundary of a notch having extremely small root radii, such as approximately 0.004 inch. This technique should be applicable to structural elements subjected to bending loads, provided that the proper precautionary measures are taken. Studying the distribution of stresses around notches having such small root radii seems preferable to proceeding with larger radii and then attempting to scale down the ratio of the radius of the notch to its depth. Also, it is interesting to investigate photoelastic techniques that may lead to a determination of stress distributions at cracks as experienced in practice. Finally, if such small root radii can be studied with precision, a much larger variation of root radii to plate width and of root radii to the depth of notches can be studied even though the size of specimen may be limited.

Studies by Liebowitz *et al.* (1967c) were concerned with a photoelastic analysis of notches with very small root radii, i.e., 0.003 inch in diameter. Such root radii are similar to those found in cracks. This chapter deals with a description of this photoelastic work, in addition to a discussion of some available stress-concentration relationships.

An elastic solution for a uniaxially loaded plate with external notches does not yet exist, but several approximate solutions are available. The best known of these are Neuber's (1937) expressions, indicated earlier in this chapter, for the deep and shallow notches. In addition, Neuber (1937) gives an average stress-concentration factor for notches geometrically placed so that they are within the limits of the solutions for the shallow and deep notches. The stress concentration, in this in-between region, is obtained from the solutions of (a) stress concentrations for shallow notches, i.e., for notches spaced appreciably apart from each other, and (b) stress concentrations for deep notches, i.e., for notches spaced fairly close to each other. The average stress concentration is determined from

$$(q-1)^{-2} = (q_S - 1)^{-2} + (q_D - 1)^{-2} \tag{36}$$

Therefore, the stress concentration is

$$q = 1 + \frac{(q_S - 1)(q_D - 1)}{[(q_S - 1)^2 + (q_D - 1)^2]^{1/2}} \tag{37}$$

where q_S is the stress-concentration factor for the case of shallow notches and q_D is the stress-concentration factor for the case of deep notches. The stress concentrations for shallow and deeply notched specimens under tensile loading may be obtained from Eqs. (6) and (18), respectively.

In a recent study of the influence of notch depth in edge-notched plates, Dixon (1962), using Neuber's solution as given in Eq. (37), applied a limiting process to Eq. (37), where the root radius ρ goes to zero. In this way, Dixon obtained an alternative expression for the stress-concentration factor for small radii in the form

$$q = \frac{1 + 2(c/\rho)^{1/2}}{[1 - (2c/h)]^{1/2} [1 + (\frac{1}{4}\pi^2 - 1)(2c/h)]^{1/2}} \tag{38}$$

For the range of variables in this study, the stress-concentration factor obtained from the above expression, Eq. (38), differs by less than 1%.

Dixon considers the inverse problem and solves Eq. (13) for σ_{max} in terms of a known stress-intensity factor. It should be noted that, in many cases, the expression for K_I is obtained from the solution of a singularity problem in elasticity in which ρ, the root radius, is not a parameter. Therefore, the resultant expression for σ_{max} is applicable only for very small root radii.

Using a polynomial mapping function, Bowie (1964) computed values for the stress-intensity factor for the opening mode, K_I, for double-edge-notched plates. Paris and Sih (1965) have shown that Bowie's (1964) results can be expressed in the form given in Eq. (24). For the range of $2c/h$ ratios considered here, $f(2c/h)$ is constant and K_I reduces to

$$K_I = 1.12\sigma(\pi c)^{1/2} \tag{39}$$

The latter equation agrees with the results of Irwin (1958) for shallow-edge notches obtained through different reasoning. Irwin (1960) had proposed that the stress-intensity factor, K_I, can be obtained from the limiting value of a known stress-concentration factor by the relation given in Eq. (13).

Therefore, equating Eqs. (13) and (39) yields

$$q = 1.12(q_\infty - 1) \tag{40}$$

where

$$q_\infty = 1 + 2(c/\rho)^{1/2} \tag{41}$$

IX. Discussion of Stress-Concentration Results

The experimental results obtained by Liebowitz *et al.* (1967c) are shown in Table V. The values obtained from theoretical calculations have also been included. In the experiments reported in this chapter, the radius of the notch ρ was varied. As a result, the ratio of notch depth to half of the shank width $c/(h/2)$ remains relatively constant. All of the stress-concentration factors in the table are based on the gross nominal cross section.

Figure 29 shows the result of plotting the stress-concentration factor versus the ratio c/ρ. The experimental results show good agreement with the results obtained from Neuber's deep-notch calculation for values up to about $c/\rho = 10$. At that point, a marked deviation takes place, and,

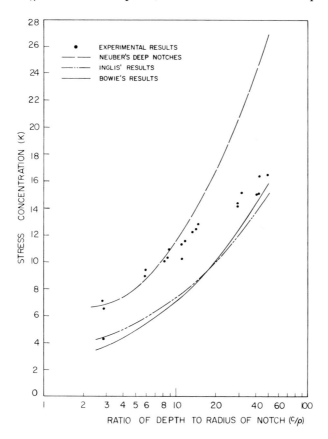

FIG. 29. Relation between the stress-concentration factor and the ratio of the depth of the notch to the root radius.

TABLE V

COMPARISON OF EXPERIMENTAL WITH THEORETICAL VALUES OF STRESS CONCENTRATION[a]

ρ	c/ρ	$2c/h$	Experimental	Stress-concentration factor (q)				
				Inglis	Bowie	Neuber deep	Neuber combined	Empirical
0.0019	49.26	0.1255	16	15.04	15.72	26.98	14.78	16.50
0.0022	42.55	0.1255	15	14.04	14.60	25.06	13.80	15.94
0.0025	42.52	0.1425	16	14.04	14.60	23.75	13.79	15.94
0.0026	40.88	0.1425	15	13.08	14.31	23.27	13.53	15.87
0.0031	31.10	0.1294	15	12.16	12.50	21.16	11.95	14.87
0.0033	29.21	0.1294	14	11.82	12.12	20.51	11.61	14.67
0.0033	29.21	0.1296	14	11.81	12.11	20.50	11.60	14.67
0.0064	14.66	0.1259	13	8.66	8.58	14.70	8.51	12.27
0.0066	14.21	0.1259	12	8.54	8.44	14.48	8.39	12.17
0.0070	13.40	0.1261	12	8.32	8.20	14.05	8.18	11.94
0.0084	11.67	0.1315	12	7.84	7.66	12.87	7.70	11.46
0.0087	11.26	0.1315	10	7.72	7.53	12.65	7.58	11.35
0.0088	11.14	0.1317	11	7.68	7.48	12.57	7.54	11.31
0.0123	8.89	0.1468	11	6.96	6.68	10.74	6.83	10.55
0.0126	8.68	0.1468	10	6.89	6.60	10.61	6.71	10.46
0.0133	8.23	0.1470	10	6.74	6.43	10.32	6.62	10.26
0.0194	5.92	0.1539	9	5.86	5.44	8.60	5.75	9.13
0.0196	5.86	0.1539	9	5.84	5.42	8.55	5.73	9.09
0.0299	2.86	0.1146	7	4.38	3.79	6.78	4.31	6.62
0.0304	2.81	0.1145	7	4.35	3.75	6.73	4.30	6.56

[a]Material: Hysol 4290.　Thickness: 0.025 inch.　$h = 1.490$ inch.

at about $c/\rho = 50$, the difference is approximately 64%. Apparently, the Neuber (1937) deep-notch calculation is not desirable in this region. It is noted that, $c/\rho = 50$, the experimental values are in fair agreement, i.e., within 5% of the Bowie (1964) solution. However, the remainder of the region shows differences of as much as 34% (at $c/\rho = 11$). Inglis' results and the fracture mechanics approximation show the same tendencies.

The stress-concentration factor has also been plotted versus the root radius in Fig. 30. Some of the theoretical K values in Fig. 29 have been replotted. Also shown are averaged experimental results obtained by combining two or three experimental results for approximately the same root radius. The experimental stress-concentration factors for the corresponding set of root radii were also averaged. It is possible to draw a straight line

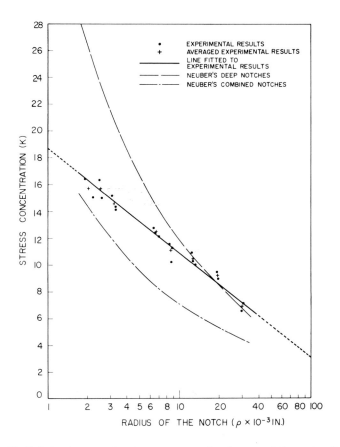

FIG. 30. Relation between the stress-concentration factor and the root radius.

very close to these points. It is interesting to point out that this line passes through $K = 3$ at the value of $\rho = 0.1$ inch for a semicircular notch.

An equation of the form

$$K = m \ln(\rho/c) + n \tag{42}$$

may be fitted to the line shown in Fig. 30. In this equation, m and n are constants. For this particular problem, the equation is

$$K = -3.45 \ln(\rho/c) + 3 \tag{43}$$

The results of this study, using small root radii, do not agree with available theoretical solutions; whereas earlier experimental results, using larger root radii, tended to confirm the theory. This appears to indicate that there is a lower limit at which geometric scaling ceases to be valid. The theoretical results for the deep notches and for the fracture mechanics approximation seem to give valid outer bounds to the experimental results, as shown in Figs. 29 and 30.

As shown above, the experiments performed in this investigation indicate the extent of the validity of using standard stress-concentration formulas for a wide range of values for the radius of the notch. This experimental study was concerned with specimens of one constant thickness. No appreciable attempt was made to treat the question of triaxial stress which may arise at the root of the notch. However, the theories with which the experimental results have been compared are also not valid for triaxiality considerations. In any event, it is interesting to note that a discrepancy exists in the results when comparing the experimental findings with the theoretical values for small notch radii, but that they agree quite well for notch radii of 0.020 inch or greater. Also significant: the experimental technique used in this study is apparently useful for determining the stress-concentration values close to the root of the notches, particularly for those having small radii. Special attention was given to the question of the possible integrating effect with use of the microscope. Results obtained with the microscope compared favorably with a conventional polariscope technique.

Another point is the question of large deformations taking place at the root of the notch. In all tests, small incremental loads were applied. After each stress-freezing cycle, the stress concentration at the root of the notch was determined. Then, the specimen was reloaded with a specified higher load and again frozen, and the cycles were repeated, as required. It was found for each small incremental step increase in load, there was a corresponding incremental increase in root radius and decrease in fringe order. Final root radii were used in all calculations and graphs. Furthermore, it is felt that the stress-optic law is linear in the cases considered because the loads were kept small, resulting in relatively low fringe orders.

X. Recommended Research

As discussed in this chapter, the experimental studies performed to date on notched slender columns have been concerned with aluminum 7075-T6511 rods of $\frac{1}{2}$- x $\frac{1}{2}$-inch dimensions for their cross section. Although tests on this particular size of section resulted in a plane strain mode of failure for most deeply notched specimens, it should be of interest to investigate other modes of failure in columns having different cross-sectional areas, column lengths, notch depths, and radii; the effect of these parameters on the load-carrying capacity and fracture characteristics should be determined for slender columns made from a variety of materials. Such columns should be studied for cases of different loadings and boundary conditions. Also, other investigations on environmental conditions, as studied by DeHart and Liebowitz (1967), should be pursued.

Concurrent theoretical studies should be undertaken to determine, from a more exact approach than previous work on this subject, the failure load of various structural elements under different loading conditions. Unfortunately, it is not simple to determine by an exact theoretical analysis the response of notched slender columns. In elastic and plastic analyses, sharp cracks require the treatment of singularities which obviously lead to mathematical complexities. In some recent studies by Liebowitz and Claus (1968), some of the difficulties in obtaining closed-form solutions were indicated by determining the failure load for sharply notched columns. Even through the use of a numerical approach, it was also difficult to obtain some meaningful results for determining the effect of cracks of various lengths on the weakening characteristics of slender columns.

Future theoretical work should be concerned with multiaxial stress conditions, as, for example, the biaxial stress problems treated by Sih and Liebowitz (1967). Experimental research on this subject is also desirable for studying the effects of various structural components having different edge conditions. Further experiments, like those of Hartbower et al. (1967), on acoustical failure criteria, should also be performed to determine the mechanical, electrical, and acoustical correlation for the critical failure characteristics of materials. Also, photoelastic and other experimental techniques need to be developed and applied to obtain the stress and strain conditions in the vicinity of sharp cracks, before and after their extension or propagation. These experimental techniques should assist the investigators in obtaining valid failure criteria on the microscopic and macroscopic levels.

It is felt that research is quite desirable and rewarding on the subject concerning the response and failure loads of structural components containing flaws. Most structures, during their life cycle, will contain flaws arising from metallurgical processing and mechanical stressing. Consequently, further insight is required to predict the behavior of such realistic structural materials. Higher strength-to-weight ratios may be obtained by properly utilizing the information being obtained by the scientists and engineers in metallurgy and applied mechanics.

XI. Summary

For the aluminum 7075-T6511 columns considered, the following conclusions may be drawn:

1. Presence of a fatigue crack in a column reduces its load-carrying capacity when the load is applied eccentrically in compression (Figs. 22 and 23).

2. The experimentally determined buckling load is not affected by the presence of two symmetrical and identical cracks for concentrically loaded straight columns (Fig. 9).

3. For slenderness ratios less than 250, the sharp notches appear to have a significant effect on the load-carrying ability of the columns (Figs. 22 and 23). This effect is especially pronounced for large eccentricity of load application. For slenderness ratios greater than 250, these notches do not appear to have quite as significant an effect on the load-carrying ability.

4. The load-carrying capacity decreases with increasing depth of notch for slenderness ratios less than 250 (Figs. 22 and 23).

5. For a column length of 12 inches, the weakening effect of a fatigue crack becomes more pronounced when loads are applied at greater eccentricities (Figs. 11–17).

6. The reduction in load-carrying ability of a 12-inch-long fatigue-cracked column having a slenderness ratio of about 92 is the same as for a sharp notch with a root radius of 0.003 inch or less, as long as all the other dimensions remain the same (Fig. 20).

7. A root radius of 0.0625 inch does not appear to result in catastrophic failures of the type exhibited by a fatigue crack in a column having a slenderness ratio of 92 (Fig. 20).

8. In loading columns to failure, a fatigue crack on one side of the column is more disastrous than a fatigue crack of half the depth on both sides of the column, as may be seen in Fig. 23 for a slenderness ratio of 92.

9. For a slenderness ratio of 92 and a given depth of fatigue crack, failure appears to occur at a near-constant horizontal deflection, when the column is loaded eccentrically in compression (Fig. 18).

10. Columns made from rolled bar stock did not show any preferred orientation resulting from manufacturing processes in these studies.

11.   It is possible to establish a reasonable failure criterion for double notched columns, from Neuber's (1937) stress-concentration equations for deep notches (Fig. 27).

12.   It is possible to establish a relation between crack length and energy required to cause crack propagation. This relation is independent of column length and eccentricity of loading (Fig. 25).

13.   Small closing cracks have little effect on the failure load or the values of failure criteria. Large closing cracks have a distinct effect on the values of failure criteria (Fig. 26).

14.   The validity of these tests performed by Liebowitz et al. (1967b), as fracture tests, is supported by the agreement of stress-intensity values, from the equivalent beam method, with those from other fracture tests.

15.   A technique has been developed by Liebowitz et al. (1967c) to study very sharp notches employing conventional photoelastic principles.

16.   In these photoelastic studies, it is possible to determine the exact boundary location to within ± 0.0004 inch and furthermore to determine accurately the fringe order very near the boundary (Fig. 7).

17.   Experimental results for determining the stress concentration appear to follow a trend different from any of the existing theories, even though the theories seem to give valid outer bounds (Figs. 29 and 30).

18.   At $c/\rho = 50$, the difference is 64% between experimental results and Neuber's solution for deep notches; the Bowie solution is within 5% at $c/\rho = 50$, but the difference becomes much more significant (up to 34%) at other points.

19.   For this range of values, scaling (using $c/(h/2)$ and c/ρ) does not appear valid; however, it may be used for notches with larger root radii.

20.   A relation for the stress concentration

$$K = -3.45 \ln(\rho/c) + 3$$

appears to be valid for the range of tests performed in this investigation.

Appendix A. Unnotched Beam Column Loaded Concentrically

1. Derivation of the Differential Equation

From equilibrium consideration, the sum of the forces in the Y direction for the structural element, as seen in Fig. A-1, is

$$- V + (V + dV/dx \, \Delta x) = 0 \tag{A.1}$$

Therefore, Eq. (A.1) gives

$$dV/dx = 0 \tag{A.2}$$

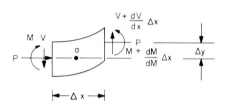

FIG. A-1. Forces on a differential element of a beam column subjected to axial loads.

Taking moments about point a gives

$$(M + dM/dx\, \Delta x) - M + V\, \Delta x/2 + (V + dV/dx)\, \Delta x/2 + P\, \Delta y \quad (A.3)$$

Consequently, Eq. (A.3) becomes

$$dM/dx + V + P\, dy/dx = 0 \quad (A.4)$$

Assuming that the deflection of a beam is due only to bending, the bending moment M is

$$M = EI\, d^2y/dx^2 \quad (A.5)$$

Substituting Eq. (A.5) into Eq. (A.4) gives

$$\frac{d}{dx}\left(EI\frac{d^2y}{dx^2}\right) + V + P\frac{dy}{dx} = 0 \quad (A.6)$$

Differentiating Eq. (A.6) with respect to x gives

$$\frac{d^2}{dx^2}\left(EI\frac{d^2y}{dx^2}\right) + \frac{dV}{dx} + P\frac{d^2y}{dx^2} = 0 \quad (A.7)$$

Substituting Eq. (A.2) into Eq. (A.7) gives

$$\frac{d^2}{dx^2}\left(EI\frac{d^2y}{dx^2}\right) + P\frac{d^2y}{dx^2} = 0 \quad (A.8)$$

For constant E and I, Eq. (A.8) becomes

$$d^4y/dx^4 + k^2\, d^2y/dx^2 = 0 \quad (A.9)$$

where

$$k^2 = P/EI \quad (A.10)$$

2. Derivation of the Critical Load

Letting $z = d^2y/dx^2$, Eq. (A.9) becomes

$$d^2z/dx^2 + k^2z = 0 \qquad (A.11)$$

The well-known solution to Eq. (A.11) is

$$z = C \sin(P/EI)^{1/2}x + D \cos(P/EI)^{1/2}x \qquad (A.12)$$

where C and D are constants of integration. Replacing z by d^2y/dx^2 and integrating twice results in

$$y = - C(EI/P)(P/EI)^{1/2}x - D(EI/P) \cos(P/EI)^{1/2}x + C_3 x + C_4 \quad (A.13)$$

Let $C_1 = -C(EI/P)$, and $C_2 = -D(EI/P)$. Therefore, the general solution to the differential equation is

$$y = C_1 \sin(P/EI)^{1/2}x + C_2 \cos(P/EI)^{1/2}x + C_3 x + C_4 \qquad (A.14)$$

The boundary conditions for an unnotched column that is pin-connected at both ends are at

$$x = 0, \quad y = 0, \quad \text{and} \quad d^2y/dx^2 = 0 \qquad \text{and}$$
$$x = L, \quad y = 0, \quad \text{and} \quad d^2y/dx^2 = 0 \qquad (A.15)$$

Using Eq. (A.15) with Eq. (A.14) gives

$$y(0) = C_2 + C_4 = 0 \qquad (A.16)$$

$$d^2y/dx^2 \big|_{x=0} = -C_2(P/EI) = 0 \qquad (A.17)$$

$$y(L) = C_1 \sin(P/EI)^{1/2}L + C_2 \cos(P/EI)^{1/2}L + C_3 L + C_4 = 0 \quad (A.18)$$

$$d^2y/dx^2 \big|_{x=L} = C_1(P/EI) \sin(P/EI)^{1/2}L - C_2(P/EI) \cos(P/EI)^{1/2}L = 0$$
$$(A.19)$$

From Eqs. (A.16) and (A.17), the constants $C_2 = C_4 = 0$. Therefore Eqs. (A.18) and (A.19) become

$$C_1 \sin(P/EI)^{1/2}L + C_3 L = 0 \qquad (A.20)$$
$$C_1(P/EI) \sin(P/EI)^{1/2} = 0 \qquad (A.21)$$

The nontrivial solution is

$$\sin(P/EI)^{1/2}L = 0 \qquad (A.22)$$

For the sine term to be equal to zero, the following relationship results:

$$(P/EI)^{1/2}L = n\pi \qquad (A.23)$$

where $n = 1, 2, 3, \ldots$. Thus, the critical load

$$P_{\text{cr}} = n^2\pi^2EI/L^2 \qquad (A.24)$$

Appendix B. Unnotched Beam Column Loaded Eccentrically

1. DERIVATION OF THE MAXIMUM DEFLECTION (AT $L/2$)

The differential equation given by Eq. (A.9) is valid for columns under any end conditions, provided that the force of gravity is neglected. The boundary conditions for a column that is pin-connected at both ends and loaded eccentrically, as seen in Fig. (10a), are

$$\text{at} \quad x = 0 \quad \text{and} \quad x = L, \quad y = 0$$
$$\text{at} \quad x = 0 \quad \text{and} \quad x = L, \quad d^2y/dx^2 = M_0/EI \tag{B.1}$$

where $M_0 = Pe$. Differentiating Eq. (A.9) gives

$$d^3y/dx^3 + k^2 \, dy/dx = C_1 \tag{B.2}$$

where C_1 is a constant of integration. Differentiating Eq. (B.2) gives

$$(d^2y/dx^2) + k^2y = C_1x + C_2 \tag{B.3}$$

where C_1 and C_2 are constants of integration. Using the boundary conditions as given by Eq. (B.1) in Eq. (B.3) gives Eqs. (B.4) and (B.5):

$$(d^2y/dx^2)(0) + k^2y(0) = C_1 \cdot 0 + C_2 \tag{B.4}$$

where $k^2y(0) = 0$ and $C_2 = M_0/EI$:

$$(d^2y/dx^2)(L) + k^2y(L) = C_1L + C_2 \tag{B.5}$$

where $M_0/EI = C_1L + (M_0/EI)$ and $C_1 = 0$. Therefore

$$(d^2y/dx^2) + k^2y = C_2 \tag{B.6}$$

The solution is

$$y = y_C + y_P \tag{B.7}$$

where $y_P = C_2/k^2$ and y_C satisfies

$$(d^2y/dx^2)_C + k^2y_C = 0 \tag{B.8}$$

The solution to Eq. (B.8) is well known and is given as

$$y_C = C_3 \sin kx + C_4 \cos kx \tag{B.9}$$

Therefore

$$y(x) = C_3 \sin kx + C_4 \cos kx + (C_2/k^2) \tag{B.10}$$

Differentiating twice, Eq. (B.10) becomes

$$d^2y/dx^2 (x) = -k^2(C_3 \sin kx = C_4 \cos kx) \tag{B.11}$$

Usually, the boundary conditions at $y(0)$ and $y(L)$ give

$$y(0) = 0, \qquad C_4 = -C_2/k^2 \tag{B.12}$$

$$y(L) = 0, \qquad C_3 \sin kL + C_4 \cos kL + (C_2/k^2) = 0 \tag{B.13}$$

Substituting Eq. (B.12) into Eq. (B.13) gives

$$C_3 = [C_4(1 - \cos kL)]/\sin kL \tag{B.14}$$

Substituting Eq. (B.14) into Eq. (B.11)

$$y(x) = C_3 \sin kx + C_4 \cos kx - C_4 \tag{B.15}$$

Rearranging terms in Eq. (B.15) gives

$$y(x) = C_3 \sin kx + C_4(\cos kx - 1) \tag{B.16}$$

Let $\delta \equiv y(L/2)$. Therefore, Eq. (B.16) becomes

$$\delta \equiv y(L/2) = C_3 \sin(kL/2) + C_4 [\cos(kL/2) - 1] \tag{B.17}$$

Substituting Eq. (B.14) into Eq. (B.17) gives

$$\delta \equiv \frac{C_4(1 - \cos kL)}{\sin kL} \sin \frac{kL}{2} + C_4\left(\cos \frac{kL}{2} - 1\right) \tag{B.18}$$

Therefore

$$\delta = C_4\left[\frac{[2 \sin^2 (kL/2)] \sin(kL/2)}{2 \sin(kL/2)\cos(kL/2)} + \cos(kL/2) - 1\right] \tag{B.19}$$

$$\delta = C_4\left[\frac{1 - \cos^2 (kL/2)}{\cos(kL/2)} + \cos(kL/2) - 1\right] \tag{B.20}$$

$$\delta = C_4\left(\frac{1}{\cos(kL/2)} - 1\right) \tag{B.21}$$

Therefore, Eq. (B.21) becomes

$$\delta = -\frac{M_0}{k^2 EI}\left(\frac{1}{\cos(kL/2)} - 1\right) \tag{B.22}$$

Using $M_0 = Pe$ and $k^2 = P/EI$, Eq. (B.22) becomes

$$\delta = -e\left(\frac{1}{\cos(kL/2)} - 1\right) \tag{B.23}$$

where $k^2 = P/EI$.

2. Derivation of the Maximum Stress (at $L/2$)

Using beam column assumptions, the bending stress is

$$\sigma_B = Md/I \tag{B.24}$$

or

$$\sigma_B = Md/Z \tag{B.25}$$

where $Z = I/d$.

It can be seen from Fig. (10a) that the bending moment

$$M = P(e + \delta) \tag{B.26}$$

Using Eq. (B.23) and changing the sign convention on the moments to conform to the deflection used in Eq. (B.26), the bending moment becomes

$$M = Pe + Pe[\sec(kL/2) - 1] \tag{B.27}$$

Therefore, the moment due to bending becomes

$$M = Pe \sec(kL/2) \tag{B.28}$$

The compressive stress due to the axially loading, as seen in Fig. (10a), is

$$\sigma_C = -P/A \tag{B.29}$$

Therefore, by using Eqs. (B.28) and (B.29), the total stress at $x = L/2$ for an unnotched column which is loaded eccentrically, as shown in Fig. (10a), is

$$\sigma_{\text{tot}} = (Pe/Z) \sec(kL/2) - (P/A) \tag{B.30}$$

Appendix C. Stress-Intensity Factors for Beam Columns Having Deep Cracks

1. Limiting Values for Stress-Intensity Factors of Hyperbolic Notched Beams under Bending Loads

The maximum stress, as given by Neuber (1937), at the hyperbolic notch for bending is

$$\sigma_{\text{max}} = \sigma_{NB}\left[\frac{\frac{4}{3}(a/\rho)(a/\rho)^{1/2}}{(a/\rho)^{1/2} + [(a/\rho) - 1]\arctan(a/\rho)^{1/2}}\right] \tag{C.1}$$

where σ_{NB} is the nominal stress for the case of bending. The stress-intensity value can be expressed as

$$K = \tfrac{1}{2}\lim_{\rho \to 0}(\pi\rho)^{1/2}\sigma_{\text{max}} \tag{C.2}$$

Consequently, the stress intensity for the case of a beam under bending loads is $K = K_B$. Substituting Eq. (C.1) into Eq. (C.2) gives

$$K_B = \frac{\pi^{1/2}}{2} \lim_{\rho \to 0} \rho^{1/2} \left[\frac{\frac{4}{3}(a/\rho)(a/\rho)^{1/2}}{(a/\rho)^{1/2} + [(a/\rho) - 1] \arctan(a/\rho)^{1/2}} \right] \sigma_{NB} \quad \text{(C.3)}$$

$$K_B = \frac{\pi^{1/2}}{2} \sigma_{NB} \cdot \frac{4}{3} \lim_{\rho \to 0} \left[\frac{(2/\rho)a^{1/2}}{(a/\rho)^{1/2} + [(a/\rho) - 1] \arctan(a/\rho)^{1/2}} \right] \quad \text{(C.4)}$$

Rearranging terms and taking the limit gives

$$K_B = \tfrac{2}{3}\pi^{1/2}\sigma_{NB}[a^{3/2}/a(\pi/2)] \quad \text{(C.5)}$$

Thus, the stress intensity for the case of bending is

$$K_B = \tfrac{4}{3}(a/\pi)^{1/2}\sigma_{NB} \quad \text{(C.6)}$$

2. LIMITING VALUES FOR STRESS-INTENSITY FACTORS OF HYPERBOLIC NOTCHED BEAMS UNDER COMPRESSIVE LOADS

The maximum stress, as given by Neuber (1937), at the hyperbolic notch under tension is

$$\sigma_{\max} = \left[\frac{2[(a/\rho) + 1](a/\rho)^{1/2}}{[(a/\rho) + 1] \arctan(a/\rho)^{1/2} + (a/\rho)^{1/2}} \right] \sigma_{NT} \quad \text{(C.7)}$$

Substituting Eq. (C.7) into Eq. (C.2) gives a stress-intensity value K_T for the tensile case. However, it is assumed that the stress-intensity factor K_C, for compression, is equal to the absolute value of K_T. Also, the nominal stress σ_{NT}, for the case of tension, is assumed equal to the nominal stress σ_{NC} for the case of compression. These are reasonable, since linearity is assumed. Therefore

$$K_C = K_T = \frac{\pi^{1/2}}{2} \lim_{\rho \to 0} \rho^{1/2} \left[\frac{2[(a/\rho) + 1](a/\rho)^{1/2}}{[(a/\rho) + 1] \arctan(a/\rho)^{1/2} + (a/\rho)^{1/2}} \right] \sigma_{NC} \quad \text{(C.8)}$$

$$K_C = \lim_{\rho \to 0} \left[\frac{(a\pi)^{1/2}}{\arctan(a/\rho)^{1/2} + (a/\rho)^{1/2}(a/\rho)^{1/2} [\rho/(a + \rho)]} \right] \sigma_{NC} \quad \text{(C.9)}$$

$$K_C = \lim_{\rho \to 0} \left[\frac{(a\pi)^{1/2}}{\arctan(a/\rho)^{1/2} + (a\rho)^{1/2}[1/(a + \rho)]} \right] \sigma_{NC} \quad \text{(C.10)}$$

Therefore, the stress-intensity factor for the case of compression is

$$K_C = 2(a/\pi)^{1/2}\sigma_{NC} \quad \text{(C.11)}$$

3. Total Stress-Intensity Factor for the Deeply Cracked Column Subjected to Bending and Compression

The total stress-intensity factor for bending and compression is

$$K_{\text{tot}} = K_B - K_C \qquad (\text{C.12})$$

It should be noted that the minus sign is used, since the compressive stress, at point a in Fig. (10a), should be subtracted from the larger tensile stress due to the bending of the column. Consequently, the total stress-intensity factor is

$$K_{\text{tot}} = \tfrac{4}{3}(a/\pi)^{1/2}\sigma_{NB} - 2(a/\pi)^{1/2}\sigma_{NC} \qquad (\text{C.13})$$

or

$$K_{\text{tot}} = 2(a/\pi)^{1/2}\left[(2\sigma_{NB}/3) - \sigma_{NC}\right] \qquad (\text{C.14})$$

Equation (C.14) is valid for columns having deep cracks; however, other equations for stress-intensity factors can also be found for columns having shallow-depth cracks. Suitable values of nominal stress should be used whether for the bending of short beams or for columns of high slenderness ratios.

Symbols

a	one-half the net sectional distance at the midpoint of the column, $2a = h - (c + c')$	$f_G(c/h)$	function given by Gross for determining the stress intensity
A	cross-sectional area	h	full depth of column
b	thickness of column	I	cross-sectional moment of inertia
c	depth of opening notch		
c'	depth of closing notch	K	stress-intensity factor
$C_1, C_2, C_3,$		K_I	stress-intensity factor, opening mode
C_4, C, D, m, n	constants		
d	distance from the geometric center of the column	K_B	stress-intensity factor for case of bending
		K_C	stress-intensity factor for case of compression
e	eccentricity of loading	K_T	stress-intensity factor for case of tension
E	modulus of elasticity		
$f(c/h)$	function for determining the stress intensity	K_{tot}	stress-intensity factor, total
$f_B(c/h)$	function given by Bowie for determining the stress intensity	K'	stress-intensity factor for an equivalent beam
		L	length of column

L/R	slenderness ratio; equal to $L/(I/A)^{1/2}$	V	shear load
M	applied moment	x	distance from one end of column
M_0	end moment	y	transverse deflection of the column
P	applied load		
P_E	Euler load	y_M	transverse deflection at the midpoint of the column
P_F	failure load		
q	stress-concentration factor	Z	section modulus, $Z=I/d$
q_D	stress-concentration factor for deeply notched specimens	δ	deflection of the midpoint of column y_{max} at failure
q_S	stress-concentration factor for shallow notched specimens	ρ	root radius of the notch
		σ	stress in the beam
		σ_B	stress due to bending
q_∞	stress-concentration factor for the case of a notch in an infinite plate	σ_C	stress due to compression
		σ_{max}	maximum stress
R	radius of gyration of section; equal to $(I/A)^{1/2}$	σ_N	nominal stress
		σ_{NB}	nominal stress for the case of bending
U_A	external energy	σ_{NT}	nominal stress for the case of tension
U_B	energy of bending		
U_C	energy of compression	σ_{tot}	total stress
U_{cr}	energy available to cause crack propagation		

ACKNOWLEDGMENTS

The author acknowledges the assistance given by The Catholic University of America, Office of Naval Research, National Science Foundation, and Reynolds Metals Co., Inc., toward this research. Also, thanks are given to the following graduate students at The Catholic University of America, who assisted the author in performing the original research on which this chapter is based: H. Vanderveldt, D. W. Harris, and R. J. Sanford. In addition, thanks should be expressed to W. D. Claus, Jr., for his assistance on part of this research.

REFERENCES

ASTM (1960). "Fracture Testing of High-Strength Sheet Materials: A Report of a Special ASTM Committee," Bulletin No. 243, pp. 29–40, and Bulletin No. 244, pp. 18–28. ASTM, Philadelphia.
ASTM (1961a). *Mater. Res. Std.* **1** (5), 389–393.
ASTM (1961b). *Mater. Res. Std.* **1** (11), 877–885.
ASTM (1962). *Mater. Res. Std.* **2** (3), 196–204.

ASTM (1964). *Mater. Res. Std.* **4** (3), 107–118.

Bowie, O. L. (1964). *Trans. ASME Ser. E, J. Appl. Mech.* **31**, 208.

Brown, W. F., Jr., and Srawley, J. E. (1967). "Plane Strain Crack Toughness Testing of High Strength Metallic Materials," STP 410. ASTM, Philadelphia.

Bueckner, H. F. (1960). "Some Stress Singularities and Their Computation by Means of Integral Equations." *In* "Boundary Value Problems in Differential Equations" (R. E. Langer, ed.), University of Wisconsin Press, Madison.

Creager, M., and Paris, P. C. (1967). "Elastic Field Equations for Blunt Cracks with Reference to Stress Corrosion Cracking," Report. Department of Applied Mechanics —Center for Surface & Coating Research, Lehigh University, Bethlehem, Pa.

Davis, S. O., Tupper, N. G., and Niemi, R. M. (1967). "Effect of Specimen Type and Crack Orientation on Fracture Toughness," Technical Report No. AFML-TR-67-38, Air Force Materials Laboratory, Wright-Patterson Air Force Base, Dayton, Ohio.

DeHart, R. C., and Liebowitz, H. (1967). "Influence of Ambient Pressures on the Stress Corrosion Susceptibility of Metals." Presented at the 1st National Symposium on Fracture Mechanics, Lehigh University. (To be published in 1968. *J. Eng. Fracture Mech.* Pergamon, New York.)

Dixon, J. R. (1960). *J. Roy. Aeron. Soc.* **64**, 141–145.

Dixon, J. R. (1962). *J. Roy. Aeron. Soc.* **66**, 320–322.

Dixon, J. R., and Strannigan, J. S. (1964). *J. Mech. Eng. Soc.* **7** (3), 132–136.

Donnell, L. H. (1966). "Applied Mechanics Surveys" (H. N. Abramson, H. Liebowitz, J. M. Crowley, and S. Juhasz, eds.), pp. 315–316. Macmillan, New York.

Euler, L. (1744). "De curvis elastices" (Additamentum). *In* "Methodus inveniendi lineas curvas maximi proprietate gaudentes." Lausanne.

Euler, L. (1757). *In* "Histoire de l'Academie," Vol. 13, pp. 252–282. Berlin.

Gerberich, W. (1962). *Proc. Soc. Exptl. Stress Anal.* **19** (2), 359–365.

Griffith, A. A. (1920). *Phil. Trans. Roy. Soc. London, Ser. A* **221**, 163.

Griffith, A. A. (1925). *In* "Proceedings of the 1st International Congress for Applied Mechanics, Delft," pp. 55–63. J. Waltman, Jr., Delft, Holland.

Hartbower, C. E., Gerberich, W., and Liebowitz, H. (1967). "Investigation of Crack Growth Stress-Wave Relationships." Presented at the 1st National Symposium on Fracture Mechanics, Lehigh University. (To be published in 1968. *J. Eng. Fracture Mech.* Pergamon, New York.)

Heyer, R. H. (1965). *In* "Symposium on Fracture Toughness Testing and Its Applications," STP 381, pp. 199–210. ASTM, Philadelphia.

Hiltscher, R. (1938). *Forsch. Gebiete Ingenieurw.* **9** (12), 91–103.

Hiltscher, R. (1944). *Forsch. Gebiete Ingenieurw.* **15** (1), 12–17.

Hoff, N. J. (1956). "The Analysis of Structures." Wiley, New York.

Inglis, C. E. (1913). *Trans. Inst. Naval Architects* **60**, 219.

Irwin, G. R. (1958). "The Crack Extension Force for a Crack at a Free Boundary," Report No. 5120. Naval Research Laboratory, Washington, D.C.

Irwin, G. R. (1960). *In* "Structural Mechanics" (J. N. Goodier and N. J. Hall, eds.), pp. 557–594. Pergamon, New York.

Kaufman, J. G., and Hunsicker, H. Y. (1965). *In* "Symposium on Fracture Toughness Testing and Its Applications," STP 381, pp. 290–310. ASTM, Philadelphia.

Kikukawa, M. (1957). *In* "Proceedings of Theoretical and Applied Mechanics," pp. 59–64. ASME, New York.

Kobayashi, A. S., Bradley, W. B., and Selby, R. A. (1965). "Transient Analysis in a Fracturing Epoxy Plate with a Central Crack," Task No. NR 064-478 (Contract Nonr-477(39)). Office of Naval Research, Washington, D.C.

Langhaar, H. L. (1962). "Energy Methods in Applied Mechanics." Wiley, New York.

Liebowitz, H., and Claus, W. D., Jr. (1968). *J. Eng. Fracture Mech.* (To be published. Pergamon, New York.)

Liebowitz, H., Harris, D. W., and Vanderveldt, H. (1967a). Presented at the Society for Experimental Stress Analysis Meeting, Ottawa. (To be published in *Exptl. Mech.*)

Liebowitz, H., Vanderveldt, H., and Harris, D. W. (1967b). *Intern. J. Solids and Structures* **3**, 489.

Liebowitz, H., Vanderveldt, H., and Sanford, R. J. (1967c). Presented at the Society for Experimental Stress Analysis Meeting, Ottawa. (To be published in *Exptl. Mech.*)

Neuber, H. (1947). "Kerbspannungslehre." Springer, Berlin. (Also available as 1958 English translation. Edwards Bros., Ann Arbor, Mich. Also, as U.S. Atomic Energy Commission (1958) report. "Theory of Notch Stresses," 2d Edition, AEC-T2-4547.)

Oppel, G. U., and Hill, P. W. (1964). *Exptl. Mech.* **4** (7), 206–211.

Paprino, R. (1962). *J. Roy. Aeron. Soc.* **66**, 323–326.

Paris, P. C., and Sih, G. C. (1965). *In* "Symposium on Fracture Toughness Testing and Its Applications," STP 381, pp. 30–84. ASTM, Philadelphia.

Payne, W. F. (1964). *In* "The 2d Annual Workshop in Fracture Mechanics, Denver Research Institute," Sec. 3, p. 38. Universal Technology Company, Dayton, Ohio.

Post, D. (1954). *Proc. Soc. Exptl. Stress Anal.* **12** (1), 99–116.

Savin, G. (1961). "Stress Concentration around Holes." Pergamon, New York.

Sih, G. C., and Liebowitz, H. (1967). *Intern. J. Solids and Structures* **3**, 1.

Timoshenko, S. P., and Gere, J. M. (1961). "Theory of Elastic Stability," 2d Edition. McGraw-Hill, New York.

Universal Technology Company (1967). "The 4th Annual Workshop in Fracture Mechanics, Denver Research Institute," Sec. 4, pp. 10, 38. Universal Technology Company, Dayton, Ohio.

Wells, A., and Post, D. (1957). *Proc. Soc. Exptl. Stress Anal.* **12** (1), 99–116.

Wigglesworth, L. A. (1957). *Mathematika* **4**, 76–96.

CHAPTER 5

PRESTRESSED BRITTLE STRUCTURES†

Ralph L. Barnett   *Paul C. Hermann*

† This chapter is based, in large part, on research supported by NASA Headquarters under Contract No. NASr-65(04). The authors gratefully acknowledge the support and encouragement of the project monitor Norman J. Mayer.

Abstract: Prestressing of monolithic and segmented elements in high performance brittle materials gives rise to special problems such as nonlinear response, statistical behavior, and transverse cracking under axial compression. These problems are investigated in connection with beams, columns, and plates, and experimental evidence is offered to support theories proposed for describing the strength and stiffness of these elements. Many examples are included to illuminate the singular characteristics associated with prestressed structures. Where experimental evidence is scanty or inadequate, the authors have speculated, perhaps too freely, about the behavior of such components.

I. Introduction

A. PRESTRESSING AND SEGMENTING

The techniques of prestressing and segmenting are studied in this chapter as possible approaches to the problems of brittleness and size limitation which usually attend the structural utilization of brittle state materials. We shall confine our discussions to materials which display simple linear elastic behavior at all stress levels below fracture; but, we shall occasionally deal with the complications associated with the stochastic nature of brittle strength, as examined in another chapter. In addition, certain geometric difficulties which give rise to both nonlinear and statistical behavior in segmented components will be investigated.

A prestress may be regarded as any stress state introduced into a structure prior to the application of its service loads. Such an initial state of stress may profoundly influence the strength, stiffness, and energy-absorbing characteristics of a structure. A brief systematic treatment of the general features of prestressing may be found in Roark (1954), and a remarkably complete account of prestressed and segmented structures is given by Harris (1957).

The ultimate utility of the prestressing technique rests on the ingenuity with which the designer resolves the practical problems of applying, monitoring, and maintaining a desired state of prestress. Our concern with this aspect of prestressing technology shall be confined to the following brief references to prestressing methods of current interest. Beginning with the oldest, and perhaps clumsiest, we single out gravity and reflect on the behavior of a masonry arch. The persistent action of the dead load forces produces compressive stresses which preclude the existence of a net tensile stress under the action of live load bending moments. Indeed, this principle forms the basis of prestressed concrete design which generally assumes a zero tensile strength for the concrete. Here, of course, steel tendons replace gravity as the means for introducing compressive stresses. We note that, unlike gravity, the presence of the tendons influences the elastic properties of the structure. For the most part, the studies reported in this chapter adopt the continuous tendon as the prestressing vehicle.

There are a number of methods for introducing compressive residual stresses into the surface of an element. In metals, shot peening is frequently employed (Fuchs and Hutchinson, 1958). Other examples utilizing inelastic deformation take advantage of the residual stresses which occur when an overstrained element is unloaded. This phenomenon is often used in the manufacture of gun barrels, hydraulic cylinders, and turbine disks (Timoshenko, 1956). Chemical strengthening methods are widely used in the glass industry to achieve compressive surface stresses. These methods expand the surface layers by chemical treatment and this creates internal tension and surface compression (Nordberg et al., 1964; Kistler, 1962). A similar action is achieved with ceramic materials by causing phase transformations in the surface layers which increase their volume. Another method which has proved effective for polycrystalline bodies involves the formation in a relatively low expansion surface layer. During cooling after firing, the main body tends to contract more than the surface, placing the surface in compression. The low expansion surface layers may result from chemical reactions to form solid solution surface layers, or formation of a completely new phase or phases (Kirchner et al., 1966).

Prestressing is often accomplished by various types of "forced fit" procedures. The basic idea is to join geometrically incompatible elements together by first altering their shapes by mechanical or thermal means. The classical application of this technique is to shrink fitting of hubs and wheels onto shafts; current interest anticipates the realization of a hydrostatic compressive prestress in ceramic components of arbitrary shape. This may be accomplished by randomly dispersing short tension resisting fibers in a matrix of the ceramic material. Using fibers with a high coefficient of thermal expansion relative to the ceramic, we would obtain a compressive prestress in the matrix after firing (Tinklepaugh *et al.*, 1960; Selsing, 1961; Bogardus and Roy, 1963).

B. ANALYSIS OF PRESTRESSED MONOLITHIC STRUCTURES

The response of monolithic prestressed components is described by linear elasticity theory. Because the overall integrity of a brittle structure is so often jeopardized by local failures, we must insist on an unusually accurate description of the stress distribution. This frequently requires that we abandon strength-of-materials theory in favor of two- or three-dimensional elasticity solutions. We should mention that this accuracy is not generally required in concrete which, because of its room temperature viscoelastic properties, is more forgiving than the ceramic materials we shall consider in this chapter.

In prestressed structures, the most severe stresses often occur under the prestressing forces alone and, for this reason, the act of prestressing a structure may constitute an effective proof test. After checking the safety of a component under the prestressing forces, the live load stresses must be superimposed on the prestress to complete the description of the stress distribution. Assuming we have obtained the stresses, we turn our attention to the difficult problem of strength analysis; i.e., will the component fracture under the applied stresses? The simplest of two current approaches to this question compares some suitable combination of the principal stresses at each point to a characteristic value determined for the material. Whether this value has been exceeded or not is supposed to be decisive in judging the integrity of the component. For plain concrete, the criterion for safety is simply that no principal stress be tensile. The second approach to strength analysis adopts the statistical point of view described in another chapter. Here, we establish the probability that the component will survive the entire load history. An example of this type of statistical treatment is given in Sect. III,B,1.

In brittle materials, localized high stresses occur at and near the surface of a component and critically influence its integrity. The exact determination of these stresses is complicated by the statistical nature of the precise traction- and displacement-type boundary conditions. This problem is discussed by Barnett and McGuire (1966) who describe a tension member with a highly variable state of parasitic bending stress which they attribute to imprecision in duplicating traction-type boundary conditions. The problem is explored in Sect. IV,A for displacement-type boundary conditions.

As our final introductory topic, we shall comment on the stability of a prestressed component. It is well known in prestressing technology that buckling of an element due to tendon forces can be eliminated by attaching the tendons to the member in such a way that they are constrained to deflect together. To see this, we shall consider the extreme case of a column formed by spherical beads. If these beads are strung on a threaded flexible rod which is subsequently tensioned by tightening nuts at both ends, it is clear that the resulting axial compressive force on the beads will tend to make them deflect laterally. On the other hand, the tension in the rod tends to keep it straight. The two effects will exactly cancel each other and, regardless of the prestressing level, no buckling can occur. We hasten to point out, however, that buckling is still possible if an external compressive force is brought onto our bead column.

In a prestressed concrete beam, primary buckling is precluded because the tendons are constrained at all stations along their length. It is not always possible or efficient to achieve such constraint, and we must sometimes compromise by attaching the tendons at discrete points along the member. Barnett (1962) has investigated the effectiveness of attaching tendons at a small number of stations along a strut prestressed by a force S and under an external compression $F = nS$. His results are shown in Fig. 1,

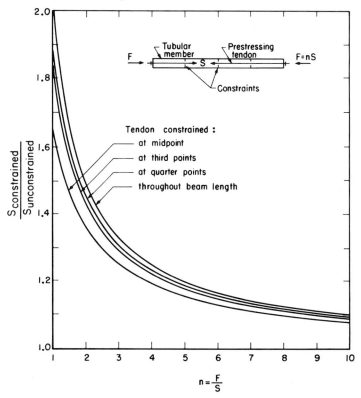

FIG. 1. Load capacity of a prestressed strut for various tendon constraints.

where we can see that the efficiency obtained by attaching the tendons at a few points may be close to that found for the tendons constrained throughout their length.

II. Prestressed and Segmented Beams

A. Nonlinear Bending Theory of Perfect Beams

1. *Problem Formulation*

We begin Sect. II, which deals with the strength and stiffness of prestressed segmented and monolithic beams, by considering the problem of predicting the load–deflection relationship of the segmented beam shown in Fig. 2. Our problem formulation will proceed under the following assumptions: (a) the segment interfaces are perfectly flat; (b) the segment material is linearly elastic up to its ultimate compressive strength; (c) the number of segments is infinite; (d) the beam-column effect due to the tendon forces is negligible (it is nonexistent if the tendons are constrained to deflect with the segments); and (e) the resultant prestressing force is located within the section kern (precluding tensile bending stresses and, hence, segment separation under zero external load).

Except for the first assumption, all the others are easy to approximate physically or they may be modified without affecting the analysis in a fundamental way. Unfortunately, departure from the "perfect flatness"

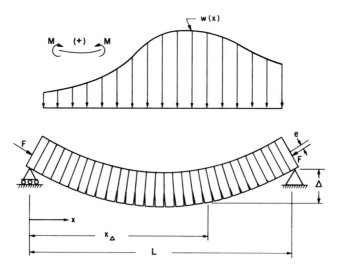

Fig. 2. Geometry of prestressed segmented beam.

assumption recasts the deterministic response problem into a statistical one which we shall discuss later.

To study the response of the prestressed beam shown in Fig. 2, we must begin with the prestressing operation. Having restricted the location of the resultant prestressing force to the section kern, the tensioning of the tendons results in compressive stresses throughout the segmented member (Timoshenko, 1955). Under our assumptions, the behavior of the segmented beam is identical to that of a monolithic elastic beam subjected to negative terminal couples of magnitude Fe. The deflection Δ for this beam at any station $x = x_\Delta$ can be determined by the virtual work expression

$$\Delta(x_\Delta) = \int_S [\mathcal{M}m/EI(x)] \, dx \tag{1}$$

in which x is the coordinate along the beam, $\mathcal{M}$ denotes the external bending moment, m is the moment due to a vertical unit load acting at the station $x = x_\Delta$, E represents the modulus of elasticity of the segments, and $I(x)$ is the variable principal moment of inertia in the plane of bending (Roark, 1954). The integration extends over the entire span S. When the lateral load $w(x)$ is zero, $\mathcal{M} = -Fe$, the resulting upward deflection is

$$\Delta(x_\Delta) = \int_0^{x_\Delta} \frac{(-Fe)}{EI} \left(\frac{L - x_\Delta}{L}\right) x \, dx + \int_{x_\Delta}^L \frac{(-Fe)}{EI} \left(\frac{L - x}{L}\right) x_\Delta \, dx$$

$$= \frac{-Fex_\Delta(L - x_\Delta)}{2EI} \tag{2}$$

where e is the eccentricity of the resultant prestressing force F.

Now, if the lateral loading on the beam is continuously increased from zero, we experience conventional elastic behavior until a net tensile stress at some station along the beam becomes incipient in, say, the bottom fibers. As the loading is increased further, cracks are formed between the segments (segment separation) at the bottom of the section. That part of the cross section which is not penetrated by cracks remains linearly elastic. The stresses in this portion of the section must be linearly distributed with a zero tensile stress in the bottom fibers and compressive stresses in the top fibers. These conditions yield the stress block shown in Fig. 3a.

Specializing to the rectangular beam, Fig. 3b, the various properties of a cracked section may be written as functions of the crack penetration f:

$$A_c = b(d - f) \tag{3}$$

$$I_c = b(d - f)^3/12 \tag{4}$$

$$n_c = (d - f)/2 \tag{5}$$

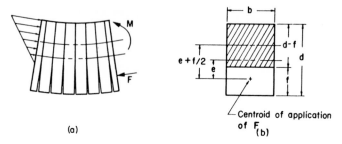

FIG. 3. (a) Stress distribution in beam with partially separated segments. (b) Rectangular section; centroid of uncracked (——·——) and cracked (——·-·——) cross section.

where A_c, I_c, and n_c are, respectively, the area, moment of inertia, and distance from the centroid to the outer fiber of the unseparated portion of a cracked beam section. The width and depth of the beam are, respectively, b and d. The condition of zero stress in the bottom fiber gives us a relationship between the penetration and the bending moment M arising from the lateral loading $w(x)$. Using the well-known fiber stress formula (Frocht, 1951) for the uncracked beam section, we have

$$\sigma_{\substack{\text{bot} \\ \text{top}}} = \frac{-F}{A_c} \pm \frac{\{M - F[e + (f/2)]\}n_c}{I_c} \tag{6}$$

Hence,

$$\sigma_{\text{bot}} = 0 = \frac{-F}{b(d-f)} + \frac{\{M - F[e + (f/2)]\}\{(d-f)/2\}}{b(d-f)^3/12} \tag{7}$$

from which

$$f = (3M/F) - (d/2) - 3e \tag{8}$$

Using this expression for f, the moment of inertia of the uncracked section given by Eq. (4) can be written as a function of the bending moment M,

$$I_c = (9b/4F^3)(M_\infty - M)^3 \tag{9}$$

where

$$M_\infty \equiv F[e + (d/2)] \tag{10}$$

We observe that I_c approaches zero as M approaches M_∞; Eq. (6) indicates that the compressive stresses in the top fibers become unbounded at this value of M. As we shall see for the case of zero stiffness tendons, both the deflections and the stresses become unbounded for a finite value of the loading. If the compressive strength of the segments is σ_c, the limiting bending moment can be found from the condition $\sigma_{\text{top}} = \sigma_c$. From Eq. (6) we obtain

$$\sigma_{\text{top}} = -\frac{2F^2}{3b\{F[e+(d/2)]-M\}} \tag{11}$$

from which

$$M_{\text{ult}} = F\left[e+\frac{d}{2}-\frac{2F}{3b\sigma_c}\right], \qquad \sigma_c > 0 \tag{12}$$

In rectangular beams which entertain no negative bending moments, one criterion defining the uncracked regions of the span is simply $f \leq 0$. The moment required to just crack or separate the segments, M_c, is found from the condition $f = 0$; thus,

$$M_c = F[e+(d/6)] \tag{13}$$

Having developed the relationships between the cross section properties and the bending moment, we may proceed to the deflection calculations. To describe the response under a given load state, the portion of the beam which is uncracked is considered to be an elastic beam under the external loading $M(x)$ and the internal loading caused by the prestressing. Since the deflection of an elastic beam can be uniquely determined for every loading, the deflection of the entire beam can be viewed as the deflection of the uncracked portion. Thus, the deflection at any station $x = x_\Delta$ may be expressed as

$$\Delta(x_\Delta) = \int_S \frac{(M-Fe)m_\Delta}{EI_0}\,dx + \int_{S_c} \frac{\{M-F[e+(f/2)]\}m_\Delta}{EI_c}\,dx \tag{14}$$

where

$$\begin{aligned} m_\Delta &= [1-(x_\Delta/L)]x, & \text{for} \quad 0 \leq x \leq x_\Delta \\ m_\Delta &= (x_\Delta/L)(L-x), & \text{for} \quad x_\Delta \leq x \leq L \end{aligned} \tag{15}$$

and where $I_0 = bd^3/12$, S represents the uncracked portion of the span defined by $M \leq M_c$, and S_c represents the cracked regions of the span defined by $M_c < M < M_\infty$.

2. Beam Deflections/Zero Stiffness Tendons

When the tendon stiffness is zero or negligible compared with the segments, the beam deflections may be computed by a direct application of Eq. (14). We shall develop the load-deflector diagrams for an I-beam and several rectangular beams.

a. Example: Rectangular Beam under Terminal Couples. When a segmented beam is subjected to a constant moment, $M = C$, either the entire beam is uncracked or the segments separate equally everywhere.

For $C \leq F[e + (d/6)]$:

In this case, no separation occurs and only the first integral in Eq. (14) contributes to the deflection. This integral was previously evaluated in Eq. (2), which gives the required result in the present case when the terminal couple $-Fe$ is replaced by $C - Fe$; hence,

$$\Delta(x_\Delta) = \frac{6(C - Fe)x_\Delta(L - x_\Delta)}{bd^3E} \tag{16}$$

For $C > F[e + (d/6)]$:

Here, the entire beam is cracked and only the second integral in Eq. (14) must be evaluated:

$$\Delta(x_\Delta) = \int_{S_c} \frac{\{M - F[e + (f/2)]\}m_\Delta}{E(9b/4F^3)(M_\infty - M)^3} \, dx = \int_{S_c} \frac{2F^3 m_\Delta}{9bE(M_\infty - C)^2} \, dx$$

$$= \frac{2F^3}{9bE(M_\infty - C)^2} \left[\int_0^{x_\Delta} \left(1 - \frac{x_\Delta}{L}\right) x \, dx + \int_{x_\Delta}^L \frac{x_\Delta}{L}(L - x) \, dx \right]$$

$$= \frac{F^3 x_\Delta(L - x_\Delta)}{9bE(M_\infty - C)^2} \tag{17}$$

Inspection of Eq. (17) indicates that the deflection is a nonlinear function of the loading C and that it becomes infinite as C approaches the finite value $M_\infty = F[e + (d/2)]$.

The theoretical load-deflection diagram for $x_\Delta = L/2$ and the crack penetration diagram are shown in Fig. 4 for a rectangular titanium carbide beam with the following characteristics:

$$L = 60 \text{ inches} \qquad E = 60 \times 10^6 \text{ psi}$$
$$b = 2 \text{ inches} \qquad F = 160 \text{ kips}$$
$$d = 4 \text{ inches} \qquad \sigma_c = 500{,}000 \text{ psi}$$
$$e = 0.5 \text{ inch} \qquad \text{zero tendon stiffness}$$

Although the curve is entirely elastic, it has the appearance of an elastic-perfectly plastic load-deflection curve. It is asymptotic to the horizontal line $C = M_\infty$, which is the critical moment corresponding to the moment of the resultant prestressing force about the upper edge of the beam. The ultimate moment resistance M_{ult} given by Eq. (12) is usually only a few percent lower than $F[e + (d/2)]$; i.e.,

$$\text{Error} = \frac{2F}{3b\sigma_c[e + (d/2)]} \times 100 \tag{18}$$

In the present case, the difference is 4.26%.

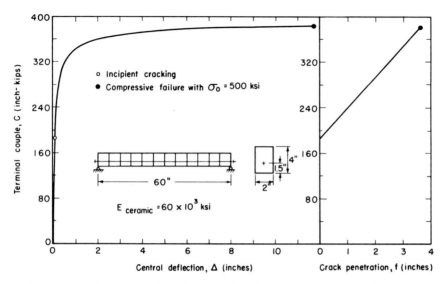

FIG. 4. Load-deflection and crack penetration diagrams for a prestressed segmented beam with zero stiffness tendon.

b. Example: Concentrated Load on a Simple or Cantilever Beam. The constant bending moment associated with terminal loading suppresses several of the complications which arise in the general loading case. For example, a number of spanwise discontinuities appear in the integrands of Eq. (14). These occur at discontinuities in the form or slope of the external bending moment diagram, at the point of application of the virtual unit load, and at stations separating the cracked and uncracked portions of the span. To illustrate how these discontinuities are handled, the general deflection analysis of an end-loaded cantilever is formulated in Fig. 5. The details are straightforward but lengthy, and they lead to a closed form solution. Instead of presenting the results, we shall describe the general solution for the deflection curve of a simply supported beam subjected to a concentrated load placed anywhere in the span. The solution for the cantilever is, of course, embedded in this solution, which is given in Fig. 6.

c. Example: I-Beam under Terminal Couples. Prestressed segmented glass beams with the cross sectional geometries shown in Fig. 7 and with $E = 10.5 \times 10^6$ psi and $L = 38$ inches, have been selected to illustrate and compare the behavior of I-beams, webless I-beams, and rectangular beams of the same overall dimensions. The response of these members is discussed in the App. A. Figure 8 illustrates the behavior of these beams under terminal couples for the case of zero stiffness tendons. We observe that the rectangular beam is the stiffest (least deflection) member in the

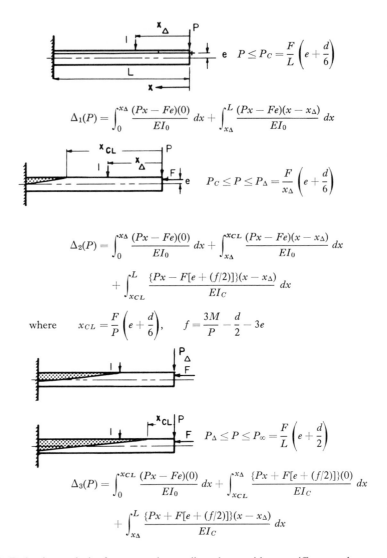

$$\Delta_1(P) = \int_0^{x_\Delta} \frac{(Px - Fe)(0)}{EI_0} \, dx + \int_{x_\Delta}^L \frac{(Px - Fe)(x - x_\Delta)}{EI_0} \, dx$$

$$\Delta_2(P) = \int_0^{x_\Delta} \frac{(Px - Fe)(0)}{EI_0} \, dx + \int_{x_\Delta}^{x_{CL}} \frac{(Px - Fe)(x - x_\Delta)}{EI_0} \, dx$$

$$+ \int_{x_{CL}}^L \frac{\{Px - F[e + (f/2)]\}(x - x_\Delta)}{EI_C} \, dx$$

where $\quad x_{CL} = \dfrac{F}{P}\left(e + \dfrac{d}{6}\right), \qquad f = \dfrac{3M}{P} - \dfrac{d}{2} - 3e$

$$\Delta_3(P) = \int_0^{x_{CL}} \frac{(Px - Fe)(0)}{EI_0} \, dx + \int_{x_{CL}}^{x_\Delta} \frac{\{Px + F[e + (f/2)]\}(0)}{EI_C} \, dx$$

$$+ \int_{x_\Delta}^L \frac{\{Px + F[e + (f/2)]\}(x - x_\Delta)}{EI_C} \, dx$$

Fig. 5. Deflection analysis of a rectangular cantilever beam with zero stiffness tendon.

initial load range, the I-beam in the middle range, and, finally, the webless I-beam in the final range.

It is interesting to note that, for a load of 18 inch-kips, the rectangular beam has a crack penetration of 2.5 inches, the I-beam has 1.7 inches, and the webless I-beam is still uncracked. We also observe, for the case of the webless I-beam, that, although abrupt changes in character occur in the terminal couple versus end rotation curve and the terminal couple versus crack penetration curve as the crack passes through the bottom flange, there is no discontinuity in slope in either of these curves. One additional noteworthy item for the case of zero stiffness tendons is the fact that, as the cracks penetrate the cross sections, eventually $(f > t_f + d)$ the uncracked sections become identical and the behavior of the three beams coincide in this range.

3. Beam Deflections/Elastic Tendons

The deflection of a segmented beam will generally produce a change in the length of the prestressing tendons. If the tendons have a nonzero stiffness, this change in length will necessarily induce a force in the tendons that will be added to or subtracted from the initial prestress force, which we shall designate as F^0. To illustrate how the tendon force F is computed, we shall once again consider a beam subjected to terminal couples C. It is possible, in this case, to obtain an algebraic relationship between the central deflection and the loading.

a. Example: Central Deflection under Terminal Couples. Consider the case of a rectangular segmented beam of length L which is prestressed by a single tendon which is constrained everywhere along its length to remain at a distance e below the centroid of the uncracked cross section. For an uncracked beam, the terminal couples resulting from the external load and the tendon forces, $C - Fe$, will bend the beam's centroid into a circular arc of radius R_1 and length L. Thus, the end cross sections will rotate through a total angle $2\theta_1 = L/R_1$. Now, since the tendon must deflect with the beam, it takes the form of a circular arc of radius $R_1 + e$ which is concentric with the centroid. The length of the stretched tendon L_1 is simply

$$L_1 = (R_1 + e)2\theta_1 = L + 2e\theta_1 \tag{19}$$

In particular, when only the prestressing force F^0 acts on the beam, the ends rotate through a total angle of $2\theta_0$. Under this loading, the tendon length L_0 becomes

$$L_0 = L + 2e\theta_0 \tag{20}$$

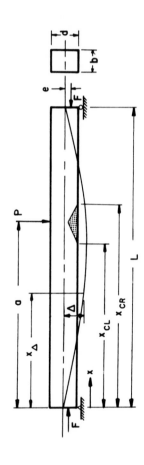

For $0 \leq P \leq \dfrac{F[e + (d/6)]}{a[1 - (a/L)]}$ and $0 \leq x_\Delta \leq a$:

$$\Delta = \frac{12}{bd^3 E} \left(\frac{x_\Delta}{L}\right) \left\{ \frac{PL^3}{6} \left(1 - \frac{a}{L}\right) \left[\left(\frac{a}{L}\right)\left(2 - \frac{a}{L}\right) - \left(\frac{x_\Delta}{L}\right)^2\right] - \frac{FeL^2}{2}\left(1 - \frac{x_\Delta}{L}\right) \right\}$$

For $\dfrac{F[e + (d/6)]}{a[1 - (a/L)]} \leq P \leq \dfrac{F[e + (d/2)]}{a[1 - (a/L)]}$, and

Case (1) $0 \leq x_\Delta \leq \dfrac{F[e+(d/6)]}{P[1-(a/L)]}$:

$$\Delta = \frac{12}{bd^3E}\left(\frac{x_\Delta}{L}\right)\left(-\frac{PL^3}{6}\left(1-\frac{a}{L}\right)\left(\frac{x_\Delta}{L}\right)^2 + \frac{FeL^2}{2}\left(\frac{x_\Delta}{L}\right) + \frac{F^2L[e+(d/6)][(d/6)-e]}{2P[1-(a/L)]} - \frac{F^3d^3}{54P^2}\left[\frac{2(a/L)-1}{\{(a/L)[1-(a/L)]\}^2}\right.\right.$$

$$\times\left\{\ln\left[\frac{3}{d}\left(e+\frac{d}{2}\right)-\frac{3PL}{Fd}\left(\frac{a}{L}\right)\left(1-\frac{a}{L}\right)\right]-\frac{3}{d}\left(e+\frac{d}{2}\right)+\frac{F[e+(d/2)]}{F[e+(d/2)]-PL(a/L)[1-(a/L)]}\right\}$$

$$\left.\left.+\frac{9[e+(d/6)]^2[(d/3)-e]}{d^3}\right]-\frac{1}{1-(a/L)}\left[\frac{PL}{F[e+(d/2)]-PL(a/L)[1-(a/L)]}-\frac{3PL}{Fd}\right]\right)$$

Case (2) $\dfrac{F[e+(d/6)]}{P[1-(a/L)]} \leq x_\Delta \leq a$:

$$\Delta = \frac{2F^3}{9P^2bE}\left(\frac{9[e+(d/6)]^2[(d/3)-e]}{d^3[1-(a/L)]^2}\left\{1-\left(\frac{x_\Delta}{L}\right)\left(\frac{L}{a}\right)^2\left[2\left(\frac{a}{L}\right)-1\right]\right\}+\frac{1}{[1-(a/L)]^2}\right.$$

$$\times\left\{\ln\left[\frac{3}{d}\left(e+\frac{d}{2}\right)-\frac{3PL}{Fd}\left(1-\frac{a}{L}\right)\left(\frac{x_\Delta}{L}\right)\right]+\frac{F[e+(d/2)]}{F[e+(d/2)]-PL(a/L)[1-(a/L)](x_\Delta/L)}-\frac{3}{d}\left(e+\frac{d}{2}\right)\right\}$$

$$+\frac{1}{1-(a/L)}\left(\frac{x_\Delta}{L}\right)\left(\frac{PL}{F[e+(d/2)]-PL(a/L)[1-(a/L)](x_\Delta/L)}-\frac{2(a/L)-1}{\{(a/L)[1-(a/L)]\}^2}\left(\frac{x_\Delta}{L}\right)\right.$$

$$\left.\left.\times\left\{\ln\left[\frac{3}{d}\left(e+\frac{d}{2}\right)-\frac{3PL}{Fd}\left(\frac{a}{L}\right)\left(1-\frac{a}{L}\right)\right]+\frac{F[e+(d/2)]}{F[e+(d/2)]-PL(a/L)[1-(a/L)]}-\frac{3}{d}\left(e+\frac{d}{2}\right)\right\}\right)\right)$$

Fig. 6. General solution of a prestressed segmented simply supported rectangular beam with zero-stiffness tendon.

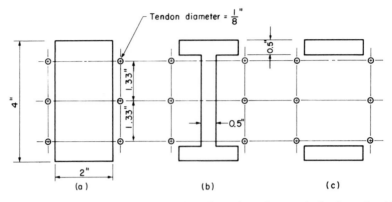

FIG. 7. Beam cross-section and tendon dimensions for equal depth and width. (a) Rectangular beam, (b) I-beam, and (c) webless I-beam.

When the terminal couples become sufficiently large, the beam segments will separate uniformly along the member and the resulting uncracked portion of the cross sections will support a uniform bending moment of $C - F[e + (f/2)]$. Under this loading, the centroid of the uncracked portion of the beam is bent into a circular arc of radius R_2 and length L. The end sections rotate through a combined angle of $2\theta = L/R_2$. Using this angle, we can compute the corresponding tendon length L_2 by recognizing that it forms a concentric circular arc of radius $R_2 + e + (f/2)$ with the centroid of the uncracked portion of the beam; thus,

$$L_2 = [R_2 + e + (f/2)]2\theta = L + [e + (f/2)]2\theta \tag{21}$$

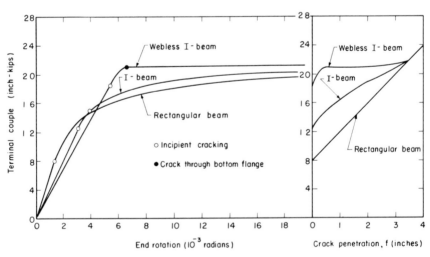

FIG. 8. Load-deflection and load-crack penetration diagrams for equal-depth-and-width rectangular beam, I-beam and webless I-beam with zero-stiffness tendons.

Using Eqs. (19)–(21), we can compute the change in the tendon length:

For an uncracked beam; $C/F < [e + (d/6)]$:

$$\Delta L = L_1 - L_0 = 2e(\theta_1 - \theta_0) \tag{22}$$

For a cracked beam; $C/F > [e + (d/6)]$:

$$\Delta L = L_2 - L_0 = [e + (f/2)]2\theta - 2\theta_0 e \tag{23}$$

To find the tendon force F, we observe that the change in the tendon length ΔL must be equal to the elongation of the tendon under the induced force $F - F^0$,

$$(F - F^0)L_t/A_t E_t = \Delta L \tag{24}$$

Before we can use this equation in conjunction with Eqs. (22) and (23), we must determine expressions for θ_0, θ_1, θ, and L_t.

If virtual unit terminal couples are applied to an uncracked beam, Eq. (1) can be used to compute $2\theta_1$, i.e.,

$$2\theta_1 = \int_0^L \frac{(C - Fe) \cdot 1}{EI_0} \, dx = \frac{12(C - Fe)L}{Ebd^3} \tag{25}$$

When $C = 0$, we obtain an expression for $2\theta_0$,

$$2\theta_0 = -12F^0 eL/Ebd^3 \tag{26}$$

For a cracked beam, Eq. (1) is used in a similar manner to find 2θ,

$$2\theta = \int_0^L \frac{\{C - F[e + (f/2)]\} \cdot 1}{EI_c} \, dx \tag{27}$$

Using the formulas for f and I_c given by Eqs. (8) and (9), we find that

$$2\theta = \frac{2F^3 L}{9Eb\{F[e + (d/2)] - C\}^2} \tag{28}$$

If we compare Eq. (25) to Eq. (16) for $x_\Delta = L/2$, we find that

$$\theta_1 = 4\Delta/L \qquad \text{uncracked range} \tag{29}$$

Similarly, when Eqs. (28) and (17) are compared, we obtain

$$\theta = 4\Delta/L \qquad \text{cracked range} \tag{30}$$

The original tendon length L_t may be found from the conditions which prevail when the beam is subjected to the prestressing force F^0 alone. Here, the tendon length is equal to its original length L_t plus the stretch caused by F^0, i.e.,

$$L_0 = L_t[1 + (F^0/A_t E_t)] \tag{31}$$

Equating this expression with that previously found for L_0, we obtain

$$L_t = L\left[\frac{1 - (12F^0 e^2/Ebd^3)}{1 + (F^0/A_t E_t)}\right] \tag{32}$$

The tendon length is usually only a few percent lower than L.

We can now proceed with the calculation of the tendon force. Substituting Eqs. (22) and (23) into Eq. (24) and using Eqs. (29) and (30), we find:

For the uncracked beam:

$$\frac{(F - F^0)L_t}{A_t E_t} = 2e\left(\frac{4\Delta}{L} - \theta_0\right) \tag{33}$$

or

$$F = F^0 + \frac{2eA_t E_t}{L_t}\left(\frac{4\Delta}{L} - \theta_0\right) \tag{34}$$

Eliminating F from Eq. (16) with $x_\Delta = L/2$, the central deflection in the uncracked range becomes

$$\Delta = \frac{3L^2}{2Ebd^3}\left[\frac{C - F^0 e + (2e^2 A_t E_t \theta_0/L_t)}{1 + (12e^2 A_t E_t L/bd^3 E L_t)}\right] \tag{35}$$

For the cracked beam:

$$\frac{(F - F^0)L_t}{A_t E_t} = \left(\frac{3C}{F} - \frac{d}{2} - e\right)\frac{4\Delta}{L} - 2\theta_0 e \tag{36}$$

or

$$F = \left\{\frac{F^0}{2} - \frac{A_t E_t}{LL_t}\left[e\theta_0 L + 2\left(e + \frac{d}{2}\right)\Delta\right]\right\}$$
$$+ \left\langle\left\{\frac{F^0}{2} - \frac{A_t E_t}{LL_t}\left[e\theta_0 L + 2\left(e + \frac{d}{2}\right)\Delta\right]\right\}^2 + \frac{12C\Delta A_t E_t}{LL_t}\right\rangle^{1/2} \tag{37}$$

Eliminating F from Eq. (17) with $x_\Delta = L/2$, the central deflection in the cracked range is given implicitly by the equation

$$C - \frac{2\alpha}{\gamma}\{(\beta - \gamma\Delta) + [(\beta - \gamma\Delta)^2 + 12\alpha C\Delta]^{1/2}\}$$
$$+ \left[\frac{L^2}{36Eb\Delta}\right]^{1/2}\{(\beta - \gamma\Delta) + [(\beta - \gamma\Delta)^2 + 12\alpha C\Delta]^{1/2}\}^{3/2} = 0 \tag{38}$$

where

$$\alpha \equiv A_t E_t/LL_t; \qquad \beta \equiv (F^0/2) - \alpha e\theta_0 L; \qquad \gamma \equiv 2\alpha[e + (d/2)]$$

Using Eqs. (35) and (38), the terminal couple–central deflection diagram was constructed in Fig. 9 for the beam shown in the figure. The initial linear portion of the curve labeled "elastic tendon" is given by the first of these equations, which governs the behavior until the tendon force F becomes greater than $C/[e + (d/6)]$. If the Δ in Eq. (34) is eliminated with Eq. (35), we obtain the tendon force as a linear function of C, thus

$$F = F^0 + C\,\frac{12R\mu}{d(1 + 12R\mu^2)} \qquad \text{uncracked range} \qquad (39)$$

where

$$R \equiv A_t E_t L/bdEL_t; \qquad \mu \equiv e/d$$

When F is set equal to $C/[e + (d/6)]$, we can readily solve for the cracking moment C_c:

$$C_c = F^0 d\,\frac{(\tfrac{1}{6} + \mu)(1 + 12R\mu)}{1 - 2R\mu} \qquad (40)$$

Taking $R = \tfrac{1}{8}$ for the beam shown in Fig. 9, the cracking moment becomes 197 inch-kips. Beyond this moment, the tendon force is given by

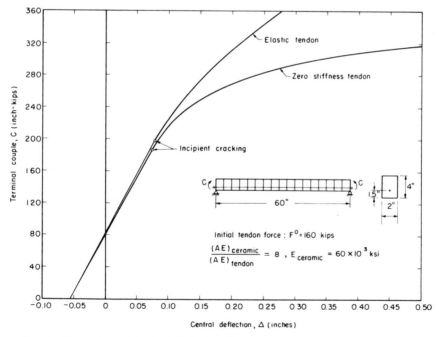

FIG. 9. Comparison of the load-deflection diagrams for a prestressed segmented beam with elastic and zero-stiffness tendon.

Eq. (37); however, to use this equation, we require the relationship between C and Δ, which must be found numerically from Eq. (38). The tendon force–terminal couple diagram for the beam described in Fig. 9 is shown in Fig. 10.

For our numerical example, we selected a tendon stiffness that was relatively high, compared to the stiffness of the beam, and, consequently, our eccentric location of the tendon gave rise to induced forces as high as 25% of the prestressing force. The influence of the elastic tendon on the load-deflection curve is quite significant in the nonlinear range when measured against the zero stiffness case, which is also included in Fig. 9.

A set of experiments corroborating our response theory is described in App. A, where we shall also find a discussion of the multiple tendon problem which includes the effects of axial shortening. These effects, omitted in our treatment of the terminal couple loading, were incorporated in an analysis by Barnett *et al.* (1964). The results were found to be nearly identical to those shown in Figs. 9 and 10.

b. Example: Central Deflection under Central Loading. For the case of elastic tendons, the general procedure for determining the load-deflection diagram begins by establishing the tendon force equation from the compatibility of the beam and tendon deformations. The tendon force F will generally be a function of the loading w, the beam shortening δ, and the beam slopes θ; i.e.,

$$F = F[w(x), \delta(w, F), \theta(w, F)] \qquad (41)$$

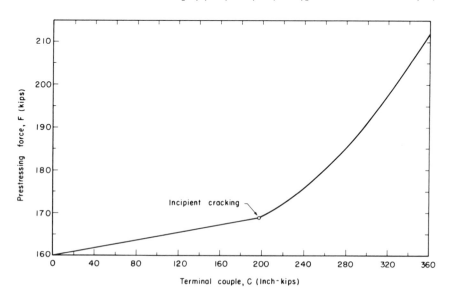

Fig. 10. Load-elastic tendon force diagram for the beam shown in Fig. 9.

The expressions for the beam response terms are readily derived in terms of w and F, using the procedures described for the zero stiffness tendons. When they are substituted into Eq. (41), we usually obtain an implicit equation for F which must be solved numerically for every loading of interest. Once a value for F has been computed for a given $w(x)$, the deflections of the beam can be determined from the zero stiffness deflection formulas. This procedure was employed in the case of a simply supported rectangular segmented beam subjected to a central concentrated load. The various properties of such beams are described in this subsection.

Certainly one of the most provocative characteristics of segmented beams stems from the possibility of approximating their load-deflection diagram by one which is elastic-perfectly plastic. This suggests the possibility of using the methods of limit analysis for segmented structures. We hasten to point out that the prestressed segmented beam is completely elastic, and, consequently, the unloading curve will differ from that of an elastic-perfectly plastic beam.

When a simply supported elastic-perfectly plastic beam is subjected to a sufficiently large central load, a plastic hinge forms in the center. Those portions of the beam away from the center remain practically undistorted. The similarity between this type of deflection pattern and that of the corresponding prestressed segmented beam can be inferred from the deflection curves shown in Fig. 11 for a segmented member.

The influence of tendon eccentricity can be ascertained from the load-deflection diagrams shown in Fig. 12 for values of e which vary within the

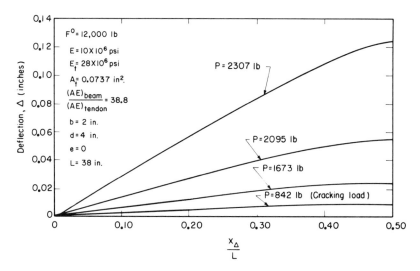

FIG. 11. Deflection curves for a simply supported centrally loaded prestressed segmented beam.

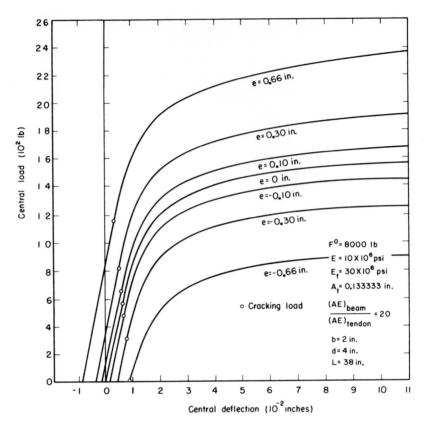

FIG. 12. Effect of tendon eccentricity on the load-deflection curves for a simply supported centrally loaded prestressed segmented beam.

limits of the kern. The stiffness and strength at large deflections are found to fall off rapidly with decreasing eccentricity. In all of the cases of zero eccentricity investigated, the influence of tendon stiffness was found to be extremely slight, suggesting that the simpler deflection analysis using zero stiffness tendons might be appropriate.

Selecting $e = 0.66$ where the tendon stiffness is the most predominant, a series of load-deflection curves were plotted for various ratios of beam stiffness to tendon stiffness. It appears from Fig. 13 that the zero stiffness approximation is not appropriate for the extreme values of eccentricity.

To complete the study of beam parameters, load-deflection diagrams are shown in Fig. 14 for different values of prestress. The maximum strength values are found to increase with the prestress level in an approximately

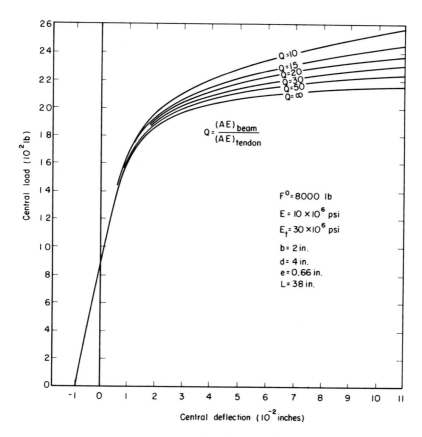

FIG. 13. Effect of tendon stiffness on the load-deflection curves for a simply supported centrally loaded prestressed segmented beam.

linear fashion. We also observe that the knee in the curves is more pronounced for the lower prestressing levels.

c. Example: I-Beams under Terminal Couples. Using the modifications described in App. A for arbitrary cross sections with multiple tendons, one can study the behavior of the three glass beams shown in Fig. 7 when the tendons are taken to be elastic. The load-deflection diagrams and the load-crack penetration diagrams for these members are shown in Fig. 15.

Comparing the behavior of beams with elastic tendons to that shown in Fig. 8 for zero stiffness tendons, we observe the following:

(1) The elastic and zero stiffness tendons produce similar effects in the initial portion of the load-deflection curves.

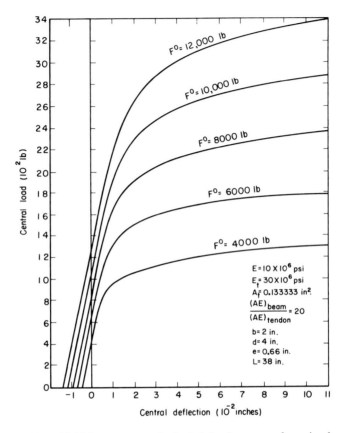

Fig. 14. Effect of initial prestress on the load-deflection curves for a simply supported centrally loaded prestressed segmented beam.

(2) In the elastic tendon case, the induced tendon force above the cracking load leads to a considerable increase in the slope of the load-deflection curve.

(3) The behavior of the three members in the elastic tendon cases does not become coincident as it does at large loads for the beams using zero stiffness tendons.

(4) The segment separation does not appear, from Fig. 15, to penetrate the entire cross section for very high loads as it does when perfectly flexible tendons are used.

Diagrams showing the increase in the tendon force and the tendon moment as the terminal couples are increased are shown in Fig. 16. The tendon force represents the resultant force of the various tendons. As this force increases because of the elasticity of the tendons, it gives rise to an

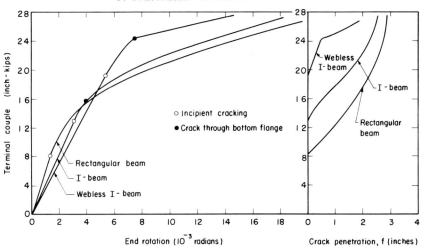

FIG. 15. Load-deflection and load-crack penetration diagrams for equal-depth-and-width rectangular beam, I-beam, and webless I-beam with elastic tendons.

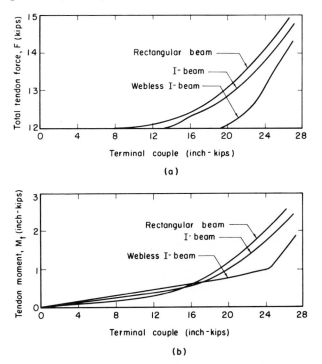

FIG. 16. (a) Tendon force and (b) tendon moment versus terminal couple diagrams for equal-depth-and-width rectangular beam, I-beam, and webless I-beam.

increase in the moment resistance which is reflected by the tendon moment M_T. This quantity is defined in App. A, together with the tendon force. Slight irregularities in the tendon force–terminal couple diagrams for the I-beams can be seen as the cracks between the segments pass through the bottom flange.

B. Limit Analysis of Segmented Beams

We shall briefly investigate the feasibility of approximating the moment–curvature relationship of a prestressed segmented beam by one which is elastic-perfectly plastic with a limiting moment of $F[e + (d/2)]$. Indeed, this possibility was exploited by Kooharian (1952) in his study of segmented concrete arches. In these arches, the compressive forces acting normal to the segment interfaces were not provided by prestressed tendons, but, rather, by the arches' reaction to live and dead loading.

The applicability of limit analysis for predicting the ultimate load-carrying capacity of prestressed segmented beams is investigated in this

FIG. 17. Prestress segmented alumina tubular beam.

section with the aid of the 16-foot segmented aluminum oxide beam shown in Fig. 17. Each segment in this member was 4 inches in both length and outside diameter with a wall thickness of $\frac{3}{16}$ inch. The beam was composed of 48 such segments, and the prestressing was accomplished by pretensioning a $\frac{1}{4}$-inch steel prestressing tendon that passed along the axes of the cylinders and was secured to steel end plates. To exclude secondary bending effects (beam-column behavior), the tendon was constrained to the centroid of the sections by five closely fitting wooden spacer inserts on 3-foot centers. Two strain gages on opposite sides of the tendon were used to monitor the prestress level. Simple end supports were provided by two saw horses and the beam was loaded with dead weights using load increments of 5 pounds.

The beam was tested under the three types of loading shown in Fig. 18. In all cases, the loading was continually increased until a 0.005-inch thick feeler gage could be inserted between the separated segments to a depth of 2 inches. The load associated with this condition is recorded in Fig. 18 as P_{Measured}. The first test run was the central loading configuration. It was noted at the conclusion of this test that longitudinal cracks had

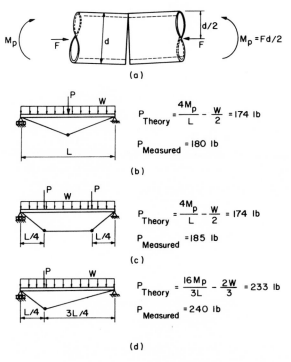

FIG. 18. Limit analysis of prestressed segmented alumina tubular beam. (a) Plastic moment M_p, (b) central loading, (c) quarter point loading, (d) single quarter point loading.

appeared on the compressive side of several segments that were close to the beam's center. For the remaining two tests, the beam was rotated such that the final bearing area was away from the cracks. During the final loading, two concentrated loads at the quarter points, horizontal cracks developed under the loads which resulted in catastrophic failure. The failure modes shown in Fig. 19 are typical of the primary segment fractures.

A similar catastrophic failure was experienced by Clanton *et al.* (1953) during a series of tests on prestressed and segmented structural clay tile

Fig. 19. Typical failures modes of alumina beam segments.

beams of 20-foot span. They remarked: "The sudden and complete compression failure forcefully points out the desirability of using smaller amounts of steel reinforcement. Beam distress should be indicated by excessive yield in the steel before there is danger of catastrophic compression failure."

The prediction of the ultimate loading of the alumina beam follows precisely the methods of limit analysis for simple beams. Here, we take the plastic moment to be the prestressing force times half the beam depth, as shown in Fig. 18a. The formulas and predictions for the limit loads are given in Fig. 18b, c, and d, where we reflect the following physical data:

(1) Prestress level, $F = 5000$ lb
(2) Weight density of tendon, 0.167 lb/ft
(3) Span length, $L = 182.5$ inches
(4) Weight of entire beam, $W = 90$ lb
(5) Weight of loading fixture, 10 lb
(6) Plastic moment, $M_p = (2)(5000) = 10,000$ in.-lb.

We observe from this figure that the predicted loads are from 2.92 to 5.41% lower than the measured loads.

C. BEAMS WITH NONFLAT INTERFACES

The casual application of the theory of perfect beams to real situations is frustrated by even minor departures from perfectly flat segment interfaces. The importance of this condition was first realized in a series of exploratory experiments conducted by Barnett (1958) as part of a minimum weight/deflection investigation of rocket launcher structures. A prestressed segmented titanium carbide beam used in that study is shown in Fig. 20.

FIG. 20. Bending test of a prestressed segmented titanium carbide beam.

The bending tests conducted with this member are described by the load-deflection diagrams plotted in Fig. 21, where we observe that the initial stiffness increases with increasing prestress.

Our theory predicts only one value for the initial stiffness; that of an equivalent monolithic beam. The surprising deviation cannot be explained by the nonlinear behavior of the segment material, since titanium carbide has a straight line compressive stress-strain curve up to its fracture strength (about 400 ksi). Consequently, the segmenting has the effect of lowering the stiffness. This effect also appeared in the direct axial compression test of the member which is described by the compressive stress-strain curve shown in Fig. 22. The observed curvilinearity is caused by the fact that the segment interfaces are not flat, and, consequently, the contact area between the segments, and, hence, the stiffness, increases monotonically with increasing axial load.

When the segment interfaces are not flat, the contact area between any two segments may vary from almost full contact to almost no contact. Furthermore, the actual contact area cannot be predicted for particular

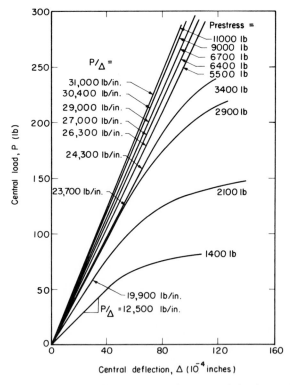

FIG. 21. Load-deflection curves for a prestressed segmented titanium carbide beam.

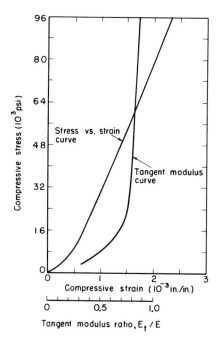

FIG. 22. Stress-strain diagram of a segmented titanium carbide column (gage length = 42 inches).

segments, since it varies randomly from interface to interface. However, when all the interfaces have been drawn from the same population, which usually happens when the same manufacturing technique is used for all the blocks, we can predict the behavior of groups of segments in a statistical sense. The compression test, for example, furnishes a measure of the average or effective contact area at every level of compression. For a given segmented column, the effective area is computed by multiplying its nominal area by the ratio of its tangent stiffness to the equivalent monolithic stiffness. In the case of a linearly elastic material, the effective area under an axial compressive stress σ is given by

$$A_{\text{eff}} = A[E_t(\sigma)/E] \qquad (42)$$

where $E_t(\sigma)$ is the tangent modulus of the compressive stress-strain curve and A is the full area of a segment. We note that, since the segments are finite in number, the average real contact area is probably less than A_{eff}.

The statistical nature of the interface contact gives rise to a number of important implications. First, a description of the compressive stress-strain diagram will be statistical and will depend on both the column area and the length. This problem is studied more thoroughly in Sect. IV,B.

Second, the moment of inertia, like the area, will be random with a lower bound equal to zero and an upper bound equal to the full moment of inertia. It follows that beam behavior will be statistical in nature and that the variability experienced will depend on the length and area of the beam, the number of segments, and on the loading. We can be a little more specific if we make the following intuitive observation: the average behavior of a 20-segment unit will show less scatter from group to group than will be found for two- or three-segment units. On this basis, we would expect more variability in the response of a beam whose behavior is very sensitive to the characteristics of a certain few segments. We would, for example, anticipate a greater scatter in the central deflection measurements of a centrally loaded beam than in the end slope measurements of a beam under terminal couples. The central segments are all-important in the first case, whereas all segments are equally important in the latter.

Let us consider the apparently simple problem of predicting the initial slopes of the titanium carbide bending tests from the results of the corresponding column test. The same member was used as both a beam and a column; it was assembled with 42 I-beam segments which measured 1 inch between their interfaces. Because of the large number of segments used, the behavior of the column varied only slightly when the segments were rearranged. Now, if the prestress σ_p and the column stress are the same, the effective area of both members should be equivalent. Assuming that, on the average, the contact area is uniformly distributed over the segment interfaces, a natural definition of the effective moment of inertia would be

$$I_{\text{eff}} = In \qquad (43)$$

where

$$n \equiv E_t(\sigma_p)/E \qquad (44)$$

and I is the moment of inertia of a segment and $\sigma_p = F^0/A$.

Unfortunately, this value of I_{eff}, based on the column test, always resulted in too low an estimate for the initial bending stiffness. We shall shortly describe another attempt to predict the initial slope of a central load-central deflection curve using rectangular glass segments. Here, this method of predicting I_{eff} gave results which were always too high.

In both the titanium carbide and the glass experiments, the response of only a single member was examined. But, as we have already discussed, the central load-central deflection curve of nonflat segmented beams may show considerable variability, and consequently, I_{eff} should be used to predict the average response of a sufficiently large number of beams and not the response of a single member. We hasten to point out that the terminal couple-end rotation diagram of a sufficiently long segmented beam will probably be deterministic and, as such, it may provide a useful tool for studying the relationship between I_{eff} and column test results.

Granting that the effective stress-strain curve of a segmented column is area and length dependent, it is clear that an equivalent nonlinear material cannot be defined which is useful for response calculations. For example, in a segmented beam under sufficiently high loads, the nominal "uncracked" area diminishes continually as the load is increased. Consequently, the stiffness of the section tends to increase as a result of increasing axial stress and decreasing nominal area; it tends to decrease because of a reduced moment of inertia. The theory of perfect segmented beams accounts only for variations in the moment of inertia. An exact solution for the response will require, in addition, that we describe the bending stiffness of any "uncracked" area subjected to a linear strain field that varies from zero at one end to some arbitrary maximum value at the other. Since the column does not produce such a strain field, its usefulness for estimating the effective statistical bending parameters is not promising. The proper strain field is, of course, realized in pure bending of a prestressed beam and perhaps the terminal couple-end rotation test would be reasonable for defining statistical beam parameters which reflect the roughness and shape of the segment interfaces. The tests are, fortunately, nondestructive.

From the preceding remarks, it is clear that considerable effort may be required to predict accurately the response of segmented structures with nonflat interfaces. This raises the question of eliminating the cause of these difficulties by physical methods which provide full segment contact. For example, brazing the segments together, buttering the interfaces with grout, using gaskets or shims, and lapping the surfaces very flat. In some situations, such techniques may be effective; in others, complications arising from elevated temperatures, hostile chemical environments, large segment sizes, and interface curvature (shell segments) preclude the achievement of full interface contact.

As an approximate approach for describing the load-deflection diagram for an imperfect segmented beam, Barnett et al. (1964) investigated the possibility of accounting for the nonflat interfaces by modifying the beam width b used in the theory of perfect beams. Specifically, they assumed that the effective beam width b_{eff} is given by

$$b_{\text{eff}} = bn \tag{45}$$

Using this definition, we obtain the same predicted value for the average initial I_{eff} that is given by Eq. (43). The predicted bending stiffness at every load level will be smaller than that described by the unmodified perfect beam theory. The influence of b_{eff} will be greatest in the initial portion of the load-deflection curve; in the "cracked" range, the detailed

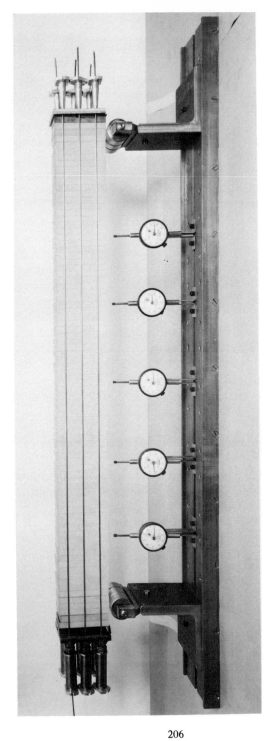

FIG. 23. Bending fixture for prestressed segmented glass beam.

segment geometry becomes less and less significant as the cracks penetrate the beam cross section. It should be emphasized that n is taken from the compressive stress-strain diagram for a column of beam segments and that the resulting modified perfect beam theory purports only to predict the average load-deflection curve.

Unfortunately, data are presently available for examining only the non-linear portion of the approximate theory. A rectangular prestressed beam with a nominal depth of 4 inches and a width of 2 inches was fabricated from segments cut from a sheet of $\frac{1}{2}$-inch plate glass. Prestressing was accomplished with six steel tendons which were symmetrically located in three rows with $1\frac{1}{4}$ inches between the tendons. Using the test fixture shown in Fig. 23, central load-central deflection diagrams were obtained for prestressing forces of 4, 6, 8, and 12 kips. The results, shown in Fig. 24, indicate a double run for the 6 and 8 kip cases. These runs indicate the scatter which results from removal and reapplication of the prestressing force.

Prior to the performance of these bending tests, the compressive load-deflection characteristics of the segments were measured *in situ* at the

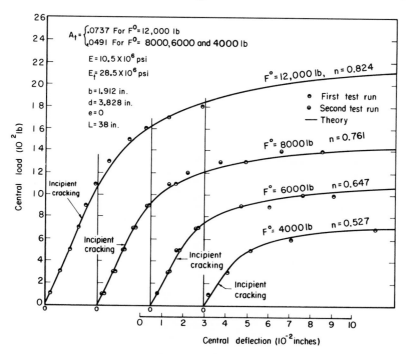

FIG. 24. Load-deflection curves for a simply supported centrally loaded prestressed segmented glass beam (fitted linear range).

middle and two ends of the member. To prevent relative movement between the segments, the axial load was never completely removed from the member. The resulting three load-deflection diagrams shown in Fig. 25 are almost identical, indicating that the 10-inch or 20-segment gage length is adequate for estimating n. The values of n obtained from the compression tests are indicated in Fig. 24 together with the detailed properties of the beam. In every case, these values of n overestimated the initial bending stiffness. Since a single beam was used, no conclusion can be drawn from this observation because n can be used to estimate only the average initial bending stiffness.

To use the data of Fig. 24 to examine the approximate theory in the nonlinear range, values of n, call them n', must be established which describe the initial slopes of the four load-deflection curves. Effective beam widths then become (bn'), and the perfect beam theory may be used to predict the bending response. We observe from Fig. 24 that the solid theo-

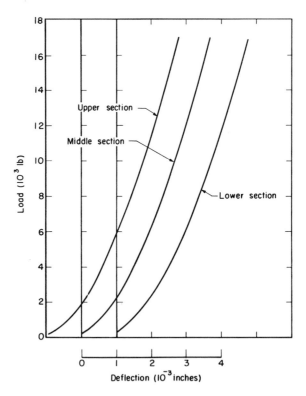

FIG. 25. Compression tests on a glass beam (gage length = 10 inches; average area = 7.32 inches²).

retical curves approximate the nonlinear behavior very closely. The linear range was, of course, selected to fit the data.

As a final observation concerning nonflat interfaces, we note that the load-deflection curves obtained for both the glass and the titanium carbide beams show an initial straight line portion. On the other hand, their associated compressive stress-strain curves are curvilinear with a monotonically increasing slope. This apparent anomaly might be explained by considering an axially prestressed beam that is free from lateral loads. The initial bending stiffness of this member is proportional to the tangent modulus of its compression curve at the given prestress level. Now, when a bending moment is applied to this member, the compression fibers will tend to get stiffer and the tension fibers will tend to become more flexible. The two effects neutralize each other and mitigate the influence of the compression nonlinearity.

III. Prestressed Monolithic Beams

A. DETERMINISTIC STRENGTH THEORY

In those circumstances where the tensile strength of a material can be approximated by a single number σ_t and the compressive strength by σ_c, the ultimate moment capacity of a prestressed beam, M_p, may be established in an elementary fashion. We shall first consider a monolithic beam prestressed by zero stiffness tendons which are constrained to deflect with the member. Since this constraint precludes any "beam column" effect, the maximum fiber stress formula can be used to define safe values for M_p. We must examine the top and bottom fiber stress in both the loaded and unloaded conditions.

Top fibers—loaded condition:

$$-\sigma_c \leq -\frac{F}{A} - \frac{(M_p - Fe)n_t}{I} \tag{46}$$

where n_t is the distance between the beam's centroid and the top fibers. Rewriting the equation, we obtain

$$M_p \leq \frac{I\sigma_c}{n_t} - F\left(\frac{I}{An_t} - e\right) \tag{47}$$

Bottom fibers—loaded condition:

$$\sigma_t \geq -\frac{F}{A} + \frac{(M_p - Fe)n_b}{I} \tag{48}$$

where n_b is the distance between the beam's centroid and the bottom fibers. Here, we obtain

$$M_p \leq \frac{I\sigma_t}{n_b} + F\left(\frac{I}{An_b} + e\right) \tag{49}$$

Top fibers—unloaded condition:

$$\sigma_t \geq -\frac{F}{A} + \frac{Fen_t}{I} \tag{50}$$

This condition leads to a bound on the prestressing force when it acts outside of the kern, i.e.,

$$F \leq \frac{A\sigma_t}{[(eAn_t/I) - 1]}, \qquad e > \frac{I}{An_t} \tag{51}$$

When $e \leq I/(An_t)$, it is not possible to produce tension in the top fibers.

Bottom fibers—unloaded condition:

$$-\sigma_c \leq -\frac{F}{A} - \frac{Fen_b}{I} \tag{52}$$

If $e > -I/(An_b)$, F is bounded by

$$F \leq \frac{A\sigma_c}{[(eAn_b/I) + 1]} \tag{53}$$

To illustrate the influence of prestressing on the moment capacity of a rectangular beam, the inequalities represented by Eqs. (47), (49), and (53) are plotted in Fig. 26, where M_p is normalized by the moment resistance of an unprestressed beam $M = I\sigma_t/n_t$. The maximum moment resistance indicated in Fig. 26 occurs at the intersection of the lines defined by Eqs. (47) and (49); thus, the optimum prestressing value becomes

$$F_{\text{opt}} = \left(\frac{\sigma_c n_b - \sigma_t n_t}{n_b + n_t}\right) A \tag{54}$$

and the associated optimum moment resistance is

$$M_{\text{opt}} = \frac{\sigma_c(I + Aen_b) + \sigma_t(I - Aen_t)}{n_b + n_t} \tag{55}$$

As the eccentricity of the prestressing force increases, the vertical bound in Fig. 26 moves to the left until the maximum moment resistance is given by the intersection of Eqs. (49) and (53); i.e.,

$$M_{\text{opt}} = \frac{I(\sigma_c + \sigma_t)}{n_b}, \qquad e \geq \frac{In_t}{An_b}\left(\frac{\sigma_c + \sigma_t}{\sigma_c n_b - \sigma_t n_t}\right) \tag{56}$$

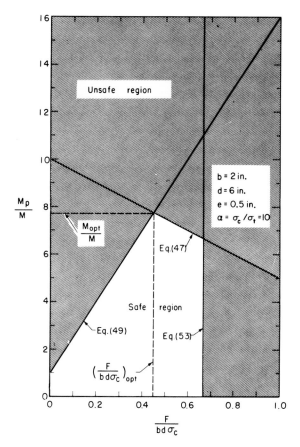

FIG. 26. Moment capacity of a prestressed segmented rectangular beam for various levels of prestress.

When the maximum bending moment on a symmetrical beam can be either positive or negative, the best location for the resultant prestressing force is, of course, at the centroid. Taking $e = 0$, $n_b = n_t$, and $\alpha = \sigma_c/\sigma_t$, Eq. (55) indicates that the largest possible increase in capacity is $M_{opt}/M = (\alpha + 1)/2$. For bending in only one direction, e should be as large as possible. Then, for a symmetrical beam, Eq. (56) gives the largest possible improvement due to prestressing as $M_{opt}/M = \alpha + 1$, which is exactly twice the previous case.

We shall now expand our deterministic strength studies to include the "buckling effect" of the axial prestressing force. This effect becomes significant when the prestressing tendons are attached only to the ends of the beam and F is of the same order of magnitude as the Euler load, F_{cr}.

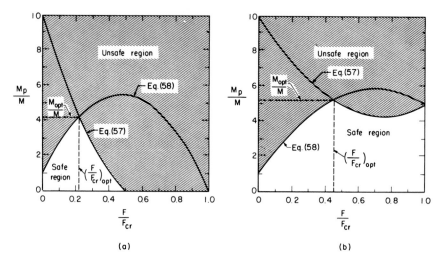

Fig. 27. Moment capacity of a prestressed segmented rectangular beam column for various levels of prestress. (a) $F_{cr}/A\sigma_t = 20$, $e = 0$, $\alpha = 10$. (b) $F_{cr}/A\sigma_t = 10$, $e = d/12$, $\alpha = 10$.

Once again, the general analysis of a prestressed beam would consider the top and bottom fiber stresses for the loaded and unloaded conditions, except that here, the bending stresses given by the second term in Eqs. (46), (48), (50), and (52) will be multiplied by the approximate magnification factor $1/(1 - F/F_{cr})$ (Timoshenko, 1955). The following inequalities are obtained for the loaded condition:

Top fibers—loaded condition:

$$\frac{M_p}{M} \leq \frac{n_b}{n_t}\left\{\left(\frac{F}{F_{cr}}\right)^2\left(\frac{F_{cr}}{A\sigma_t}\right) + \left(\frac{F}{F_{cr}}\right)\left[\left(\frac{F_{cr}}{A\sigma_t}\right)\left(\frac{Aen_t}{I} - 1\right) - \alpha\right] + \alpha\right\} \quad (57)$$

Bottom fibers—loaded condition:

$$\frac{M_p}{M} \leq -\left(\frac{F}{F_{cr}}\right)^2\left(\frac{F_{cr}}{A\sigma_t}\right) + \left(\frac{F}{F_{cr}}\right)\left[\left(\frac{F_{cr}}{A\sigma_t}\right)\left(\frac{Aen_b}{I} + 1\right) - 1\right] + 1 \quad (58)$$

These equations are plotted in Fig. 27 for two eccentricities; we observe that the maximum moment capacity occurs at their intersection. The optimum prestressing force and the associated optimum are given, respectively, by

$$\left(\frac{F}{F_{cr}}\right)_{opt} = \frac{(\alpha\lambda - 1)}{B(\lambda + 1)} \quad (59)$$

and

$$\left(\frac{M_p}{M}\right)_{\text{opt}} = \frac{-(\alpha\lambda - 1)^2}{B(\lambda + 1)^2} + \frac{(\alpha\lambda - 1)}{B(\lambda + 1)}\left[B\left(\frac{Aen_b}{I} + 1\right) - 1\right] + 1 \quad (60)$$

where

$$\lambda \equiv n_b/n_t; \qquad B \equiv F_{\text{cr}}/A\sigma_t \qquad (61)$$

B. STATISTICAL STRENGTH THEORY

1. *Bending Strength*

The usual practice in the design of monolithic prestressed concrete is to assume that the concrete has zero tensile strength. The tendon positions and the associated prestressing forces are selected on this conservative basis. Because the tensile strength of many brittle materials is substantial, we have been motivated in this section to take advantage of this latent load-carrying capacity. Clearly then, our first step must be the characterization of the tensile strength of the brittle materials to be utilized. For this purpose, we shall adopt the methods of statistical fracture theory which are treated in another chapter.

This theory recognizes that the strength of a brittle material cannot be specified by a single number; that indeed, a distribution of strength values will be obtained on repeated testing of nominally identical specimens. It is most convenient to organize these strength values into a cumulative distribution curve, such as that shown in Fig. 28 for the so-called four point bend tests of rectangular plaster beams. The data in this figure have been ordered and the probability of failure at the stress associated with the ith observation is estimated to be $P = i/(N + 1)$, where N is the total number of observations. The resulting distribution curve may be thought of as a tradeoff relationship between the strength and the reliability of the elements.

The principal objective of statistical strength analysis is to establish a cumulative distribution function for complex prototype components from information obtained from laboratory specimens or small scale models. In both cases, we begin by determining the strength distribution for a basic building block associated with the component. We must then provide a rule relating the behavior of the entire component to the behavior of the individual building blocks. For an ideal brittle material, the series rule governs the behavior; i.e., failure in any unit necessarily constitutes overall failure of a component. Here, the building block may be taken as an infinitesimal volume.

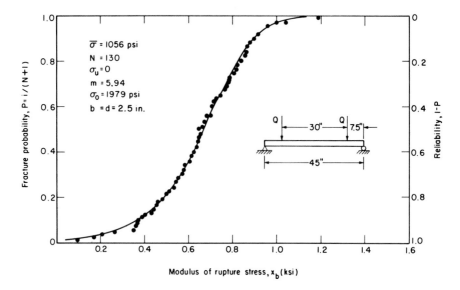

FIG. 28. Cumulative distribution curve for unprestressed monolithic rectangular beams.

Adopting the series model, Weibull (1939) proposed a very simple form for the strength distribution which represents the general behavior patterns of most brittle materials. For a uniaxial stress distribution, his fracture probability P may be written as

$$P(\sigma) = 1 - \exp\left[-\frac{1}{v}\iiint g \, d\xi_1 \, d\xi_2 \, d\xi_3\right]$$

$$g = \left[\frac{\sigma\phi(\xi_1, \xi_2, \xi_3) - \sigma_u}{\sigma_0}\right]^m; \qquad \sigma\phi \geq \sigma_u \geq 0 \qquad (62)$$

$$g = 0; \qquad \sigma\phi \leq \sigma_u$$

where σ is an intensity level; $\sigma\phi$ is the actual uniaxial stress distribution resulting from the live loads; ξ_1, ξ_2, and ξ_3 are space coordinates; v is a unit volume; and m, σ_u, and σ_0 are statistical distribution parameters. To illustrate how this equation is used, we shall establish a formula for the fracture probability of the beams considered in Fig. 28. The stress distribution in a rectangular beam subjected to terminal couples is simply

$$\sigma\phi = \sigma_b[y/(d/2)] \qquad (63)$$

where σ_b is the maximum fiber stress and y is the vertical coordinate measured downward from the centroid of the beam. Equation (62) may be written

$$-\log(1-P) = \frac{1}{v} \int_V \left(\frac{\sigma\phi - \sigma_u}{\sigma_0}\right)^m dV = \frac{1}{v\sigma_0{}^m} \int_{y_u}^{d/2} \left[\frac{\sigma_b y}{(d/2)} - \sigma_u\right]^m bL \, dy$$

$$= \frac{V}{2v(m+1)} \left(\frac{\sigma_b - \sigma_u}{\sigma_b}\right)\left(\frac{\sigma_b - \sigma_u}{\sigma_0}\right)^m \tag{64}$$

where L is the span length under pure bending, $y_u = (d/2)(\sigma_u/\sigma_b)$, and V is the beam volume bdL. When $\sigma_u = 0$, this expression reduces to

$$P(\sigma_b) = 1 - \exp\left[-\frac{V}{2v(m+1)} \left(\frac{\sigma_b}{\sigma_0}\right)^m\right] \tag{65}$$

To fit $P(\sigma_b)$ to the data of Fig. 28, that is, to estimate the statistical parameters σ_0 and m, we have adopted the efficient method of maximum likelihood. Following the development by Barnett *et al.* (1965), the maximum likelihood estimates of the parameters σ_0 and m are found from the simultaneous solution of

$$\frac{N}{m} + \sum_{i=1}^{N} \log \sigma_i - N \frac{\sum_{i=1}^{N} \sigma_i{}^m \log \sigma_i}{\sum_{i=1}^{N} \sigma_i{}^m} = 0 \tag{66}$$

and

$$\sigma_0{}^m = \frac{V}{N(m+1)} \sum_{i=1}^{N} \sigma_i{}^m \tag{67}$$

where the σ_i are the observed fiber stresses at fracture. When the results of Eqs. (66) and (67), $\sigma_0 = 1979$ psi and $m = 5.94$, were checked by a chi-squared test, the response was at the 50% level, indicating a very good fit.

To find the fracture probability of an element which entertains a uniaxial state of prestress $-\sigma_p$, we simply superimpose this stress state onto the live load stresses and replace $\sigma\phi$ in Eq. (62) by $(\sigma\phi - \sigma_p)$. For a uniformly prestressed beam with $\sigma_u = 0$, the probability of fracture is found from

$$P = 1 - \exp\left[-\frac{1}{v} \int_V \left(\frac{\sigma\phi - \sigma_p}{\sigma_0}\right)^m dV\right] \tag{68}$$

FIG. 29. Prestressed monolithic plaster beam.

When the prestressing tendons are unconstrained, as illustrated in Fig. 29, the deflection u of the resulting beam column is as described in Timoshenko and Gere (1961),

$$u = \frac{Q \sin kc}{Fk \sin kl} [\sin kx + \sin k(l-x)] - \frac{Qc}{F}, \qquad c \leq x \leq l-c \quad (69)$$

where $k = (F/EI)^{1/2}$ and Q, c, and l are defined in Fig. 30. The associated bending stress is

$$\sigma\phi = Qy \frac{Ek \sin kc}{F \sin kl} [\sin kx + \sin k - (lx)] \qquad (70)$$

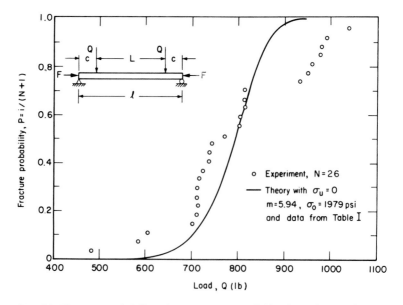

FIG. 30. Fracture probability of prestressed monolithic plaster beam columns.

Considering only the central portion of the beam column shown in Fig. 29, we can establish its cumulative distribution curve from Eq. (68) when the stress for any load Q is given by Eq. (70) and when the integration extends over that portion of the beam between c and $l - c$. Using the data in Table I together with the distribution parameters established with the unprestressed beams of Fig. 28, Eq. (68) was numerically integrated to produce the solid curve drawn in Fig. 30. The fixture shown in Fig. 29 was used to test 26 plaster beams. The associated fracture loads are plotted in Fig. 30 where, in spite of their sparseness, they tend to corroborate the

TABLE I

EXPERIMENTAL DATA FOR PRESTRESSED MONOLITHIC
PLASTER BEAM COLUMNS

$b = 2.5$ inches	$E = 2.8 \times 10^6$ psi (plaster)
$d = 2.5$ inches	$I = 3.26$ inches^4
$l = 45$ inches	$F = 10,000$ pounds
$c = 7.5$ inches	$k = 0.0321$ inch^{-1}

predicted distribution curve. We should mention that the center deflection of one of the plaster beams was measured to be 0.183 inch at the fracture load of 702 pounds. Using Eq. (70), we predicted a deflection of 0.179 inch, a satisfactory agreement.

2. Transverse Strength

When structures are employed in real situations, they are invariably subjected to loads which cannot be precisely characterized or anticipated in the design process. These loads arise, for example, during the fabrication, handling, testing, and inspection of brittle components, and they usually cause some damage to these unforgiving materials. Even under laboratory conditions, the authors have observed that specimens of various sizes and shapes in a half dozen different brittle materials gradually suffer damage by chipping or spalling. On the other hand, experience has also shown that prestressed members are considerably less sensitive to the impacts and bruising normally found in a structures laboratory.

In this closing section on beams, we shall briefly attempt to account for the apparent increase in transverse tensile strength which is observed in prestressed members. An investigation of this type falls under the general category of combined stress theories for brittle state materials. The development of such theories has been seriously hampered by a dearth of experimental data and a lack of appreciation for the underlying statistical nature of the problem.

The objective of a combined stress theory is to establish a fracture surface; i.e., to find a relationship among the strengths achieved under various stress states. The usual approach to this problem in either ductile or brittle materials is to find a property common to all stress states that will indicate failure or nonfailure. In ductile materials, the distortion energy represents such a property, since incipient flow occurs in any stress state in which the distortion energy is equal to the distortion energy obtained in a tension specimen at yield. Stated another way, we can correlate yielding under any stress state with the distortion energy. Our approach for brittle materials is completely analogous—we shall try to find a property that will correlate with the reliabilities associated with the various possible combined stress conditions.

We shall consider only those failures of a brittle material which are caused by tensile stresses. On this basis, it seems natural that we examine the collection of all tensile stresses associated with every stress state. One way of doing this, for example, in the plane stress problem, would be to construct the figure enclosing all of the tensile normal stress vectors $\bar{\sigma}_n$ acting in the plane about a point. Since the area of the resulting figure would, in general, be different for every stress state, there is a possibility that we can correlate this area with the failure or nonfailure of the small material volume ΔV associated with the point.

Such a procedure recognizes that every tensile normal stress may contribute to failure; however, it does not account for the possibility that the stresses may exert an influence on fracture that is not proportional to their magnitudes. To deal with this situation, we could weight each vector $\bar{\sigma}_n$ and then calculate the area of the figure enclosing the weighted vectors, which we shall designate as $\bar{f}$. In two-dimensional polar coordinates, $\bar{f} = \bar{f}[f(\sigma_n), \theta]$, and the area of the weighted tensile normal stress diagram g is

$$g = 4 \int_0^{\pi/2} [f^2(\sigma_n)/2] \, d\theta \qquad (71)$$

where

$$\begin{aligned} f &= f(\sigma_n), & \sigma_n &\geq 0 \\ f &= 0, & \sigma_n &\leq 0 \end{aligned} \qquad (72)$$

Written in terms of the principal stresses S_1 and S_2, σ_n becomes

$$\sigma_n = S_1 \cos^2 \theta + S_2 \sin^2 \theta \qquad (73)$$

where θ is the angle between $\bar{\sigma}_n$ and $\bar{S}_1$.

Now, putting aside the question of the function f, we can proceed to correlate $g(S_1, S_2)$ with the fracture probabilities associated with different stress states. This may be done by recognizing that any cumulative distribution function may be written in the form

$$P(S_1, S_2) = 1 - \exp[-(\Delta V/v)g] \tag{74}$$

where $\Delta V/v$ is merely a convenient constant. If P is to represent the fracture probability for our small volume ΔV, the function f must satisfy certain conditions. We see from Eqs. (73) and (72) that, if $S_1 \leq 0$ and $S_2 \leq 0$, f becomes zero. It follows, from Eqs. (71) and (74), that P also becomes zero.

At the other extreme, we expect that fracture is a certainty when either S_1 or S_2 is positive and unbounded; hence, $P = 1$ implies that

$$f \to \infty \quad \text{when} \quad S_1, S_2 \to +\infty$$

Furthermore, we would expect, on physical grounds, that the failure probability would increase continuously with increasing principal tensile stresses; thus,

$$f \quad \text{continuous and monotonically increasing}$$

Finally, f must be chosen in such a way that the associated $P(S_1, S_2)$ fits the cumulative distribution curves obtained from fracture tests conducted using various stress states. In particular, it is necessary that fracture data obtained under pure tension be represented by $P(S_1, 0)$ or $P(0, S_2)$. This is a standard problem in curve fitting and one proceeds by selecting a reasonable and versatile form for f which contains n parameters a_i; i.e., $f = f[\sigma_n; a_1, a_2, \ldots, a_n]$. These parameters are chosen so that the curve for P passes "as close as possible" to each data point. For a series material, we note that the parameters which provide an exact fit to an infinite amount of data are intrinsic phenomenological strength properties of the material.

One of the simplest candidates for f is the power form

$$f = (\sigma_n/\sigma_0)^m \tag{75}$$

where m and σ_0 have been taken as parameters. We may now specialize Eq. (74), using Eqs. (71)–(73) and (75); thus,

$$P = 1 - \exp\left[-\frac{2\,\Delta V}{v}\int_0^{\theta_0}\left(\frac{S_1\cos^2\theta + S_2\sin^2\theta}{\sigma_0}\right)^{2m} d\theta\right] \tag{76}$$

where the range of integration from zero to θ_0 extends over the region where $\sigma_n \geq 0$. This inequality leads to three distinct cases:

Case 1: $S_1 \geq S_2 \geq 0$

$$\theta_0 = \pi/2 \tag{77}$$

Case 2: $S_1 \geq 0,\ S_2 \leq 0$

$$\theta_0 = \cos^{-1}[-S_2/(S_1 - S_2)]^{1/2} \tag{78}$$

Case 3: $S_1 \leq 0,\ S_2 \leq 0$

$$\theta_0 = 0 \qquad (P = 0) \tag{79}$$

Together with Eq. (76), these equations describe the fracture probability for any stress state (S_1, S_2); we shall determine particular expressions for pure tension and pure shear.

Pure tension   (Case 1: $S = \sigma_t$, $S_2 = 0$)

$$P(\sigma_t) = 1 - \exp\left[-\frac{2\,\Delta V}{v} \int_0^{\pi/2} \left(\frac{\sigma_t}{\sigma_0}\right)^{2m} \cos^{4m}\theta\ d\theta \right]$$

$$P(\sigma_t) = 1 - \exp\left[-\frac{\sqrt{\pi}\,\Delta V}{v} \frac{\Gamma(2m + \tfrac{1}{2})}{\Gamma(2m + 1)} \left(\frac{\sigma_t}{\sigma_0}\right)^{2m} \right] . \tag{80}$$

This equation may be used in conjunction with tension data to establish the statistical parameters m and σ_0. The maximum likelihood method described by Eqs. (66) and (67) can be used for this purpose with only slight modification.

Pure shear   (Case 2: $S_1 = \sigma_s$, $S_2 = -\sigma_s$)

$$P(\sigma_s) = 1 - \exp\left[-\frac{2\,\Delta V}{v} \int_0^{\pi/4} \left(\frac{\sigma_s}{\sigma_0}\right)^{2m} (\cos^2\theta - \sin^2\theta)^{2m}\ d\theta \right]$$

$$P(\sigma_s) = 1 - \exp\left[-\frac{\sqrt{\pi}\,\Delta V}{2v} \frac{\Gamma(m + \tfrac{1}{2})}{\Gamma(m + 1)} \left(\frac{\sigma_s}{\sigma_0}\right)^{2m} \right] \tag{81}$$

As an example of how we may estimate the increase in transverse strength due to prestressing, we shall consider a volume ΔV on the surface of a beam. If the compressive prestress acting on this volume is taken to be equal in magnitude to the transverse tensile resistance, we can calculate the transverse strength from the pure shear example. Without prestress, the transverse tensile strength of ΔV is given by the pure tension example. Comparing these strengths at the same reliability level, $P(\sigma_s) = P(\sigma_t)$, we find

$$\frac{\sigma_s}{\sigma_t} = \left[\frac{2\Gamma(m + 1)\Gamma(2m + \tfrac{1}{2})}{\Gamma(m + \tfrac{1}{2})\Gamma(2m + 1)} \right]^{1/2m} \tag{82}$$

When $m = 1$, $\sigma_s/\sigma_t = 1.225$; $m = 2$, $\sigma_s/\sigma_t = 1.099$; $m = \infty$, $\sigma_s/\sigma_t = 1$. Thus, in the first two cases, prestressing increases the transverse tensile strength by 22.5 and 10%, respectively.

We should remark in closing this subject that, when a series material is used, the fracture probability of a component P_c may be established by observing that survival of the component requires the simultaneous survival of each constituent volume. Therefore, the survival probability $(1 - P_c)$ is given by

$$1 - P_c = \prod_{i=1}^{N} (1 - P_i) \tag{83}$$

where P_i is the fracture probability of the ith volume ΔV_i and N is the total number of volumes. Substituting from Eq. (76) for P_i and taking the limit as $\Delta V \to 0$, we obtain

$$P_c = 1 - \exp\left\{-\frac{2}{v}\iiint_V \left[\int_0^{\theta_0} \left(\frac{S_1 \cos^2 \theta + S_2 \sin^2 \theta}{\sigma_0}\right)^{2m} d\theta\right] dV\right\} \tag{84}$$

where the triple integral is taken over the volume of the component and θ_0 is given by Eqs. (77)–(79).

An enlarged treatment of combined stress theories in two and three dimensions is given by Barnett *et al.* (1967) for brittle state materials under varying mechanical and thermal loading.

IV. Segmented Columns

A. STRENGTH-TRANSVERSE CRACKING

Cracking in a direction transverse to a uniaxial compressive load was first recognized by Shanley *et al.* (1955) to be a major deterrent to the application of prestressing to segmented members. As part of his investigations of high performance prestressing, the four high alumina porcelain wing structures shown in Fig. 31 were fabricated and tested. In the first three of these wings, gaskets were used between the interfaces, and failure occurred while the prestressing loads were being applied. The failures were quite interesting in that the initial cracks were formed parallel to the wing axis, suggesting the presence of transverse tension. This subsection deals with the explanation for this behavior. In the test of ceramic wing No. IV, the gaskets were eliminated and the interfaces were lapped. Here, no distress was apparent under a prestress of 2000 psi. Under a uniform lateral loading, failure occurred once again by spanwise cracks which developed when the maximum bending stress was 1590 psi. The net compressive stress of 3590 psi which was realized in the member represented a small fraction of the measured compressive strength of the material; 12,000 psi for individual wing sections and about 40,000 psi for smaller compression specimens.

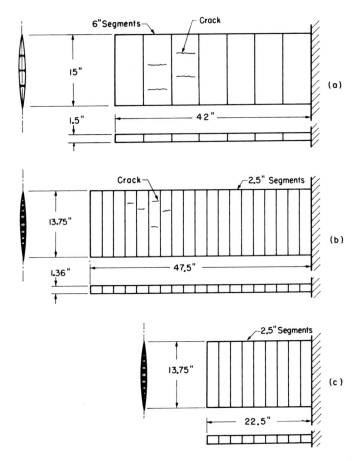

Fig. 31. Prestressed segmented ceramic wings (after F. R. Shanley *et al.*, 1955); (a) types I and II, (b) type III, (c) type IV.

Because the roughness of segment interfaces played such a significant role in the stiffness experiments described in Sect. II,C for the titanium carbide member, it seemed reasonable to adopt this premise as a first hypothesis for explaining the transverse cracking of segmented elements under axial compressive loads. Indeed, our studies appear to support this position.

We shall begin our investigation of the roughness hypothesis by considering a simple compression test of a segmented plate glass column conducted by Barnett *et al.* (1964). The glass segments were in the form of blocks with nominal dimensions of $2 \times 4 \times \frac{1}{2}$ inches where the contacting surfaces (8 square inches) were 5 to 7 lightbands out of flat. The tests were terminated at about 10,000 psi when spalling was observed on the periphery of the glass segments. Examination of the segments subsequent to their testing revealed that all of the blocks contained lenslike cracks such as those shown in Fig. 32. The normals to these crack lenses were perpendicular to the axis of loading, and their centers were located near the central plane of the segments. The cracks did not penetrate to the surfaces.

a. Lateral Tensile Stresses. In a segmented column, the roughness of the segments gives rise to a nonuniform distribution of axial stresses across their interfaces. This, in turn, causes tensile stresses to be developed in the transverse direction to the loading. This principle has been used as an indirect method of obtaining the tensile strength of brittle materials. The method has been described by Berenbaum and Brodie (1959), who conducted a two-dimensional photoelastic analysis of the nonuniformly loaded block shown in Fig. 33a. The results shown in Fig. 33b indicate that the transverse stress under the load assumes a maximum tensile value at the

FIG. 32. Transverse internal crack in glass segment resulting from direct compression.

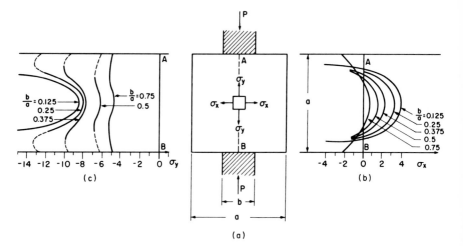

FIG. 33. Indirect tension test (after R. Berenbaum and I. Brodie, 1959). (a) Non-uniformly loaded block, (b) transverse stress, (c) axial stress. Note: Stresses result from an applied load of 50 units and $AB = a = 10$ units.

center of the block and becomes compressive at the top and bottom surfaces. This corresponds to our observations concerning the internal crack lenses which did not penetrate to the surfaces.

Additional insight into the nature of the transverse tensile stresses can be gained by studying the stress distribution in the strip shown in Fig. 34. The intensity of the vertical forces acting on the top and bottom surfaces is $A[1 + \sin(m\pi x/L)]$, where the integer m represents the number of waves and L is the strip length. Referring to Timoshenko and Goodier (1951), the stress distribution becomes

$$\sigma_x = 2A \frac{(a \cosh a - \sinh a) \cosh \alpha y - \alpha y \sinh \alpha y \sinh a}{\sinh 2a + 2a} \sin \alpha x$$

$$\sigma_y = -2A \frac{(a \cosh a + \sinh a) \cosh \alpha y - \alpha y \sinh \alpha y \sinh a}{\sinh 2a + 2a} \sin \alpha x - A \quad (85)$$

$$\tau_{xy} = -2A \frac{a \cosh a \sinh \alpha y - \alpha y \cosh \alpha y \sinh a}{\sinh 2a + 2a} \cos \alpha x$$

where $a = m\pi c/L$ and $\alpha = m\pi/L$ and c is half the strip depth. Specializing these formulas to give the maximum stresses in the middle plane ($y = 0$, $\sin \alpha x = 1$), the ratio of transverse to axial stress becomes

$$-\frac{\sigma_x}{\sigma_y} = \frac{a \cosh a - \sinh a}{(1 + \cosh a)(a + \sinh a)} \quad (86)$$

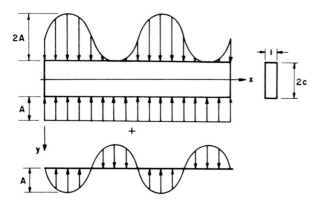

Fig. 34. Strip subjected to a nonuniform axial load.

This relationship has been plotted in Fig. 35, where we observe that somewhere between very few waves and very many waves there exists a "worst" condition. We observe further that tensile failures can occur if the tensile strength of the strip material is less than 15.3% of its compressive strength. For most ceramic materials, the tensile strength is less than 10% of their compressive strength.

There are two important similarities between the photoelastic and the elasticity solutions considered. Both show the existence of transverse tensile stresses of one order of magnitude less than the axial stresses, and both show the transverse stresses to be maximum in the middle plane and compressive near the top and bottom surfaces. Equation (85) demonstrates that σ_x is negative at $y = \pm c$.

b. Flatter Specimens and Smaller Specimens. Examination of the interfaces of the $2 \times 4 \times \frac{1}{2}$ inch glass blocks with optical flats seemed to indicate that the surfaces contained a relatively small number of waves. The amplitudes of these waves can be reduced by lapping which, according to our roughness hypothesis, should increase the ultimate compressive strength of a segmented column. Further, if the larger amplitude waves are the more influential in controlling surface contact, it follows that smaller specimens should be stronger than larger ones. This observation is based on a result from extreme value statistics that the maximum amplitudes are smaller in small specimens.

The ultimate compressive strengths of segmented columns were determined for two glass sizes and two levels of interface roughness for each size. Some of the $2 \times 4 \times \frac{1}{2}$ inch "as received" glass blocks (five to seven lightbands) were lapped to a flatness of two to three lightbands. A portion of the segments from each of the resulting groups were then cut to produce $1 \times 2 \times \frac{1}{2}$ inch segments. The columns corresponding to the four types

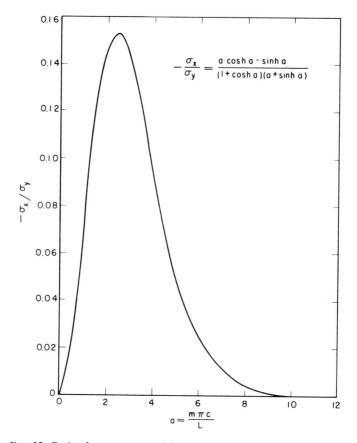

$$-\frac{\sigma_x}{\sigma_y} = \frac{a \cosh a - \sinh a}{(1 + \cosh a)(a + \sinh a)}$$

$$a = \frac{m \pi c}{L}$$

FIG. 35. Ratio of transverse to axial stresses in a nonuniformly loaded block.

of segments were slowly loaded in compression until catastrophic failure occurred and the maximum nominal stress was recorded. These ultimate compressive strengths are given in Table II. Each value listed represents the average strength of three "five-segment" columns. It can be seen that the strength increases as the segments become flatter and as they become smaller.

Although the tests appear to support the roughness hypothesis, it should be pointed out that there are other possible explanations for the observed behavior. First, the small sample sizes used may not lead to a valid statistical inference concerning the average values. Second, if a weakest link mechanism controls the strength of glass in compression, the observed size effect would also appear in monolithic columns. Lastly, the cross-sectional-area-to-circumference ratio of the larger segments is greater than that of

TABLE II

ULTIMATE COMPRESSIVE STRENGTHS OF SEGMENTED GLASS
COLUMNS

Nominal size (inches)	Ultimate compressive stress	
	"As received" 5–7 lightbands (psi)	"Lapped" 2–3 lightbands (psi)
$2 \times 4 \times \frac{1}{2}$	52,450	53,445
$1 \times 2 \times \frac{1}{2}$	56,966	66,533

the smaller segments; consequently, a "skin strength" theory could produce the observed size effect.

c. Triaxial Compression Tests. If, as we contend, premature failure of a segmented column is caused by the presence of transverse tensile stresses, dramatic increases in axial compressive strength can be anticipated through the application of a lateral compressive prestress. In the tests described in this subsection, it was pragmatic to apply the lateral prestress by means of a hydrostatic pressure. In real members, the lateral prestress may be achieved by tension wrapping the member with high strength tendons or perhaps shrink fitting a jacket about them.

A triaxial compression setup was used which subjected "eight-segment" columns to an axial force in addition to a hydrostatic pressure. The test results are summarized in Table III, where we observe that the increase in axial failure stress is greater than the lateral pressure. When interpreting the test results, one must bear in mind that only the axial force can produce

TABLE III

COMPRESSION EXPERIMENTS ON 4-INCH SEGMENTED GLASS PLATE COLUMNS
IN A HYDROSTATIC PRESSURE ENVIRONMENT

Test No.	Segment size (inches)	Mean hydrostatic pressure (psi)	Environment	Axial stress at failure (psi)
1	2×2	0	Air	29,600
2	1×1	0	Air	30,400
3	1×1	10,000	Mil-H-5606A hydraulic	58,400
4	1×1	20,000	Oil (Red)	72,200

transverse tensile stresses; fluid surrounding the segments on all faces produces a hydrostatic state of compression.

d. Backbone Column. We have established that imperfect contact between the interfaces of a segmented column cause transverse compressive stresses near the interfaces and tensile stresses in the interior of the segment. Consequently, it appears that, if the lateral geometry of the segments could be appropriately altered, we might induce compression in the interior and tension near the interfaces of the segments. Thus, the two effects would tend to cancel one another and thereby give rise to a segmented column with a higher strength-to-weight ratio than a prismatic column. To test this supposition, the backbone column shown in Fig. 36 was constructed using three segments. In each of the 46 columns tested, the lips or flanges of the segments were stripped off, to failure, leaving a prismatic column to provide the ultimate resistance.

Fig. 36. Test setup for backbone segmented columns.

When stress concentrations appear in a compressive field, it is possible to achieve "intelligent behavior" from materials which usually provide no stress redistribution mechanism. In addition to the backbone specimen, another example of such behavior was described to the senior author by H. A. Perry of the Naval Ordnance Laboratory. Glass spheres were fabricated from two hemispheres that were attached in such a way that a bead appeared around the equator on the inside. When the sphere was submerged in the ocean, the bead was stripped off and appeared as chips in the bottom of the sphere.

As a final observation on the transverse cracking of segmented members, it should be pointed out that the cracks often propagate across the segment interfaces. This is illustrated in Fig. 37, using a three segment plaster cylindrical column.

FIG. 37. Crack propagating across the interface of a plaster segmented column.

B. Stiffness

In situations where perfect interface contact cannot be achieved, the statistical behavior of a segmented column may be determined from full-scale tests. From a practical point of view, the alternative to such tests is to develop a scaling procedure that will enable us to predict the compression stress-strain diagrams for columns of any length and area from information obtained from a single segmented column. We begin our search for such a scaling law by examining the effects of column length. Let us assume that all the interfaces have been drawn from the same population and that, for a specified axial stress, there exists a frequency distribution for the inter-face contact areas. It follows, then, that the deflection of each segment will be a random variable which also possesses a frequency distribution. Now, the total deflection of a multisegment column will represent the sum of the random deflections of the constituent blocks. Therefore, the frequency distribution of the responses of many nominally identical columns repre-sents the distribution of the sums of the random segment responses.

From the central limit theorem of statistics, we are assured that the sums of random variables are normally distributed regardless of the form of the distribution for the random variables themselves. Thus, we can hypothesize that the stiffness of segmented columns of a given length and under a specified load are normally distributed. On this basis, the following theorem provides the length scaling rule.

THEOREM (Hoel, 1954). *If x is normally distributed with mean μ and standard deviation σ and a random sample of size n is drawn, then the sample mean $\bar{x}$ will be normally distributed with mean μ and standard deviation $\sigma/\sqrt{n}$.*

We note that n is proportional to the column height h.

It is considerably more difficult to speculate on the column area scaling problem; however, we do have a hypothesis that we feel is worth exploring. Let us examine the assumption that the interface contact is controlled primarily by the highest asperities on the surface. If the maximum asperity were measured on each of many nominally identical surfaces, we could construct the frequency distribution. The resulting frequency curve repre-sents the distribution of largest values in a sample of size n (or rather area A). Methods for scaling such distributions to larger areas are treated quite systematically by the methods of extreme value statistics (Gumbel, 1960). Assuming that the stiffness is inversely proportional to the maximum asper-ity heights, the cumulative stiffness distribution $P(E_t)$ might scale as the distribution of smallest values; i.e.,

$$P_L(E_t) = 1 - [1 - P_S(E_t)]^n \qquad (87)$$

where the subscripts L and S refer, respectively, to the large and small area columns, E_t is the tangent modulus, and $n = A_L/A_S$. This hypothesis conforms to our past observations that smaller area columns are stiffer.

Unfortunately, no satisfactory set of compression stress-strain curves is available for examining the area and length scaling hypotheses for segmented columns. An attempt was made by Barnett and Hermann (1966) to establish such a data base, but an error in technique considerably reduced the value of the effort. Nevertheless, their data did show that the distribution curves for the tangent moduli of 13 different circular segmented glass columns were, indeed, normal distributions.

Thirty column tests were conducted on members fabricated from five different diameter disks which were core drilled from a single sheet of $\frac{1}{4}$-inch window glass in sizes ranging from $\frac{1}{2}$ to 3 inches. Compression stress-strain curves were obtained for 3 column heights associated with 10, 20, and 30 segments; 7 such curves are shown in Fig. 38, which clearly indicates the highly individual behavior of segmented columns with nonflat interfaces.

The tangent modulus was measured for all test columns at a stress level of 120 psi, which represents the region around the knee of most of

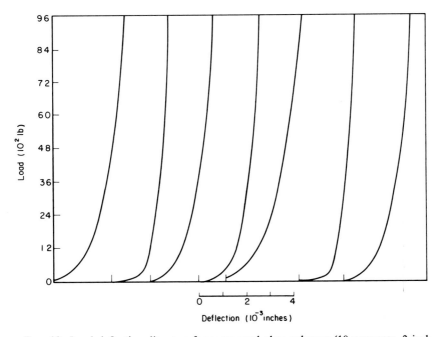

FIG. 38. Load-deflection diagrams for segmented glass columns (10 segments, 2-inch diameter).

the load-deflection curves. The cumulative distribution curve for the tangent moduli of each size column was plotted on " normal probability paper," and, in all cases, a linear relationship was obtained which establishes the validity of the normality hypothesis. Typical distribution curves are shown in Fig. 39, where the solid lines represent the normal curves generated from the computed means and standard deviations of the data which are indicated on the curves.

As part of our examination of the $\frac{1}{2}$-inch plate glass specimens described in Sect. IV,A, compressive stress-strain diagrams were obtained for different size segments with different levels of flatness. Three of these diagrams are shown in Fig. 40, where we observe that the stiffness at every stress level increases when the specimen area decreases and the interface flatness increases. As we have pointed out previously, the apparent size effect precludes the possibility of describing a segmented linear material by an equivalent nonlinear material. Because of the monotonically increasing stiffness, the possibility exists that a segmented column can be stable at high loads and unstable at low ones. This problem may be circumvented by prestressing the column, but not without a weight penalty.

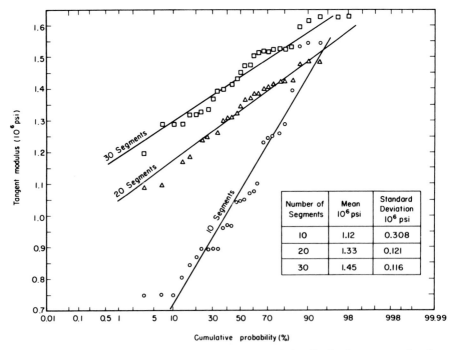

FIG. 39. Plot of segmented glass column tangent modulus distribution on normal probability paper (nominal stress = 120 psi, 1.0-inch diameter).

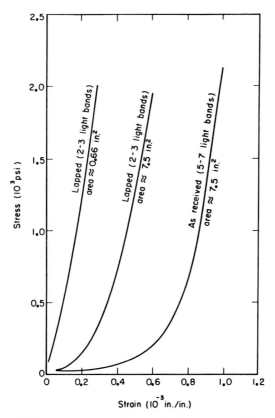

FIG. 40. Effect of size on the compressive nominal stress-strain diagram of segmented glass columns.

As a final observation, we note that, as long as a column is never completely unloaded, the compressive stress-strain curve is almost perfectly reproducible. However, if the relative positions of the segments are disturbed after loading and unloading, the subsequent stress-strain curve will be different and, sometimes, quite different.

C. THEORETICAL RESULTS FOR PERFECTLY FLAT INTERFACES

If, as in the case of the nonlinear bending theory of segmented beams, we assume that perfect contact exists between segments, the behavior of segmented beam columns is amenable to analytical treatment. However, owing to the fact that this area has received much less attention than the behavior of beams under transverse loading, only one problem has been investigated: the response of an eccentrically loaded segmented beam column. The rather lengthy development of the solution has been placed in App. B; here, we shall briefly summarize results.

The geometry of the eccentrically loaded beam column is shown in Fig. 41 together with curves representing nondimensional end load versus nondimensional central deflection. The curves are drawn for two eccentricities; $e = 0$ and $e/d = \frac{1}{12}$. A degenerated curve for $e/d = \frac{1}{6}$ can be represented by a point at the origin. The solid portion of the curves represents the response when the beam column is behaving as though it were monolithic and the dashed portion indicates the response when some of the

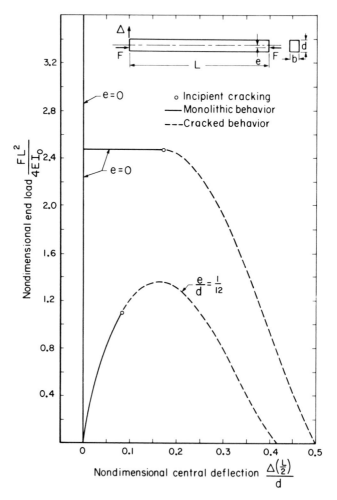

FIG. 41. Load-deflection diagram for a segmented beam column.

segments begin to separate. The value of the load at which cracking is incipient is

$$F_c = (4EI_0/L^2)[\cos^{-1}(6e/d)]^2 \qquad (88)$$

and we note that $\lim_{e \to 0} F_c = \pi^2 EI_0/L^2$, which is the Euler buckling load for a monolithic column.

Referring to Fig. 41, we observe that, when the deflection goes from zero to $(d/2) - e$, the load goes from zero to F_{max} and then back to zero. Consequently, for any given load $0 < F < F_{max}$, two deflection curves exist which satisfy equilibrium. This feature distinguishes the segmented beam column from the monolithic one which exhibits only one equilibrium configuration for loads below the buckling load.

The existence of two equilibrium configurations, at least one of which is in the cracked range, raises the question of whether these forms are stable or unstable. Below the Euler load, monolithic beam column behavior is well known to be stable. The stability in the cracked equilibrium positions has not been studied. We note, however, that any deflections greater than or equal to $(d/2) - e$ are definitely unstable, because there is no possible way for the beam column to remain intact under these conditions.

Many interesting aspects of segmented beam columns remain to be investigated; for example, the effects of cross section geometry and lateral loads. The results of this section are applicable to the problem of eccentrically loaded masonry walls. They also apply to the case of the zero stiffness unconstrained tendon on a segmented beam. This suggests that it should be fruitful to investigate the segmented beam column which incorporates unconstrained elastic tendons.

V. Prestressed Plates

A. SEGMENTED PLATES

The similarity between prestressed segmented beam behavior and that of ductile bending made it possible to successfully apply the techniques of limit analysis to describe the ultimate load-carrying capacity of prestressed segmented beams. The extension of these techniques to prestressed segmented plates is investigated in this section, and exploratory experiments are described which examine both monolithic and segmented plates.

We begin by considering a plate of arbitrary shape and constant thickness t which is prestressed by a system which produces and maintains a homogeneous and isotropic state of compressive forces which act in the middle plane of the plate. For example, the randomly dispersed short fibers mentioned in the Introduction constitute such a system when they are tensioned by differential contraction. Any and all cracks in such a plate will tend to close up, and, in particular, the ultimate bending resistance along such cracks will be calculated in the same manner used for segmented beams. The prestressing forces give rise to a plane hydrostatic stress field in the uncracked plate which we shall denote by $-\sigma_p$. Then, ignoring any stiffness of the prestressing system, we may refer to Fig. 18a to establish the limiting moment per unit length in the plate as

$$M_0 = \sigma_p t^2/2 \qquad (89)$$

where we note that $-\sigma_p$ acts normal to any potential crack interface. This limiting moment capacity would not be affected by moments acting transverse to the crack, which suggests the application of the square yield criterion shown in Fig. 42 where M_1 and M_2 are principal moments. The analysis of plates, using a square yield diagram, has been treated extensively under the name "yield line theory," and an excellent description of this technique may be found in Wood (1961).

We shall now use yield line theory to analyze a circular plate of radius R which is simply supported on a circular ring of radius r and is subjected to a central load P brought onto the plate through a blunt circular rod of radius a. Assuming the yield (or crack) pattern shown in Fig. 43, we observe that the loading die will ultimately contact the centerline of each segment at only one point at a distance a from the plate center. The loading at such points will be P/n, where n is the number of segments. The virtual work done by these loads in the assumed displacement pattern is

$$n(P/n)\Delta[(b-a)/b]$$

where Δ is the central plate deflection. The energy dissipated at the yield line is given by

$$nRM_0\, 2\omega\, \sin(\pi/n)$$

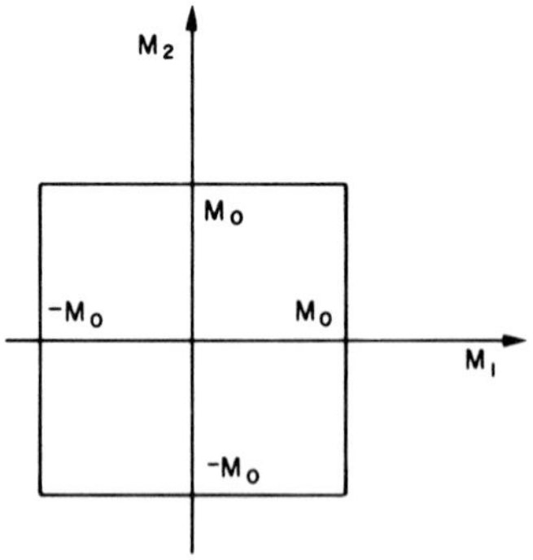

FIG. 42. Square yield diagram, $M_0 = \sigma_p t^2/2$.

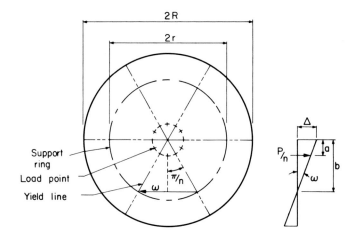

Rotation $\omega = \dfrac{\Delta}{b} = \dfrac{\Delta}{r \cos \frac{\pi}{n}}$

Radial rotation component $= 2\omega \sin \frac{\pi}{n}$

$b = r \cos \frac{\pi}{n}$

FIG. 43. Collapse pattern for a circular plate. Deflection of load $= \Delta(b - a)/b$, rotation $\omega = \Delta/b = \Delta/[r \cos(\pi/n)]$, radial rotation component $= 2\omega \sin(\pi/n)$, $b = r \cos(\pi/n)$.

where the rotation ω is defined in Fig. 43. Equating these virtual energies, we obtain

$$nR\left(\frac{\sigma_p t^2}{2}\right)2\left(\frac{\Delta}{r \cos (\pi/n)}\right)\sin\frac{\pi}{n} = n\frac{P}{n}\Delta\left(1 - \frac{a}{r \cos (\pi/n)}\right)$$

or

$$P = \sigma_p t^2 n \tan \frac{\pi}{n}\left(\frac{R}{r - [a/\cos(\pi/n)]}\right) \qquad (90)$$

This load represents an upper bound on the true collapse load of the plate, and, consequently, we should choose from among this class of collapse mechanisms the one which gives the lowest load. This occurs when $n \to \infty$, and hence,

$$P = \pi\sigma_p t^2[R/(r - a)], \qquad n \to \infty \qquad (91)$$

The true collapse load is realized only when the correct yield pattern is chosen. In the present case, symmetry suggests that we have made the right choice.

We can cause yielding to occur along a finite number of radial lines by strengthening the material between them. We would expect the capacity of the plate to increase with such a procedure, and this is exactly what Eq. (90) predicts. As we force failure to occur along fewer and fewer lines, the required strength of the segments will correspondingly increase. As a rule, to avoid fracturing the elements in a segmented component, we should select geometries that approximate the true yield patterns for the structure. On the other hand, if the segments are sufficiently strong, we can force the plate to deform in any kinematically admissible pattern formed by the interfaces.

To establish the potential of the proposed analysis procedure, Barnett and Hermann (1966) conducted exploratory experiments with two segmented circular plates each fabricated from eight plaster segments. The prestressing was accomplished by making a double wrap of steel strapping about the periphery of the plate, as shown in Fig. 44, and tightening with a standard banding tool until yielding occurred near the grip. Seven mono-

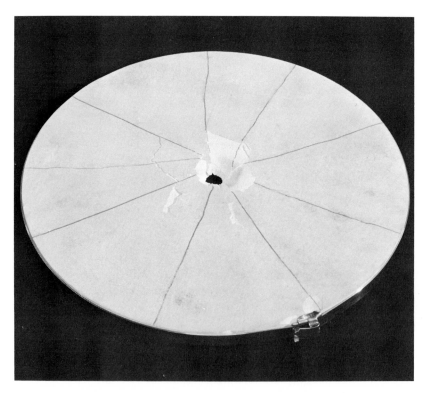

FIG. 44. Prestressed monolithic circular plaster plate.

TABLE IV

PRESTRESSED MONOLITHIC AND SEGMENTED CIRCULAR PLATE STRENGTHS

Plate No.	Strain $\times 10^{-6}$ inch/inch [a]			Yield load (lb)	Ultimate load (lb)
	(a)	(b)	(c)		
Monolithic 1	[b]	50	45	400	540
Monolithic 2	70	55	65	345	582
Monolithic 3	30	50	55	370	520
Monolithic 4	40	45	55	410	624
Monolithic 5	60	70	[b]	330	706
Monolithic 6		No gages		300	535
Monolithic 7		No gages		350	430
Segmented 1	50	40	10	270	—
Segmented 2		No gages		288	—

[a] Average strain-gage reading: 49.4×10^{-6} inch/inch.
[b] Defective.

lithic plates and two segmented plates were prestressed in this way, and the resulting strains in six of the plates were recorded by radially positioned electrical resistance foil strain gages. The strain gage readings and measured loads for these plates are tabulated in Table IV. The loading setup is shown in Fig. 45, where the support fixture is constructed like a large ball bearing race. The load-deflection diagrams for the segmented beams are shown in Fig. 46, where we observe well-defined horizontal regions. On unloading, we obtained complete deflection recovery with only occasional chipping at the segment edges.

As evidenced from Table IV, the straps did not apply a uniform radial prestress; however, since care was taken to tighten the straps in the same way for all cases, it is felt that the average prestress in the various plates were about the same. On this basis, the prestrain was taken as the average of 16 gage readings; i.e., 49.4×10^{-6} inch/inch. Using this value, together with the plate properties tabulated in Table V, Eq. (90) predicts a yield load of $P = 309$ lb. This value differs from the measured values of 280 and 288 lb by 14.4 and 7.3%, respectively.

B. MONOLITHIC PLATES

When a prestressed monolithic plate is slowly loaded, conventional elastic behavior is experienced until the net tensile stress at some point exceeds the material strength, and a crack develops. In a constant strain

FIG. 45. Test setup for loading circular plates.

rate machine, the load would fall off abruptly and then increase again as the strain continued to increase. This behavior is depicted in the central load-central deflection diagram shown in Fig. 47 for the second monolithic plate referenced in Table IV. As we see, other cracks continue to form until the strength of the surviving material is sufficient to force unconstrained collapse in the existing crack pattern. The radial crack pattern

TABLE V

PHYSICAL PROPERTIES OF HYDROSTONE PLATES

Plate radius	$R = 7.5$ inches
Support ring radius	$r = 6.75$ inches
Central load die radius	$a = 0.906$ inches
Plate thickness	$t = \frac{5}{8}$ inches
Average plate strain	$\varepsilon_p = 49.4 \times 10^{-6}$ inch/inch
Modulus of elasticity of plaster	$E = 2.79 \times 10^6$ psi
Poisson's ratio for plaster	$\nu = \frac{1}{4}$
Average prestress level	$\sigma_p = \varepsilon_p \left[E/(1 - \nu) \right] = 184$ psi
Number of segmented beam elements	$n = 8$

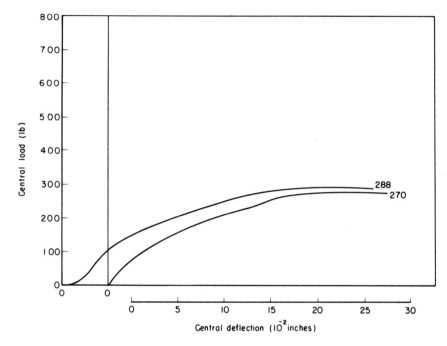

FIG. 46. Central load-central deflection diagrams of prestressed segmented circular plaster plates.

(artificially darkened) shown in Fig. 44 is exactly what limit analysis theory anticipates. The visible crushing at the center of this early plate test was caused by a steel ball that was used originally to load the plate. Subsequent tests employed a circular die to distribute the central load over a greater area.

The punching shear mode of failure is also reported by Ali *et al.* (1964). Using a low performance ceramic, they subjected square plates (6 × 6 × $\frac{1}{2}$ inch) to various levels of biaxial prestress and loaded them laterally in the center with a $1\frac{1}{2}$-inch diameter hydraulic ram. They comment: "If a substantial level of prestressing existed, the fracture was characterized by formation of a hole in the plate by the penetrating transverse-loaded ram. In most such cases, the plate maintained its monolithic integrity after failure and could be removed from the fixture in monolithic form."

Seven load tests were conducted with monolithic plates, and their yield and ultimate strengths are recorded in Table IV. The average ultimate strength for these members is 562 lb, which represents a considerable increase in the average strength of monolithic plates without prestressing— 328 lb. The distribution curve for the strength of these unprestressed

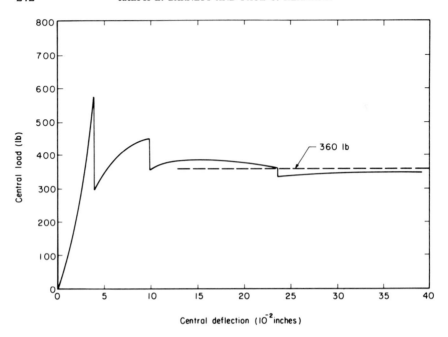

FIG. 47. Central load-central deflection diagram of prestressed segmented circular plaster plates.

control plates is shown in Fig. 48, where we observe a considerable spread in the data. This implies that very low strength values will be present in a population of even a few hundred. Consequently, very "low strength" operating levels must be used to obtain reasonable reliability. For the prestressed plates, on the other hand, there is a built-in fail-safe mechanism. Although the ultimate load is statistical and may be subject to wide variability, the yield load is bounded from below. We observe that the weakest plate is achieved when an infinite number of radial cracks develop, in which case their yield load is computed from Eq. (91). Real plates will crack in a finite number of places and will therefore be stronger. For our prestressed monolithic plates, Eq. (91) predicts a yield load of 289 lb, and we observe from Table IV that all of the collapse strengths reported are higher than this value; the average load is 358 lb.

We should point out that our mathematical model for segmented beams assumes an infinite number of segments and should, therefore, predict a lower bound on the behavior of monolithic prestressed beams. In the exceptional case of a beam column, however, we cannot make this statement, since the resistance at a section can be lowered by virtue of the beam deflection. Finally, since a monolithic segment sustains no separation, it is

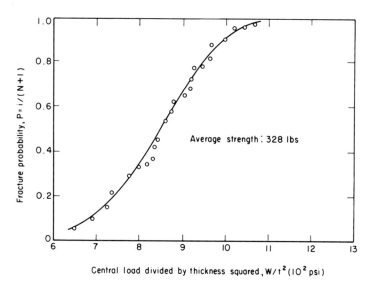

FIG. 48. Failure probabilities for monolithic circular plaster plates without prestressing.

stiffer than an equivalent length of several segments. Consequently, beams constructed with a finite number of elements will be stiffer than predicted from an infinite number of elements.

VI. Recommended Research

There are, at present, only a few promising techniques for utilizing brittle materials in structural applications; among these we find proof testing, prestressing, and methods which provide for alternative load paths in a material such as we find in fiber composites. In spite of the success of prestressed concrete, prestressing of high performance brittle materials has not enjoyed the interest of many investigators. The potential of this technique demands such attention, and we shall suggest a few general and a few specific areas where it will be welcomed.

A. METHODS OF APPLYING PRESTRESS

Several of the prestressing methods of current interest are briefly mentioned in the Introduction, and each of these should be the subject of greatly expanded inquiry. A general program which would systematically identify and catalog the various possible prestressing techniques is badly needed. Research in this area will most certainly demand the involvement of many disciplines.

B. Maintaining Prestress

The oldest problem in connection with the maintenance of a state of prestress is the development of suitable gripping devices for single tendons and cables. Ideally, grips are expected to be positive no-slip mechanisms which are of minimum weight and which develop 100% of the tendon strength. Clearly, devices of large weight or cost can jeopardize the weight/strength or cost/strength characteristics of prestressed systems. Advances in gripping technology have heretofore sprung from the ingenuity of designers rather than from natural consequences of the scientific process.

A second problem in maintaining a state of prestress arises from the viscoelastic behavior of a prestressed system. Relaxation in the tendons and creep in the matrix material both result in a loss in the magnitude of the prestress. The problem is routinely dealt with in prestressed concrete, where the initial prestress is increased in anticipation of creep losses. The possibility of distress in the unloaded member acts to limit the over-stressing of the tendons. Furthermore, when differential shrinkage is used as the prestressing mechanism, the possibility of overstressing to account for relaxation may not exist. Very little work has been directed to this problem for materials other than concrete. Its importance will grow as elevated temperature environments are considered.

C. Monitoring Prestress Levels

The critical conditions for a prestressed member may be realized in both the loaded and unloaded states. The range between too little prestress and too much prestress can be quite narrow in highly efficient designs. Under these circumstances, precision is required in the application and maintenance of the prestress. The technology for monitoring the prestress state must be improved especially for embedded fibers and tendons and for compressive residual stresses induced into the surface layers of components.

D. Interface Treatment

We have observed that the behavior of segmented members is greatly influenced by interfaces which are not flat. Research is needed to discover physical means for eliminating or minimizing this influence. A preliminary investigation of this matter was undertaken by Barnett (1958). Load-deflection diagrams for a segmented titanium carbide column were obtained when shims of various materials and thicknesses were placed between the segments, when the interfaces were buttered with plaster, and when the interfaces were lapped. The shims were not found to be effective; lapping was. At low loads, the plaster provided the greatest stiffness. We note that segmented concrete structures and masonry structures use mortar between their elements with apparent success.

E. ANALYSIS OF SEGMENTED MEMBERS WITH NONFLAT INTERFACES

If the influence of imperfect interfaces cannot be eliminated because of hostile environments or limitations in technology, a considerable effort is contemplated to deal with the analysis of segmented structures. An excellent starting point for such investigations would be the column scaling problem, which might provide the basic input for all other types of components. Special difficulties can be visualized with shell segments because of their more complex interface geometries.

F. SEGMENTED PLATES WITH PERFECT INTERFACES

When separation occurs in a prestressed segmented plate, a method must be found for relating the effective moment of inertia of the cracked section to the external loading. Some features of the plate response problem are present in a prestressed segmented hyperstatic beam. We recommend that the latter element be studied prior to the plate investigation.

G. STABILITY OF PERFECT SEGMENTED ELEMENTS

Buckling problems arise naturally in segmented beams, plates, and shells; they are present whenever prestressing is accomplished with unconstrained tendons. We have observed that segmented beam columns entertain two equilibrium positions; one corresponds to the conventional response of a monolithic beam column and the other to rather large deflection states which are associated with behavior in the " cracked " range. Little is known about the stability of these latter equilibrium positions, and it is quite important that such information be developed. Several applications of segmented structures utilize the constant resistance and the energy absorbing characteristics one finds in the separated segment range. Investigations are required of the stability of plates and shells together with arbitrarily loaded segmented beams with multiple elastic tendons.

H. MINIMUM WEIGHT DESIGN OF PRESTRESSED ELEMENTS

Almost all of the work in the area of high performance prestressing has been concerned with analysis rather than design. There is a sufficient background to begin work on the design problem and the authors strongly advocate such an undertaking. There are several reasons for adopting this recommendation. First, the development of optimum designs of simple elements will enable the engineering community to evaluate rationally the potential of the prestressing technique. Second, minimum weight design tends to expose the inadequacies in the analysis capability. Also, the design orientation makes it possible to display the relative importance of the various problems entering into a design without fully or accurately characterizing their solution.

The design point of view will be helpful, and perhaps decisive, in selecting the best prestressing system in a given situation. Performance in various environments, such as elevated temperature, will be subject to quantitative evaluation. Further, we can expect an optimum design capability to outline shortcomings in our current manufacturing technology as it relates to prestressing and segmenting.

VII. Summary

To realize the considerable potential of brittle materials such as ceramics and cermets in high performance structures, it is necessary to circumvent the problems which attend brittleness and small available section size. One approach to this problem utilizes the techniques of prestressing and segmenting, and, indeed, the principal objective of this chapter has been the development of an analytical capability for predicting the behavior of prestressed monolithic and segmented brittle structures from a knowledge of the behavior of their component elements. An attempt is made to describe the significant characteristics of basic beam, column, and plate structures, and the main features of our investigation of these elements are outlined in this summary.

There are several topics of considerable importance that have been summarily dealt with because they are either too little known or too well known, e.g., techniques for applying, maintaining, or monitoring states of prestress, deterministic analysis of monolithic structures, such as prestressed concrete components, and the stability of segmented elements. .

A. The Theory of Perfect Segmented Beams

A mathematical model is developed to describe the linear and nonlinear response of prestressed segmented beams with perfectly flat interfaces. The theory is verified by carefully performed experiments on a member fabricated from precision tungsten carbide gage blocks. The characteristics of rectangular beams under simple loadings are explored when the prestress is applied with zero stiffness or elastic tendons. The theory is then extended to arbitrary cross sections with multiple elastic tendons.

B. LIMIT ANALYSIS OF SEGMENTED BEAMS

The load-deflection curves of segmented beams are found to possess features similar to those of an elastic-perfectly plastic member. This suggests the possibility of using limit analysis to describe the collapse load of segmented beams, and this idea is briefly explored by means of tests conducted on a 16-foot tubular aluminum oxide beam with a circular cross section. Remarkably accurate predictions are obtained for several different types of loading.

C. MONOLITHIC PRESTRESSED BEAMS

After reviewing the important properties of conventional deterministic analysis of prestressed monolithic beams with constrained tendons, a modification is introduced to include beam column action. This work is expanded to account for materials whose tensile strength is statistically characterized. A reasonable correlation is obtained between the predicted strength distribution for square prestressed beams and that obtained experimentally for plaster beam columns. The local transverse tensile strength of beams and the attendant spalling and chipping resistance generally improve under an axial compressive prestress. A combined stress theory is proposed from which this improvement may be estimated.

D. TRANSVERSE CRACKING PHENOMENON

Cracking in a direction transverse to a uniaxial compressive load was first recognized by F. R. Shanley to be a major deterrent to the application of prestressing to segmented members. The authors hypothesize that the interface roughness causes this cracking. To support this view, the following evidence was established:

a. Column strength increases with increasing flatness.

b. Specimens increase in compressive strength with decreasing cross sectional area.

c. Internal transverse crack lenses can be observed in glass columns ($2 \times 4 \times \frac{1}{2}$ inches).

d. Photoelastic and two-dimensional elasticity results indicate that an uneven load distribution on a segment will cause internal tensile stresses in directions parallel to the interfaces.

e. Triaxial compressive tests indicate a substantial increase in axial strength when a lateral prestress is imposed.

E. STIFFNESS OF SEGMENTED MEMBERS WITH NONFLAT INTERFACES

The slopes associated with the compressive stress-strain diagram of a segmented column increase with increasing stress. This behavior is explained by observing that the contact area increases with axial load, and, hence, the stiffness correspondingly increases. A statistical theory is proposed for scaling the tangent moduli of different height segmented columns. Data obtained for various size segmented glass columns provides partial support of the height scaling hypothesis; i.e., the distribution of tangent moduli is Gaussian. A brief experimental investigation of plaster columns indicates that cracks are not necessarily arrested at the segment interfaces and, further, that nature may prefer the prismatic shape for short struts.

The behavior of segmented beams is greatly influenced by nonflat

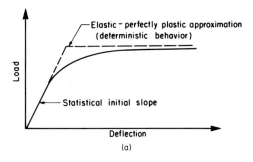

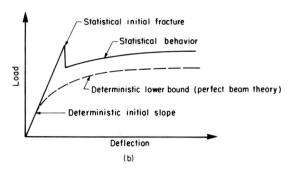

Fig. 49. General response characteristics of prestressed bending members: (a) prestressed segmented bending behavior for nonflat interfaces; (b) prestressed monolithic bending behavior.

interfaces. The linear response is highly statistical in nature; the limiting behavior in the nonlinear range tends to be deterministic. A slight modification of the perfect segmented beam theory is described which provides a promising technique for approximating the load-deflection curve for beams with nonflat interfaces; an exact treatment of the problem is expected to be quite demanding. The general response characteristics of an imperfect segmented beam prestressed with zero stiffness tendons are summarized in Fig. 49a.

F. PRESTRESSED PLATES

The theory of limit analysis was applied to prestressed segmented circular plates, and the resulting predictions agreed closely with results obtained from preliminary experiments performed on plaster disks. Theoretically, this theory provides a lower bound to the strength of monolithic prestressed brittle plates, and tests conducted on such elements support this prediction. The bending characteristics of prestressed elements are typified in Fig. 48b, where we observe that the integrity is not forfeit when local fractures occur.

Appendix A. Segmented Beams with Arbitrary Cross Sections and Multiple Tendons

1. GENERAL RELATIONSHIPS FOR MULTIPLE TENDONS

In this appendix, relationships are developed for extending the perfect beam theory to arbitrary symmetric cross sections with multiple elastic tendons. The resulting theory is verified experimentally using a segmented beam constructed from tungsten carbide gage blocks.

Referring to the beam cross section shown in Fig. A-1, let us define the

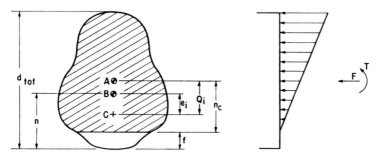

FIG. A-1. Geometry of cracked arbitrary symmetric cross section: A, cracked centroid; B, uncracked centroid; C, ith tendon.

following geometric quantities: d_{tot}, total beam depth; f, crack penetration or total segment separation; e_i, eccentricity of the ith tendon about the uncracked centroid; Q_i, eccentricity of the ith tendon about the cracked centroid; n_c, distance from the cracked centroid to the bottom fiber of the cracked cross section; n, distance from the uncracked centroid to the bottom fiber of the uncracked beam. From these definitions, Q_i may be written as

$$Q_i = e_i + f + n_c - n \tag{A.1}$$

Then if F_i is the force in the ith tendon and M is the bending moment acting at the cross section, the resultant moment T about the cracked centroid becomes

$$T = M - \sum_{i=1}^{N} F_i Q_i \tag{A.2}$$

where N is the total number of tendons. We have found it convenient in our numerical computations to introduce the following definitions:

Resultant prestressing force F^0

$$F^0 = \sum_{i=1}^{N} F_i^0 \tag{A.3}$$

Resultant tendon force F

$$F = \sum_{i=1}^{N} F_i \tag{A.4}$$

Eccentricity of F^0 about the uncracked centroid e

$$e = \frac{\sum_{i=1}^{N} F_i^0 e_i}{F^0} \tag{A.5}$$

Total algebraic eccentricity of the tendons about the uncracked centroid Q

$$Q = \sum_{i=1}^{N} Q_i \tag{A.6}$$

Moment of F about F^0, M_T

$$M_T = F\left(\frac{\sum_{i=1}^{N} F_i e_i}{F} - \frac{\sum_{i=1}^{N} F_i^0 e_i}{F^0}\right) \tag{A.7}$$

Note: $M_T = 0$ when $F_i = F_i^0$

$M_T = 0$ when $e_1 = e_2 = \cdots = e_N$

2. CRACK PENETRATION

Using the various definitions, we can rewrite T as

$$T = M - M_T - F(e + f + n_c - n) \qquad (A.8)$$

Now, referring to Eq. (6), we can determine the crack penetration f from the "zero stress" condition at the top of the crack,

$$\sigma_{bot} = 0 = -(F/A_c) + (Tn_c/I_c) \qquad (A.9)$$

Combining Eqs. (A.8) and (A.9) yields

$$(M - M_T)/F = e + f + n_c - n + (I_c/n_c A_c) \qquad (A.10)$$

where

$$I_c = I_c(f), \qquad n_c = n_c(f), \qquad \text{and} \qquad A_c = A_c(f) \qquad (A.11)$$

In general, except for the rectangular cross section, Eq. (A.10) cannot be solved explicitly for f. To deal with this problem, we can define $W \equiv (M - M_T)/F$, tabulate W versus f, and use the table to accomplish

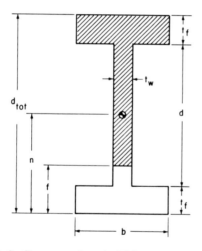

FIG. A-2. Geometry of cracked I-beam cross section.

inversion and, thus, obtain $f = f(W)$. The cross sectional properties of the I-beam dramatically illustrate the possible complexity of the terms entering into Eq. (A.10).

Using the dimensions of the I-beam shown in Fig. A-2, we obtain the following cross sectional properties:

Uncracked section properties ($f \equiv 0$)

$$A_0 = 2bt_f + dt_w$$

$$n = n_c = \frac{d_{tot}}{2} = t_f + \frac{d}{2} \tag{A.12}$$

$$I_0 = \frac{t_w d^3}{12} + \frac{bt_f^3}{6} + \frac{bt_f}{2}(d + t_f)^2$$

Cracked section properties

Case I: $(0 \leq f \leq t_f)$

$$A_c = b(t_f - f) + dt_w + bt_f$$

$$n_c = \frac{1}{A}[\tfrac{1}{2}b(t_f - f)^2 + dt_w(t_f + \tfrac{1}{2}d - f) + bt_f(\tfrac{3}{2}t_f + d - f)] \tag{A.13}$$

$$I_c = \tfrac{1}{12}[b(t_f - f)^3 + t_w d^3 + bt_f^3] + b(t_f - f)(n_c - \tfrac{1}{2}t_f + \tfrac{1}{2}f)^2$$
$$+ dt_w(n_c - \tfrac{1}{2}d - t_f + f)^2 + bt_f(\tfrac{3}{2}t_f + d - n_c - f)^2$$

Case II: $(t_f \leq f \leq t_f + d)$

$$A_c = (t_f + d - f)t_w + bt_f$$

$$n_c = \frac{1}{A}[\tfrac{1}{2}t_w(t_f + d - f)^2 + bt_f(\tfrac{3}{2}t_f + d - f)] \tag{A.14}$$

$$I_c = \tfrac{1}{12}[t_w(t_f + d - f)^3 + bt_f^3] + t_w(t_f + d - f)$$
$$\cdot (n_c - \tfrac{1}{2}t_f - \tfrac{1}{2}d + \tfrac{1}{2}f)^2 + bt_f(\tfrac{3}{2}t_f + d - n_c - f)^2$$

Case III: $(t_f + d \leq f \leq 2t_f + d)$

$$A_c = b(2t_f + d - f)$$

$$n_c = t_f + \tfrac{1}{2}d - \tfrac{1}{2}f \tag{A.15}$$

$$I_c = \tfrac{1}{12}b(2t_f + d - f)^3$$

3. Beam Deflections

Using the virtual work method described by Eq. (1), we can write down all of the deflection and end rotation relationships of interest.

Uncracked beam

$$M = 0: \qquad \Delta_0(x_\Delta) = \frac{-F^0 e x_\Delta (L - x_\Delta)}{2EI_0} \qquad (A.16)$$

$$2\theta_0 = \frac{-F^0 e L}{EI_0} \qquad (A.17)$$

where I_0 is the uncracked moment of inertia.

$$M > 0: \qquad \Delta_1(x_\Delta) = \int_0^L \frac{(M - Fe)}{EI_0} m_\Delta \, dx \qquad (A.18)$$

$$2\theta_1 = \int_0^L \frac{(M - Fe) \cdot 1}{EI_0} \, dx \qquad (A.19)$$

where the virtual moments are

$$m_\Delta = \left(1 - \frac{x_\Delta}{L}\right) x, \qquad \text{for} \quad 0 \leq x \leq x_\Delta$$

$$\qquad\qquad\qquad\qquad\qquad\qquad\qquad\qquad\qquad (A.20)$$

$$m_\Delta = \frac{x_\Delta}{L} (L - x), \qquad \text{for} \quad x_\Delta \leq x \leq L$$

Cracked beam

$$\Delta_2(x_\Delta) = \int_S \frac{(M - Fe)}{EI_0} m_\Delta \, dx + \int_{S_c} \frac{T m_\Delta}{EI_c} \, dx \qquad (A.21)$$

$$\theta_{L,R} = \int_S \frac{(M - Fe)}{EI_0} m_{L,R} \, dx + \int_{S_c} \frac{T m_{L,R}}{EI_c} \, dx \qquad (A.22)$$

where

$$m_L = [1 - (x/L)], \qquad m_R = x/L \qquad (A.23)$$

4. TENDON FORCES

a. Unconstrained Tendons

When the tendons are attached only at the ends of a beam, an accurate determination of the tendon forces can be obtained by taking three separate length changes into account:

$\Delta L'$ caused by end rotations
$\Delta L''$ caused by axial compression
$\Delta L'''$ caused by beam deflections

These effects are listed in descending order of importance. The total change in length at any stage is

$$\Delta L = \Delta L' + \Delta L'' + \Delta L''' \tag{A.24}$$

We shall separately consider each load range for the ith tendon.

Uncracked range, $M = 0$. $\Delta L'$: under the influence of an eccentric resultant prestressing force, each end of the beam will rotate through a small angle θ_0. Since the ith tendon is held at a distance e_i from the uncracked centroid, the ends of the tendon will move apart. The horizontal movement is approximately

$$(\Delta L_0')_i = 2\theta_0 e_i \tag{A.25}$$

$\Delta L''$: the compression stresses due to the prestress tend to shorten the beam by an amount

$$\Delta L_0'' = -F^0 L / A_0 E \tag{A.26}$$

$\Delta L'''$: whenever a change in the shape of the deflection curve takes place on a simply supported beam, the centroids at the ends of the beam move together. This displacement is equal to the difference between the length of the deflection curve and the length of the chord L; L is the length of the unstressed beam. We note that the difference between the length of an element ds of the curve and the corresponding element dx of the chord is equal to

$$ds - dx = dx \, [1 + (d\Delta/dx)^2]^{1/2} - dx \approx \tfrac{1}{2}(d\Delta/dx)^2 \, dx \tag{A.27}$$

Hence,

$$\Delta L_0''' = \frac{1}{2} \int_0^L \left\{ \frac{d[\Delta_0(x_\Delta)]}{dx_\Delta} \right\}^2 dx_\Delta \tag{A.28}$$

The total change in the length of the ith tendon for $M = 0$ is

$$(\Delta L_0)_i = (\Delta L_0')_i + \Delta L_0'' + \Delta L_0''' \tag{A.29}$$

Uncracked range, $M > 0$.

$$(\Delta L_1')_i = 2\theta_i e_i \tag{A.30}$$

$$\Delta L_1'' = -FL/EA_0 \tag{A.31}$$

$$\Delta L_1''' = \frac{1}{2} \int_0^L \left\{ \frac{d[\Delta_1(x_\Delta)]}{dx_\Delta} \right\}^2 dx_\Delta \tag{A.32}$$

$$(\Delta L_1)_i = (\Delta L_1')_i + \Delta L_1'' + \Delta L_1''' \tag{A.33}$$

Cracked range.

$$(\Delta L_2')_i = \theta_L(Q_L)_i + \theta_R(Q_R)_i \tag{A.34}$$

where the subscripts L and R refer to the left and right ends of the beam, respectively.

$$\Delta L_2'' = -\int_S \frac{F}{AE_0}\,dx - \int_{S_c} \frac{F}{EA_c}\,dx \tag{A.35}$$

$$\Delta L_2''' = \frac{1}{2}\int_0^L \left\{\frac{d[\Delta_2(x_\Delta)]}{dx_\Delta}\right\}^2 dx_\Delta \tag{A.36}$$

$$(\Delta L_2)_i = (\Delta L_2')_i + \Delta L_2'' + \Delta L_2''' \tag{A.37}$$

We shall now use the geometric relationships given in Eqs. (A.24)–(A.37) to find the tendon forces in the cracked and uncracked ranges. In the uncracked range, the total change in the length of the ith tendon is

$$(\Delta L)_i = (\Delta L_1)_i - (\Delta L_0)_i \tag{A.38}$$

This change in length must match that produced in the ith tendon by the action of the induced force $F_i - F_i^0$. Thus,

$$\frac{(F_i - F_i^0)l_i}{A_t E_t} = (\Delta L)_i = (\Delta L_1)_i - (\Delta L_0)_i \tag{A.39}$$

where l_i is the original length of the ith tendon before prestressing and where every tendon has the same stiffness $A_t E_t$. To find l_i, we observe that, when the prestress acts alone, the distance between the points of attachment of the ith tendon $L + (\Delta L_0)_i$, must equal the length of the tendon under F_i^0, $l_i + (l_i F_i^0/E_t A_t)$. Therefore,

$$l_i = \left[\frac{L + (AL_0)_i}{1 + (F_i^0/E_t A_t)}\right] \tag{A.40}$$

Substituting for the ΔL's in Eq. (A.39), we obtain expressions for the individual tendon forces F_i:

$$\frac{(F_i - F_i^0)l_i}{E_t A_t} = 2e_i(\theta_1 - \theta_0) - \frac{(F - F^0)L}{EA_0} + \frac{1}{2}\int_0^L \left[\left(\frac{d\Delta_1}{dx_\Delta}\right)^2 - \left(\frac{d\Delta_0}{dx_\Delta}\right)^2\right]dx_\Delta,$$
$$i = 1, 2, \ldots, N \tag{A.41}$$

Summing over the i's, approximating l_i by L, and using the definitions given by Eqs. (A.3) and (A.4), we arrive at

$$\frac{(F - F^0)L}{E_t A_t} = 2(\theta_1 - \theta_0)\sum_{i=1}^{N} e_i - \frac{(F - F^0)LN}{EA_0} + \frac{N}{2}\int_0^L \left[\left(\frac{d\Delta_1}{dx_\Delta}\right)^2 - \left(\frac{d\Delta_0}{dx_\Delta}\right)^2\right]dx_\Delta \tag{A.42}$$

from which F may be determined numerically for every specified loading. Once F has been obtained, the F_i's can be found from Eq. (A.41).

In the cracked range, the total change in the tendon length $(\Delta L)_i$ is

$$\frac{(F_i - F_i{}^0)l_i}{E_t A_t} = (\Delta L)_i = (\Delta L_2)_i - (\Delta L_0)_i \tag{A.43}$$

Again, eliminating the ΔL's, we obtain

$$\frac{(F_i - F_i{}^0)l_i}{E_t A_t} = \theta_L (Q_L)_i + \theta_R (Q_R)_i - 2\theta_0 e_i$$

$$-\frac{F}{E}\left[\int_S \frac{dx}{A_0} + \int_{S_c} \frac{dx}{A_c}\right] + \frac{F^0 L}{EA_0}$$

$$+\frac{1}{2}\int_0^L \left[\left(\frac{d\Delta_2}{dx_\Delta}\right)^2 - \left(\frac{d\Delta_0}{dx_\Delta}\right)^2\right] dx_\Delta, \tag{A.44}$$

$$i = 1, 2, \ldots, N$$

Approximating l_i by L, we may sum these equations for each i; thus,

$$\frac{(F - F^0)L}{E_t A_t} = \theta_L Q_L + \theta_R Q_R - 2\theta_0 \sum_{i=1}^N e_i$$

$$-\frac{FN}{E}\left[\int_S \frac{dx}{A_0} - \int_{S_c} \frac{dx}{A_c}\right] + \frac{F^0 NL}{EA_0}$$

$$+\frac{N}{2}\int_0^L \left[\left(\frac{d\Delta_2}{dx_\Delta}\right)^2 - \left(\frac{d\Delta_0}{dx_\Delta}\right)^2\right] dx_\Delta \tag{A.45}$$

This equation must be solved numerically for F for every specified loading. With F determined, Eqs. (A.44) furnish us with the individual tendon forces. It should be noted that we have ignored any beam column effect that might be present in the unconstrained tendon problem. This procedure is justified only as long as the tendon force F is much smaller than the buckling load of the beam as is frequently the case.

b.   Constrained Tendons

To preclude buckling, the tendons can be constrained to deflect with the beam. In such cases, the axial shortening $\Delta L''$ is the same as that calculated for the unconstrained tendons; the change in length due to bending will be treated in this subsection.

Let us begin by finding the length of the ith tendon when the beam is in the cracked range. From Fig. A-3, it is clear that the angle $d\theta$ associated

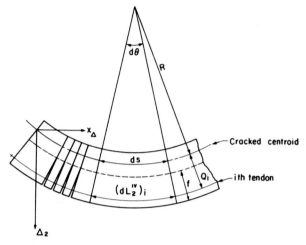

FIG. A-3. Prestressed segmented beam with constrained tendons.

with the arc ds on the cracked centroid is given by

$$d\theta = ds/R = (dx_\Delta/R)[1 + (d\Delta_2/dx_\Delta)^2]^{1/2} \tag{A.46}$$

where R is the radius of curvature of the uncracked portion of the beam. The radius is related to the moment on the section by the familiar relationship

$$1/R = T/EI_c \tag{A.47}$$

We may now calculate the infinitesimal tendon length $(dL_2^{iv})_i$ by observing that the tendon radius is $R + Q_i$,

$$(dL_2^{iv})_i = d\theta(R + Q_i) \tag{A.48}$$

Then, the length $(L_2^{iv})_i$ is given by

$$(L_2^{iv})_i = \int_0^L \left(1 + \frac{TQ_i}{EI_c}\right)\left[1 + \left(\frac{d\Delta_2}{dx_\Delta}\right)^2\right]^{1/2} dx_\Delta \tag{A.49}$$

For the uncracked range in which $M > 0$, we find

$$d\theta = \frac{dx_\Delta}{R}\left[1 + \left(\frac{d\Delta_1}{dx_\Delta}\right)^2\right]^{1/2} \tag{A.50}$$

$$\frac{1}{R} = \frac{M - Fe}{EI_0} \tag{A.51}$$

$$(dL_1^{iv})_i = d\theta(R + e_i) \tag{A.52}$$

$$(L_1^{iv})_i = \int_0^L \left[1 + \frac{(M - Fe)e_i}{EI_0}\right]\left[1 + \left(\frac{d\Delta_1}{dx_\Delta}\right)^2\right]^{1/2} dx_\Delta \tag{A.53}$$

Finally, when the beam is subjected only to the prestressing force F^0, we have

$$d\theta = \frac{dx_\Delta}{R} \left[1 + \left(\frac{d\Delta_0}{dx_\Delta}\right)^2\right]^{1/2} \tag{A.54}$$

$$\frac{1}{R} = \frac{-F^0 e}{EI_0} \tag{A.55}$$

$$(dL_0^{\text{iv}})_i = d\theta(R + e_i) \tag{A.56}$$

$$(L_0^{\text{iv}})_i = \int_0^L \left(1 - \frac{F^0 e e_i}{EI_0}\right)\left[1 + \left(\frac{d\Delta_0}{dx_\Delta}\right)^2\right]^{1/2} dx_\Delta \tag{A.57}$$

The tendon forces in the uncracked beam may be calculated by recalling that the increased length of the ith tendon is caused by the induced force $F_i - F_i^0$; consequently,

$$\frac{(F_i - F_i^0)l_i}{(A_t E_t)_i} = [(L_1^{\text{iv}})_i + \Delta L_1''] - [(L_0^{\text{iv}})_i + \Delta L_0''], \tag{A.58}$$

$$i = 1, 2, \ldots, N$$

where $(A_t E_t)_i$ is the product of the area and Young's modulus for the ith tendon. For the cracked range,

$$\frac{(F_i - F_i^0)l_i}{(A_t E_t)_i} = [(L_2^{\text{iv}})_i + \Delta L_2''] - [(L_0^{\text{iv}})_i + \Delta L_0''], \tag{A.59}$$

$$i = 1, 2, \ldots, N$$

To find l_i we equate the tendon length under F_i^0 to $[(L_0^{\text{iv}})_i + \Delta L_0'']$,

$$l_i = \left[\frac{L_0^{\text{iv}} + \Delta L_0''}{1 + [F_i^0/(A_t E_t)_i]}\right] \tag{A.60}$$

When the appropriate expressions for the L's and ΔL's are substituted into Eqs. (A.58) and (A.59), each set of these equations, together with Eq. (A.4), may be solved simultaneously for F and the F_i's. Once the tendon forces are known for a given loading, all of the associated response quantities may be readily determined; e.g., W, f, M_T from Eq. (A.7) and the beam deflections from Eqs. (A.16), (A.18), and (A.21). If the quantity $(l/A_t E_t)$ is the same for all tendons, we may sum Eqs. (A.58) and (A.59) over i to obtain a single equation for F in both the cracked and uncracked ranges.

5. VERIFICATION OF THE PERFECT BEAM THEORY

Of the various assumptions entering into the deflection analysis of segmented beams, the most difficult to realize physically is that the segment interfaces be perfectly flat. To approach this condition experimentally, a segmented beam was fabricated from 80 tungsten carbide gage blocks with the dimensions $1 \times 2 \times \frac{1}{4}$ inches. The gage block faces were no more than one-half lightband out of flat as measured with optical flats using a monochromatic helium light source with a wavelength of 23.1×10^{-6} inch. As shown in Fig. A-4, the compression load-deflection diagram for an 18.75-inch column is linear down to very low loads and has a slope equal to that of a monolithic tungsten carbide bar in the higher load range, the slope corresponds to a modulus of elasticity of about 92×10^{6} psi.

Using the experimental setup shown in Fig. A-5, two terminal couple-end rotation diagrams were obtained for prestressing forces of 4 and 14 kips. These diagrams are compared, in Fig. A-6, with theoretical predictions based on the perfect beam theory. Excellent agreement is found in the 14-kip case and good agreement in the 4-kip case. We expect that the influence of the nonlinearity in the compressive load-deflection diagram is better suppressed with the higher prestressing force.

The tendon forces in the upper and lower pairs of tendons used on the

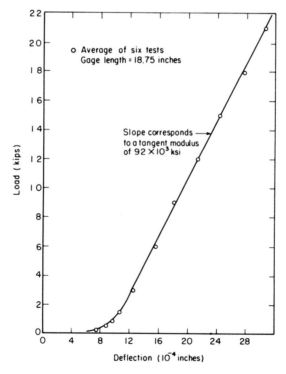

FIG. A-4. Compression load-deflection diagram for a segmented tungsten carbide column (gage length = 18.75 inches).

FIG. A-5. Prestressed segmented tungsten carbide beam with experimental setup.

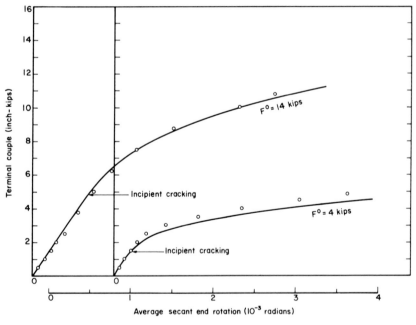

FIG. A-6. Terminal couple-end rotation diagrams for a prestressed segmented tungsten carbide beam.

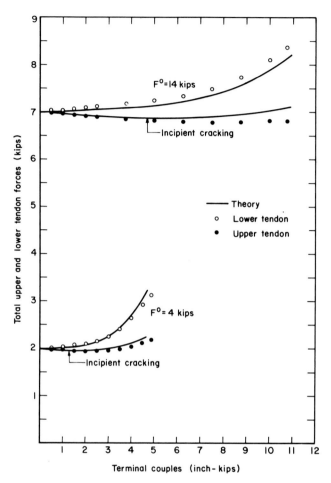

FIG. A-7. Tendon force-terminal couple diagrams for a prestressed segmented tungsten carbide beam.

beam were monitored by strain gages. The predicted tendon forces are compared to the measured values in Fig. A-7 where the agreement is found to be quite good. A detailed description of the tungsten carbide beam experiments can be found in Barnett and Hermann (1966).

Appendix B. Eccentrically Loaded Segmented Beam Columns

In this appendix, the response of an eccentrically loaded segmented beam column of rectangular cross section will be determined. Referring to Fig. B-1, we define T to be the resultant moment acting upon an arbitrary

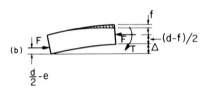

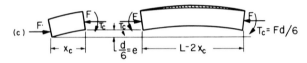

FIG. B-1. Free body diagram of a segmented beam column. (a) beam column geometry, (b) free body for determination of resultant moment T, (c) free body diagrams for cracked and uncracked regions.

section of the beam column and thus,

$$T = F(\Delta + e - \tfrac{1}{2}f) \tag{B.1}$$

The crack penetration f, which is determined from the condition that the stress at the tip of the crack is zero (see Sect. II,A,1), is readily found to be

(a) For uncracked sections: $f = 0$

(b) For cracked sections: $f = d - (6T/F)$

$$\tag{B.2}$$

Eliminating T between Eqs. (B.1) and (B.2), we obtain for cracked sections

$$f = 3\Delta + 3e - (d/2) \tag{B.3}$$

Thus, it is readily observed that the requirement for the cross section to be cracked, $0 < f < d$, implies that $d/6 - e < \Delta < d/2 - e$. Thus, Eq. (B.2) becomes

$$f = 0 \qquad\qquad \text{when} \quad 0 \leq \Delta \leq (d/6) - e$$
$$f = d - (6T/F) \qquad \text{when} \quad (d/6) - e < \Delta < (d/2) - e$$

$$\tag{B.4}$$

and Eq. (B.1) may be written as

$$T = F(\Delta + e) \qquad \text{when} \quad 0 < \Delta < (d/6) - e$$
$$T = (F/2)[(d/2) - e - \Delta] \qquad \text{when} \quad (d/6) - e < \Delta < (d/2) - e \qquad \text{(B.5)}$$

Recalling Eq. (4) for the moment of inertia of a rectangular cross section

$$I_c = b(d - f)^3/12 \qquad \text{(B.6)}$$

and using Eq. (B.4), we obtain

$$I = I_0 \equiv bd^3/12 \qquad \text{when} \quad 0 \leq \Delta \leq (d/6) - e$$
$$I = 18b(T/F)^3 \qquad \text{when} \quad (d/6) - e < \Delta < (d/2) - e \qquad \text{(B.7)}$$

Now, the governing differential equation for the deflection curve from elementary beam theory is

$$EI\, d^2\Delta/dx_\Delta{}^2 = -T \qquad \text{(B.8)}$$

Using Eqs. (B.5) and (B.7) to express T and I in terms of Δ, the differential equation becomes:

(1)   Uncracked region $(0 \leq \Delta \leq (d/6) - e)$

$$d^2\Delta/dx_\Delta{}^2 + k^2\Delta = -k^2 e \qquad \text{(B.9)}$$

where

$$k^2 \equiv F/EI_0 \qquad \text{(B.10)}$$

(2)   Cracked region $((d/6) - e < \Delta < (d/2) - e)$

$$d^2\Delta/dx_\Delta{}^2 = -(k^2 d^3/54)[(d/2) - e - \Delta]^{-2} \qquad \text{(B.11)}$$

Thus, it appears that two situations are possible; (1) the entire beam column is uncracked, and (2) a central portion of the beam column is cracked with the remainder being uncracked. The case of the entire beam column being cracked is not permitted due to the boundary conditions requiring zero deflections at the ends.

Case I: Monolithic Behavior. The entire beam column is uncracked; thus, $\Delta_{max} = \Delta(L/2) \leq (d/6) - e$. The associated differential equation is

$$d^2\Delta/dx_\Delta{}^2 + k^2\Delta = -k^2 e \qquad \text{(B.12)}$$

and the boundary conditions are

$$\Delta(0) = \Delta(L) = 0 \qquad \text{(B.13)}$$

The solution for the deflection curve is readily found to be

$$\Delta = e\left[\frac{\cos k[x_\Delta - (L/2)]}{\cos (kL/2)} - 1\right] \tag{B.14}$$

If we define $k = k_c$ when $\Delta(L/2) = (d/6) - e$, we obtain

$$k_c = (2/L) \cos^{-1}(6e/d) \tag{B.15}$$

and, since $k_c{}^2 = F_c/EI_0$, the load which causes incipient cracking, F_c, becomes

$$F_c = (4EI_0/L^2)[\cos^{-1}(6e/d)]^2 \tag{B.16}$$

Note that taking the limit of F_c as e goes to zero yields the monolithic Euler buckling load. Also observe that, in the special case $e = 0$, we obtain $\Delta \equiv 0$, unless $F = \pi^2 EI_0/L^2$, in which case $\Delta(L/2)$ is indeterminate, and any value less than or equal to $(d/6) - e$ is permissible.

Case II: Cracked Behavior. It is convenient to utilize the fact that the deflection curve is symmetric about $x_\Delta = L/2$ and consider only the left half of the beam column. Referring to Fig. B-1, let $x_\Delta = x_c$ designate the location of the boundary between the uncracked portion (region I) and the cracked portion (region II) of the beam column. Note, by definition, $\Delta(x_c) = (d/6) - e$.

In region I, we again have the differential equation

$$d^2\Delta/dx_\Delta{}^2 + k^2\Delta = -k^2e \tag{B.17}$$

only now the boundary conditions are

$$\Delta(0) = 0 \tag{B.18}$$

$$\Delta(x_c) = (d/6) - e \tag{B.19}$$

$$d\Delta/dx_\Delta\big|_{x_\Delta = x_c} = \theta \tag{B.20}$$

The extra boundary condition arises from the unknown location of x_c. The solution of this set of equations may be expressed as

$$\Delta = \left[\frac{\theta + ek \sin kx_c}{k \cos kx_c}\right] \sin kx_\Delta + e(\cos kx_\Delta - 1) \tag{B.21}$$

where θ is related to x_c through

$$\theta = \frac{k[(d/6) \cos kx_c - e]}{\sin kx_c} \tag{B.22}$$

In region II, the differential equation is

$$d^2\Delta/dx_\Delta{}^2 = -(k^2d^3/54)[(d/2) - e - \Delta]^{-2} \tag{B.23}$$

and the boundary conditions are

$$d\Delta/dx_\Delta\big|_{x_\Delta=L/2} = 0 \tag{B.24}$$

$$\Delta(x_c) = (d/6) - e \tag{B.25}$$

$$d\Delta/dx_\Delta\big|_{x_\Delta=x_c} = \theta \tag{B.26}$$

Equation (B.24) ensures symmetry about $x_\Delta = L/2$ and Eqs. (B.25) and (B.26) preserve continuity in deflection and slope between regions I and II. We can integrate Eq. (B.23) at once to yield

$$\frac{dx_\Delta}{d\Delta} = \left[C_1^2 - \frac{k^2 d^3}{27[(d/2) - e - \Delta]} \right]^{1/2} \tag{B.27}$$

It is convenient to introduce the following change in the dependent variable:

$$\Delta = \frac{d}{2} - e - \frac{k^2 d^3}{27 C_1^2} \cosh^2 z \tag{B.28}$$

Then, Eq. (B.27) becomes

$$\frac{dz}{dx_\Delta} = -\frac{27 C_1^3}{2 k^2 d^3} (\cosh z)^{-2} \tag{B.29}$$

which is readily integrated to yield

$$x_\Delta = -\frac{k^2 d^3}{27 C_1^3} (z + \tfrac{1}{2} \sinh 2z) + C_2 \tag{B.30}$$

Using Eq. (B.24), it is found that $z = 0$ when $x_\Delta = L/2$, and, hence, Eq. (B.30) yields $C_2 = L/2$. Now, when $x_\Delta = x_c$, we define $z = z_c$, and, thus, Eq. (B.30) implies that

$$x_c = -\frac{k^2 d^3}{27 C_1^3} (z_c + \tfrac{1}{2} \sinh 2z_c) + \frac{L}{2} \tag{B.31}$$

Using Eqs. (B.26) and (B.28) we obtain

$$\theta = C_1 \tanh z_c \tag{B.32}$$

Finally, Eq. (B.25), together with Eq. (B.28), yields

$$\cosh z_c = 3C_1/kd \tag{B.33}$$

Thus, the four parameters θ, C_1, x_c, and z_c are determined by the simultaneous solution of Eqs. (B.22), (B.31), (B.32), and (B.33).

A somewhat simpler form is obtained if we define

$$\alpha \equiv \cosh z_c \tag{B.34}$$

and then eliminate θ, C_1 and z_c:

$$\frac{kL}{2} = \phi - \psi \pm \cos^{-1}[(6e/d) \cos \psi] \tag{B.35}$$

$$\frac{2x_c}{L} = 1 - \frac{\phi}{\phi - \psi + \cos^{-1}[(6e/d) \cos \psi]} \tag{B.36}$$

where

$$\phi \equiv (1/\alpha^3)[\cosh^{-1}\alpha + \alpha(\alpha^2 - 1)^{1/2}] \tag{B.37}$$

$$\psi \equiv \tan^{-1} 2(\alpha^2 - 1)^{1/2} \tag{B.38}$$

The solution for the deflection curve becomes

(1)   for $0 \le x_\Delta \le x_c$

$$\Delta = \left[\frac{(d/3)(\alpha^2 - 1)^{1/2} + e \sin kx_c}{\cos kx_c}\right] \sin kx_\Delta + e(\cos kx_\Delta - 1) \tag{B.39}$$

(2)   for $x_c \le x_\Delta \le L/2$

$$\Delta = (d/2) - e - (d/3\alpha^2) \cosh^2 z \tag{B.40}$$

$$x_\Delta = (L/2) - (1/k\alpha^3)(z + \tfrac{1}{2} \sinh 2z) \tag{B.41}$$

By definition given in Eq. (B.34), we find that $\alpha \ge 1$, and, hence, that the central deflection

$$\Delta(L/2) = (d/2) - e - (d/3\alpha^2) \tag{B.42}$$

increases with increasing α and the $\lim_{\alpha \to \infty} \Delta(L/2) = (d/2) - e$. The behavior of $kL/2$ and $2x_c/L$ as functions of α are depicted in Figs. B-2a and B-2b, where they are plotted for the cases $e = 0$ and $e/d = \tfrac{1}{12}$. It is significant to note that, except for a possible brief rise, $kL/2$ decreases with increasing α and that $2x_c/L$ seems to have a minimum value with respect to α.

Using the results of both Case I and Case II and Eq. (B.42), the load parameter $kL/2$ can now be plotted as a function of the central deflection for $0 \le \Delta(L/2) \le (d/2) - e$. These curves for the cases $e = 0$ and $e/d = \tfrac{1}{12}$ are depicted in Fig. B-3, where the deflection has been nondimensionalized by dividing by d.

The most significant observation, with respect to Fig. B-3, is that it is possible for two different equilibrium deflection curves to exist for the same value of $kL/2$. For $e/d < \frac{1}{6}$ and $k < k_c$, Case I and Case II each yield an equilibrium deflection curve; for $0 < e/d < \frac{1}{6}$ and k slightly larger than k_c, Case II alone yields two different equilibrium deflection curves. A slightly modified version of Fig. B-3, in which the ordinate was squared to yield a plot of $FL^2/4EI_0$ versus $\Delta(L/2)/d$, is presented in Fig. 41.

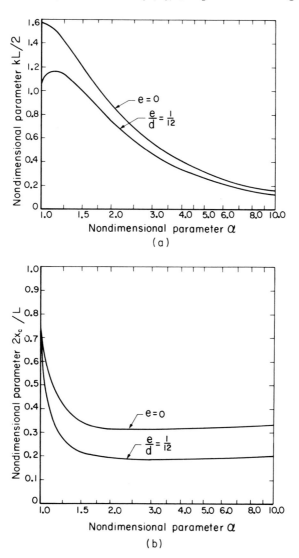

FIG. B-2. Analysis parameters for segmented beam columns. (a) Plot of $kL/2$ vs. α; (b) plot of $2x_c/L$ vs. α.

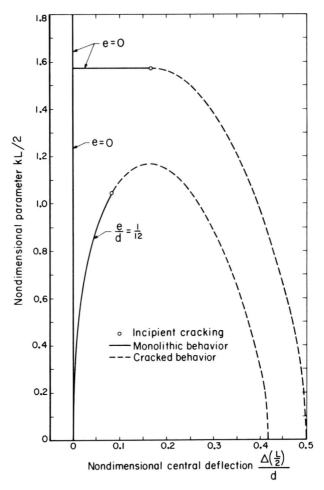

FIG. B-3. Response of a segmented beam column.

Symbols

A	(1) area of uncracked cross section	A_0	area of uncracked cross section
	(2) mean value of non-uniform loading on a strip	A_s	area of small column
		A_t	area of a tendon
		a	(1) $\equiv m\pi c/L$, parameter in nonuniformly loaded strip
A_c	area of cracked cross section		
A_{eff}	effective area		(2) radius of circular rod
A_L	area of large column		

$a_1, a_2, \ldots, a_n$	arbitary statistical parameters	F_c	(1) Euler buckling load for a monolithic column
$B \equiv F_{cr}/A\sigma_t$	dimensionless parameter in prestressed monolithic beams		(2) axial load at which cracking becomes incipient in segmented beam column
b	(1) width of rectangular cross section		
	(2) radius of support ring	F_{cr}	Euler load for beam
b_{eff}	effective rectangular beam width	F_i	force in the ith tendon
C	magnitude of terminal couples applied to beam	F_{opt}	optimum value for prestressing force for monolithic beams
C_c	value of C which causes cracking to become incipient	F^0	(1) initial single tendon force
C_1, C_2	integration constants		(2) resultant prestressing force
c	(1) distance between concentrated load Q and the end of the beam	f	(1) depth of crack penetration
	(2) half the depth of a strip		(2) function of the normal stress
d	(1) depth of uncracked rectangular cross section	$\bar{f}$	weighted normal stress vector
	(2) I-beam web depth	g	(1) function of stress appearing as integrand of Weibull statistical distribution
d_{tot}	total beam depth		(2) area of the weighted normal stress diagram
E	modulus of elasticity of beam		
E_t	(1) modulus of elasticity of tendon	h	height of column
	(2) tangent modulus of compressive stress-strain curve	I	moment of inertia of uncracked cross section
		I_c	moment of inertia of cracked cross section
e	(1) eccentricity of single tendon with respect to centroid of uncracked cross section	I_{eff}	moment of inertia of effective area
	(2) eccentricity of resultant prestressing force about uncracked centroid	I_0	moment of inertia of uncracked cross section
		i	integer number
		$k \equiv (F/E I_0)^{1/2}$	beam column parameter
e_i	eccentricity of the ith tendon about the uncracked centroid	L	(1) beam length
			(2) distance between concentrated loads Q in beam column
F	(1) single tendon force	L_t	tendon length
	(2) resultant tendon force	L_0	length of tendon with no transverse load on beam

L_1 length of tendon with load in uncracked range

L_2 length of tendon with load in cracked range

l length of beam column

l_i original length of ith tendon before prestressing

$(L_j^{iv})_i$ length of ith constrained tendon in: $j = 0$, unloaded condition; $j = 1$, uncracked range; $j = 2$, cracked range.

$M(x)$ applied bending moment distribution

$M \equiv I\sigma_t/n_t$ moment resistance of unprestressed beam

M_c value of applied bending moment which produces incipient cracking

M_0 limiting moment per unit length in plate

M_{opt} optimum moment resistance

M_p plastic moment of cross section

M_T moment due to F about the line of action of F^0

M_{ult} ultimate value of applied bending moment based on the compressive strength of the beam material

M_1, M_2 principal moments in plate

M_∞ value of applied bending moment which causes I_c to go to zero

$\mathcal{M}$ resultant bending moment

$m(x)$ bending moment distribution due to virtual loading

m (1) parameter of Weibull statistical distribution

(2) integer number

$m_\Delta(x)$ bending moment distribution due to virtual load at $x = x_\Delta$ and in the direction of the deflection

N (1) number of strength values

(2) total number of tendons

n (1) ratio of tangent modulus to asymptotic modulus

(2) statistical sample size

(3) $= A_L/A_S$, scaling parameter for segmented columns

(4) number of segments in circular plate

(5) distance from the uncracked centroid to the bottom fiber of the uncracked beam

n_b distance from the cracked centroid to the bottom fiber of the cracked cross section

n_c (1) distance from the cracked centroid to the outer fibers of the cracked rectangular cross section

(2) distance from the cracked centroid to the bottom fiber of the cracked cross section

n_t distance between the beams centroid and the top (compression) fibers

$P(E_t)$ cumulative stiffness distribution

$P_L(E_t)$ cumulative stiffness distribution for large column

$P_S(E_t)$ cumulative stiffness distribution for small column

$P(S_1, S_2)$ — probability of failure under the biaxial state of stress S_1, S_2

P — (1) central load on beam
(2) probability of failure
(3) central load on plate

P_c — fracture probability of a component

P_i — fracture probability of the ith volume

Q — (1) concentrated transverse load
(2) total algebraic eccentricity of the tendons about the uncracked centroid

Q_i — eccentricity of the ith tendon about the cracked centroid

R — (1) $\equiv (A_t E_t L)/(bd E L_t)$, nondimensional parameter in segmented beam under terminal couples
(2) outer radius of circular plate
(3) radius of curvature

r — arbitrary radius

S — (1) entire span of beam
(2) uncracked portion of beam

S_c — cracked portion of beam

S_1, S_2 — magnitude of the principal stresses in two dimensions

$\bar{S}_1, \bar{S}_2$ — principal stress vectors in two dimensions

s — arc length along beam

T — resultant moment about the cracked centroid

t — plate thickness

t_f — I-beam flange thickness

t_w — I-beam web thickness

u — deflection of a beam column

V — total volume of structural member

v — unit volume associated with Weibull statistical distribution

W — (1) resultant of uniform load on beam
(2) $\equiv (M - M_T)/F$, convenient variable in segmented I-beam

$w(x)$ — distributed load distribution

x — (1) coordinate along beam
(2) random variable

$\bar{x}$ — sample mean

x_c — location of boundary between cracked and uncracked portions of beam

x_Δ — location on beam where deflection is sought

y — coordinate perpendicular to axis of beam

y_u — limit of integration for probability of failure of beam

z — convenient segmented beam column variable

α — (1) $\equiv (A_t E_t)/(L L_t)$, parameter in segmented beam under terminal couples
(2) $\equiv \sigma_c/\sigma_t$, dimensionless parameter in prestressed monolithic beams
(3) $\equiv m\pi/L$, parameter in nonuniformly loaded strip
(4) $\equiv \cosh z_c$, parameter for segmented beam column

$\beta \equiv (F^0/2) - \alpha e\theta_0 L$ — parameter in segmented beam under terminal couples

$\gamma \equiv 2\alpha[e + (d/2)]$ — parameter in segmented beam under terminal couples

Δ — central plate deflection

$\Delta(x_\Delta)$ — deflection of beam at $x = x_\Delta$

Δ_0 deflection of beam under zero transverse loading

Δ_1 deflection of beam under less than cracking load

Δ_2 beam deflection for loads greater than cracking load

ΔL change in tendon length

$(\Delta L_j)_i$ total change in length of the ith unconstrained tendon in: $j = 0$, unloaded condition; $j = 1$, uncracked range; $j = 2$, cracked range

$(\Delta L_j')_i$ change in length of the ith unconstrained tendon due to end rotations in: $j = 0$, unloaded condition; $j = 1$, uncracked range; $j = 2$, cracked range

$\Delta L_j''$ change in length of unconstrained tendon due to axial compression in: $j = 0$, unloaded condition; $j = 1$, uncracked range; $j = 2$, cracked range

$\Delta L_j'''$ change in length of unconstrained tendon caused by beam deflections in: $j = 0$, unloaded condition; $j = 1$, uncracked range; $j = 2$, cracked range

δ beam shortening

ε_p average strain in plate due to prestress

θ (1) end rotation of beam (2) angle between $\overline{\sigma}_n$ and $\overline{S}_1$

θ_c slope of deflection curve at $x_\Delta = x_c$

$\theta_{L,R}$ left, right end rotation of beam

θ_0 (1) upper limit of integration (2) end rotation of beam under zero transverse loading

θ_1 end rotation of beam under less than cracking load

$\lambda \equiv n_b/n_t$ dimensionless parameter in prestressed monolithic beams

μ (1) $\equiv e/d$ nondimensional parameter in segmented beam under terminal couples (2) parameter and mean value of normal distribution

ν Poisson's ratio

ξ_1, ξ_2, ξ_3 space coordinates

σ (1) normal stress (2) magnitude of stress distribution (3) parameter and standard deviation of normal distribution

$\overline{\sigma}$ mean fracture stress

σ_b maximum fiber stress in bending

σ_{bot} stress in bottom fiber of beam

σ_c compressive strength of beam material

σ_i ith value of the fiber stress of fracture

σ_n magnitude of the normal stress at an angle θ with respect to $\overline{S}_1$

$\overline{\sigma}_n$ normal stress vector

σ_0 parameter of Weibull statistical distribution

σ_p magnitude of state of prestress

σ_s magnitude of shear stress in state of pure stress

σ_t	tensile strength of beam	ϕ	(1) normalized stress distribution
σ_{top}	stress in top fiber of beam		(2) convenient function of α for segmented beam column
σ_u	parameter of Weibull statistical distribution	ψ	convenient function of α for segmented beam column
$\sigma_x, \sigma_y, \tau_{xy}$	state of stress in two dimensions	ω	angle of rotation

REFERENCES

Ali, M. A., Chipman, R. D., Jurtz, P., and Knapp, W. J. (1964). "Load-Bearing Characteristics of Biaxially Prestressed Ceramic Plates," Report No. 64-40 (NASA Grant NsG-427). Department of Engineering, University of California.

Barnett, R. L. (1958). "Lightweight Structures and Prestressed Launcher Components" (Contract No. DA-11-070-508-ORD-588, Project No. TU2-70, Phase 2). Rock Island Arsenal.

Barnett, R. L. (1962). "On the Lifting Capacity of Crane Booms," Paper No. 62-WA-43. ASME, New York.

Barnett, R. L., and Hermann, P. C. (1966). "Studies in Prestressed and Segmented Brittle Structures," NASA CR-505.

Barnett, R. L., and McGuire, R. L. (1966). Am. Ceram. Soc. Bull. 45 (6), 595–602.

Barnett, R. L., Hermann, P. C., and Costello, J. F. (1964). "Prestressed Monolithic and Segmented Brittle Structures," NASA CR-113.

Barnett, R. L., Costello, J. F., Hermann, P. C., and Hofer, K. E. (1965). "The Behavior and Design of Brittle Structures," Report No. AFFDL-TR-65-165. Flight Dynamics Laboratory, Air Force Systems Command, Wright-Patterson Air Force Base, Dayton, Ohio.

Barnett, R. L., Hermann, P. C., Wingfield, J. R., and Connors, C. L. (1967). "Fracture of Brittle Materials under Transient Mechanical and Thermal Loading," Report No. AFFDL-TR-66-220. Flight Dynamics Laboratory, Air Force Systems Command, Wright-Patterson Air Force Base, Dayton, Ohio.

Berenbaum, R., and Brodie, I. (1959). Brit. J. Appl. Phys. 10, 281–287.

Bogardos, E. A., and Roy, R. (1963). J. Am. Ceram. Soc. 46, 573–576.

Clanton, J. R., Mueller, J. I., and Powell, H. R. (1953). The Trend in Engineering, July, 5–8.

Frocht, M. M. (1951). "Strength of Materials," pp. 227–228. Ronald Press, New York.

Fuchs, H. O., and Hutchinson, E. R. (1958). Machine Design 30 (3), 116–125.

Gumbel, E. J. (1960). "Statistics of Extremes," p. 76. Columbia Univ. Press, New York.

Harris, A. J. (1957). Engineering 184 (4772), 244–246.

Hoel, P. (1954). "Introduction to Mathematical Statistics," 2nd Edition, pp. 103. Wiley, New York.

Kirchner, H. P., Gruver, R. M., and Walker, R. E. (1966). "Chemical Strengthening of Ceramic Materials" (Contract No. NOw-0407-c). Bureau Naval Weapons, Department of the Navy.

Kistler, S. S. (1962). J. Am. Ceram. Soc. 45, 59–68.

Kooharian, A. (1952). *J. Am. Concrete Inst.* (24), 317–328, December 1952.

Nordberg, M. E., Mochel, E. L., Garfinkel, H. M., and Olcott, J. S. (1964). *J. Am. Ceram. Soc.* **47**, (5), 215–219.

Roark, R. J. (1954). "Formulas for Stress and Strain," 3rd Edition, pp. 42–44, 143–145. McGraw-Hill, New York.

Selsing, J. (1961). *J. Am. Ceram. Soc.* **44**, 419.

Shanley, F. R., Knapp, W. J., and Needham, R. A. (1955). "Prestressed Ceramic Structures," WADC Technical Report No. 54–75, Pt. 2, p. 43. Wright Air Development Center, Wright-Patterson Air Force Base, Dayton, Ohio.

Timoshenko, S. (1955). "Strength of Materials," 3rd Edition, Pt. 1, pp. 254–258. Van Nostrand, Princeton, New Jersey.

Timoshenko, S. (1956). "Strength of Materials," 3rd Edition, Pt. 2, pp. 214–221. Van Nostrand, Princeton, New Jersey.

Timoshenko, S. P., and Gere, J. M. (1961). "Theory of Elastic Stability." McGraw-Hill, New York.

Timoshenko, S., and Goodier, J. N. (1951). "Theory of Elasticity," 2nd Edition, pp. 47–49. McGraw-Hill, New York.

Tinklepaugh, J. R., Funk, J. E., and Sullivan, R. M. (1960). "Metal Fiber Reinforced Ceramics," WADC Technical Report No. 58–452, Pt. 3. Wright Air Development Center, Wright-Patterson Air Force Base, Dayton, Ohio.

Weibull, W. (1939). *Ing. Veterskaps Akad.* **151**, 1–45.

Wood, R. H. (1961). "Plastic and Elastic Design of Slabs and Plates." Ronald Press, New York.

CHAPTER 6

DESIGN OF ATTACHMENTS AND
CONNECTIONS WITH BRITTLE MATERIALS

Wilfred H. Dukes   *Frank M. Anthony*

Abstract: This chapter is concerned with the problem of designing reliable structural joints and attachments for structural components fabricated from nonmetallic refractory materials. Such materials fail mechanically in a completely brittle manner. Successful design with this class of material requires many departures from conventional practices as used for metallic materials. These departures are discussed and form the basis for a design philosophy appropriate to the use of brittle materials. It is shown that brittle materials are prone to fail at points of stress concentration, which means that an appropriately refined stress analysis method is required so that peak stresses can be determined. Also inherent in these materials and developing from their brittleness is a wide variability in mechanical properties for nominally identical specimens. This leads to a statistical definition of strength in which stress level is associated with the probability of failure. Special attention must also be given to the definition of loads, particularly those created by internal restraints and by deformation of supporting structures. Other areas where the use of brittle materials requires a different design approach include design criteria, where the conventional safety factors must be replaced by an acceptable failure probability, and the specification of material failure modes, particularly under complex stress systems. The designer must also pay particular attention to material processing and quality control to a degree which is unnecessary with metallic materials. He must do this in order to ensure a minimum of variability in mechanical properties.

Having established the principles of brittle material design, in general, this chapter then considers joining methods in particular, and describes potential applications for refractory nonmetallic materials. These applications are principally in the high temperature areas of high performance aerospace structures. Specific joining methods appropriate to each application are described. The design problems associated with each of these methods are reviewed; it is shown that these will generally involve (a) eliminating constraints against deformation and, hence, avoiding unknown induced loads, and (b) properly defining the areas of peak stress.

Having established the types of joints and the related problem areas, a subsequent section presents the special methods of analysis required. The method of carrying out a failure probability analysis for a brittle component is given; it is supplemented with charts to facilitate the numerical calculations. The finite element method of stress analysis, which is necessary to obtain a sufficiently detailed analysis of stresses in a brittle component of complex shape, is described, and numerous references are given from which this analytical capability can be established. However, because this technique requires an extensive computer capability which is not available to all agencies, a stress-concentration method of stress analysis is described and again supplemented with design charts which facilitate making the numerical calculations.

The final section reviews all of the examples which have been found in the open literature of joints and connections made with brittle materials. In those examples where comparisons between analysis and test can be made, the test results justify surprisingly well the design approach presented in this chapter.

I. Introduction

Brittle materials have been used for structural and nonstructural applications for centuries, because these materials have always been much more abundant and in a more immediately useful form than the ductile metallics. In the past, the problems posed by brittleness were avoided by using such materials primarily in compression, and always at very low working stresses. Low structural efficiency was of no concern for a ground installation; the success of this approach is demonstrated by many building structures, some representing considerable achievements in terms of height or span or size, etc., which are still functioning satisfactorily in the structural sense, after many hundreds of years.

In recent years, there has been an increasing interest in the use of brittle nonmetallic materials for aerospace systems applications, primarily because high performance introduces high temperatures, in various forms, and the most refractory construction materials are brittle, nonmetallic compounds. However, for aerospace applications, much higher structural efficiencies must be achieved, and, in particular, it must be possible to use such materials in tension with the same level of reliability and confidence presently associated with metallic structures. It is clear that the designer will always prefer to use ductile metallic materials if he can accomplish his design objectives with them; it is unlikely, for instance, that nonmetallic refractories will ever match the structural efficiency obtainable with metals. However, many advanced applications, particularly in high performance airframe and propulsion systems as well as industrial processing equipment, involve operating temperatures and environmental conditions for which the refractoriness of brittle ceramic materials is particularly attractive.

The general idea of attempting to design efficient aerospace structures with materials which exhibit no ductility whatever has usually been sufficient to discourage most designers. Where attempts have been made to design and build such structures, they have frequently been made using commercially available materials, and more or less conventional design practice, and the result has been failure. The important difference in approach, which must be recognized, is that a material which is completely lacking in ductility is sensitive to every stress concentration produced by the component configuration or the loads or environmental conditions, and it is sensitive to every flaw or defect within the material. Successful design with this class of material is believed, therefore, to require meticulous attention to the details of the stresses, greatly improved processing control and quality control to minimize material flaws, and a method of specifying material strength which recognizes the significance of material defects. Such concepts are set forth in this chapter; however, this technology is at an early stage of development and it is not at all clear whether all of the techniques that will be advanced for brittle material design are necessary for satisfactory performance or whether they are sufficient. Where these concepts have been applied completely, the results have been surprisingly successful, but the number of applications is extremely small and certainly it cannot be claimed, at this time, that following the practices presented in this chapter will invariably lead to success.

Inevitably, in any construction technique, methods of joining must be available, since it is impractical to make large complex structures in one piece. From the little that has already been said about brittle refractory materials, it will be evident that the problems are greatest at joints, since they always involve many sources of stress concentration due to complex geometry, redundancy, manufacturing tolerances, etc. This chapter is therefore concerned with the subject of joining, for structures constructed with brittle refractory materials, although it necessarily embraces design philosophies which are equally applicable to those elements of brittle refractory structures other than joints.

The present early development stage of brittle material design technology has already been mentioned; methods of joining are even less advanced than the technology generally. No more than three or four U.S. publications exist, at present, which describe original work on brittle material joining. Consequently, it is not possible to present, in a chapter of this type, well substantiated design rules or substantial quantitative data or even empirical "rule-of-thumb" methods. The experience and the data simply do not exist. Instead, the chapter defines a design philosophy, supports this where possible with analytical data to facilitate its application, and presents also a number of brittle material joining concepts. While it is hoped that this work will find application in actual joint design for practical brittle material components, an equally important purpose will have been served if it encourages further development by showing that a logical and promising approach to the problem is available.

Specifically, this chapter presents, in the following section, the philosophy of designing with brittle materials, and it brings out those areas where, so far as is known, departures are required from the design approach used for metallic materials. The subsequent section presents a number of brittle material joining concepts and emphasizes, for each one, the anticipated problems and the general approach to resolving the difficulties. Another section presents information on some of the special analytical methods necessary for brittle material joint design, and includes design charts to facilitate particular aspects of the stress analysis and the statistical analysis of component failure probability. Still another section gives recommendations for future research—necessarily very broad recommendations in view of the large amount of development work still to be done. A final section reviews such experience as is available in the unclassified literature, with actual hardware developments in brittle material joining.

II. Design Considerations

Experience shows that structural design techniques which have been developed and used successfully for structures fabricated from ductile metallic materials require modification if the same degree of structural reliability is required with brittle materials. The considerations involved in brittle material design result from the condition that the material shows no yielding prior to failure, that is, that the stress-strain curve is a straight line to the stress level at which failure occurs. This assumption of no yielding leads to failure at points of maximum stress, regardless of the fact that these high stresses might be very localized. As a consequence, refined stress analysis methods are necessary so that these localized maximum stresses can be determined. Joints and connections, changes in cross section, holes, concentrated loads, are all sources of stress concentration and impose a particular need for detailed and accurate stress analysis.

Another source of localized high stresses is the imposed loadings; and in brittle material design it is, as a consequence, necessary to know all sources of loading accurately. While it is always necessary to know applied loads accurately, regardless of whether the material is ductile or brittle, many sources of load which are normally neglected with ductile materials must be included when brittle materials are used, unless the design is such that they are deliberately avoided. Such loads include built-in assembly stresses, constraints at joints, loads induced by deformation of supporting structures, and thermal expansion constraints.

Another source of localized high stresses is flaws within the material; thus, the apparent strength of the material becomes dependent on the size, type, and frequency of such flaws. This produces a requirement for new material failure theories, particularly under complex stresses.

Since the material strength is affected by flaws, which are random phenomena, a variability in material strength results, and it becomes necessary to use a statistical rather than a deterministic definition of material strength. This variability also requires particular attention to material processing and quality control so that the probability of flaws may be minimized, and, hence, the strength that can be expected with a specified level of reliability may be maximized. With such changes in the mechanical characteristics of materials, corresponding changes in the method of specifying structural design criteria are required. Since material strength is defined statistically, the conventional factor of safety must be replaced by an acceptable failure probability.

In the remainder of this section these six areas, where a unique design philosophy is necessary in order to use brittle materials, are discussed in more detail, with particular reference to the problem of joining brittle material components; a subsequent section presents the analytical methods necessary to apply these new techniques.

A. Stress Analysis

Conventional stress analysis involves such assumptions as constant cross section, no distortion of cross section, beams having sufficiently large length to depth ratios for end effects to be neglected, and no abrupt change of stress distribution at points of load application. Such methods neglect many effects which are particularly significant at joints. Such effects include, among others, short deep beam sections, rapid changes in cross section, probably involving fillets; the presence of holes, stiffening members and reinforcements; and points of application of concentrated loads, probably involving clamping due to bolt heads.

All of these effects will generally produce local strains which are greater, at some point, than those predicted by simple theory. Generally, with ductile metallic materials, such localized strains can be absorbed by yielding and redistribution of stress, providing that the average strength across the section is sufficient to resist the external loads. Sometimes, the yielding causes fatigue cracks under repeated loads, but such effects can be examined analytically with sufficient accuracy by applying correction factors which have been computed with the theory of elasticity for a number of idealized cases. If the material is completely brittle, however, and if these local effects include regions of maximum strain, they will be the source of failure, and they cannot be neglected however localized they may be.

It is particularly important to apply these considerations to thermal stresses. In a typical metallic structure, thermal stresses will rarely produce failure, since they represent a balanced internal load system, which is relieved by local yielding at points of excessive strain. No such relief is possible with brittle materials, and peak thermal stresses are just as likely to produce failure as the peak stresses resulting from externally applied loads.

The most important principle of successful design with brittle materials is believed, therefore, to be the use of stress analysis methods which avoid both the approximations of the simple strength theory and the geometric simplifications of the classical theory of elasticity. Fortunately, an analytical tool which meets these requirements is available; it is called finite element analysis and is described fully in a later section. Finite element analysis, however, requires substantial computer capability, which may not be available to all agencies interested in brittle material design. A later section therefore presents graphical data from which a stress analysis which is still approximate, but nevertheless more refined than usual, can be made. These data have been selected and prepared with the particular requirements of brittle material joint design in mind.

B. Loads

For any satisfactory structural design, it is desirable to know the applied loadings accurately, and, in this respect there is no particular difference between design with brittle materials and designing with ductile materials.

Some minor added difficulty may arise with brittle materials, since they will generally be used for high temperature applications, and the calculation of internal heat transfer by both conduction and radiation will be necessary if an accurate assessment of internal loads is to be made. Calculation of internal heat transfer by radiation is not difficult, but is particularly laborious. Fortunately, the neglect of radiant heat transfer will generally be conservative, although, at temperatures above, say, 2000° F, it may be unduly so.

Loadings of a class which receive little attention when ductile materials are used, but which may be of paramount importance with brittle materials, are loads induced by the installation itself. Such loads can be caused by misalinement during installation of components, by strains induced from the deformation of supporting structures, by restrictions on thermal expansion and thermal deformation, by constraints on deformation under external loads, by thermal expansion differences between metallic and nonmetallic elements at mating surfaces, etc. These effects are likely to be most pronounced at joints, particularly the joints and connections between nonmetallic structural components and supporting metallic structures. In each case, the effects are not relieved by local yielding, and the resulting forces or displacements must be accommodated by strain in the brittle material.

While the above considerations impose a requirement to assess the effect, in terms of material strain, of all induced deformations and internal load systems, the limited strain capability of all brittle metallic materials makes it more practical, in most cases, to design the component so that all of these effects are avoided. This approach is of particular significance in joint and connection design, since it is at the joints where essentially all of these accommodations must be made. The main principle is to avoid indeterminacy of loadings at joints; this may be done by using single bolt connections, hinged supporting brackets, and similar devices. The support arrangement for a brittle component, for instance, should be such that force and moments in three planes can be resisted, but nothing more. For instance, a bracket which is intended to support a vertical load should provide no significant resistance to twist, in case deformations of the brittle component involve rotation of the attachment lug. A single pin will generally provide rotational freedom about only one axis. Unknown moments may be introduced about the other two axes due to component deformation, and critical stresses which would be relieved by yielding in a metallic component may be introduced into the nonmetallic elements of the connection.

These principles should be carried to considerable lengths in order to achieve successful brittle material joint design, at least until a substantial body of experience is available to determine the extent to which such measures are necessary. Similarly, with expansion differences between metallic and nonmetallic elements of a joint, methods for accommodating these differences are available and are discussed in the next section, though they produce relatively complex joints. Nevertheless, these complexities should be faced unless and until experience shows that they are unneccessary.

This discussion is not intended to imply that redundancy in a properly designed connection is undesirable. Indeed, the use of redundant load paths to increase structural reliability without reduction in allowable stresses is important. However, the redundancy must be of the type which permits the loads through each load path to be accurately determined.

Instances have been found where partial restraint against deformation due to temperature and temperature gradients can be beneficial. In materials which have much greater compression strength than tensile strength (which is true of essentially all full density brittle materials), restraints which increase compressive thermal stresses but thereby reduce tensile thermal stresses could improve reliability. Whether it is practical to control restraints to such a degree is not known.

C. FAILURE THEORIES

A discussion of material failure can be either a discussion of fracture mechanics, which attempts to explain in physical terms the initiation and progression of failure in the material, or a discussion of failure theories, which define material strength under complex stress conditions but which are based on gross considerations. With a brittle material, in which a source of critical stresses may be flaws in the material, it is probable that both the mechanics of fracture and the definition of material strength will differ from conventional metallic practice. Fracture mechanics do not at present provide the designer with quantitative information, although it is desirable that fracture be understood so that the failure theories used for design reflect the proper parameters. Failure theories, on the other hand, provide quantitative statements of the stress conditions which will result in material failure. Such theories are based on gross assumptions about material behavior, such as the assumption that fracture will occur when the maximum tensile stress reaches some limiting value, and they require empirical verification, but they do provide quantitative data which can be used in design. Only the latter subject will therefore be discussed in this section.

For brittle materials, the maximum stress theory is most commonly used. This theory predicts that fracture will occur when the maximum tensile stress in the body reaches a limiting value. It assumes fracture to be independent of the other two principal stresses, which is contrary to observation, and it neglects both compressive stresses and the compression strength of the material. There is also the so-called stress invariant theory, which does realistically predict compression strength values six times the tension strength, although there is no evidence in the literature of its application.

The Griffith crack theory and the Weibull theory have also been extended to complex stress conditions so that they become failure theories relating strength values. The Griffith theory predicts failure under biaxial tension when the maximum normal stress acts on a flaw of critical size. It is thus equivalent to the maximum stress theory in the tension-tension quadrant, but it also predicts a uniaxial compressive strength equal to eight times the uniaxial tensile strength, so that it also defines the compression quadrant of the failure envelope. In the compression-tension quadrant, however, the theory does not predict an increase in allowable tensile stress due to a normal compressive stress, though limited test data suggest that this may be the case.

The Weibull theory predicts values less than the maximum stress theory in the tension-tension quadrant, and, in the compression-tension quadrant, it predicts that the presence of compression will increase the allowable tension in the normal direction.

Very little quantitative experimental data are available to verify which failure theory should be used for brittle materials. Furthermore, very few materials have been examined under complex stress states, so it is not known whether different failure theories are required for different types of brittle materials. Certainly, it must be anticipated that the material manufacturing process will have a significant effect, since it controls such factors as porosity, grain size, and the absence, presence, and degree of microcracks. Nothing is yet known, for example, about the effects of anisotropy under complex stress conditions. In view of these severe limitations, it is recommended that material tests be conducted for any significant application in order to define a material failure theory.

D. STATISTICAL DEFINITION OF FAILURE STRENGTH

The processing of nonmetallic inorganic materials of interest for structural applications has not generally reached the stage of development and refinement of control associated with the processing of metals, so a substantially greater variation in the mechanical properties of supposedly identical samples is apparent. Of more significance, however, is the sensitivity of mechanical properties to flaws, as a consequence of the lack of ductility. These flaws include pores, microcracks, and inclusions of foreign materials, and will generally be random in size and distribution. They will produce local stress concentrations dependent on the size and configuration of the flaws, and, since the apparent material strength will be controlled by these peak stresses, a corresponding randomness will exist in the strength of the material. In design, therefore, the usable strength level must be associated with an acceptable probability of failure. The use of material strength as a matter of probability is another of the more important differences between brittle material design technology and the technology used with ductile materials. In the latter case, it is usual to treat material strength as a singular value, although, in fact, there is still a variability in strength from sample to sample, but the strength distribution is very narrow.

The techniques required to determine the material strength variability and to calculate the probability of failure for a complex structure are given in a subsequent section. Strength level becomes dependent on volume of material, since the greater the volume, the greater the probability of a critical flaw. The failure probability, however, is tempered by the stress distribution, and its prediction becomes dependent not only on the maximum stress at some particular location but on the summation of the failure probabilities of each element of the component. The characteristic shape of the strength distribution curve, however, is such that only the material in a region of high stress is likely to contribute significantly to failure probability.

The question of a material failure theory to describe failure under complex stress systems was discussed previously. Apparently, however, any mechanical property test conducted on a sample of material with the expectation of defining a point on the failure envelope is associated with a probability of occurrence. Each point on the failure envelope, therefore, requires a series of identical tests defining a strength distribution curve under the particular stress ratios and other environmental conditions. Thus the failure envelope becomes a series of envelopes, each associated with a particular probability of failure.

E. Material Process Control

The present variability in the mechanical properties of brittle materials requires large reductions from the average strength in order to achieve low probabilities of failure. To maximize working stresses and minimize weight, it is therefore, necessary that the designer minimize variability by giving attention to control of processing and inspection methods. This contrasts with the practice with metallic materials where a simple reference to a material specification is sufficient to ensure very closely controlled material.

The purpose of process and inspection control is not necessarily to maximize strength, but, rather to minimize the variation in strength; the concern is therefore to ensure that each step is repeated identically for each piece of material. It is also important that the process be identical for both structural components and the test specimens used to establish material properties.

In the present state of brittle material development, process control is complicated by a number of factors which may become less significant as development proceeds. One of these is the exercise of proprietary restrictions, which results from the fact that many of these materials have been developed by long and closely guarded processes of trial and error. Another problem is the fact that the significance of various processing parameters on the variability of mechanical properties is not generally known, so that it is not possible to determine which parameters should be closely controlled and to what extent. At present, the only approach seems to be to control every processing step and every processing variable from the preparation of the raw ingredients to the final machining of a component.

Consideration should also be given to inspection techniques, including— in addition to the more conventional methods—various crack detection techniques, such as the use of dye penetrant to detect surface cracks; acoustic techniques for detecting internal cracks; X-ray inspection for porosity and density variations; and similar methods. Evidently, the design task with brittle materials includes preparation of detailed material and component processing and inspection specifications, and it is important that these be prepared before extensive mechanical property testing of the material is undertaken so that such testing can be performed on specification material.

One other technique which can provide the designer with components of reduced performance variability is proof testing. This involves subjecting each component to a predetermined stress to eliminate, by destructive testing, the occasional sample of low strength. In addition to reducing performance variability across an acceptable batch of components, the proof test permits a much more accurate description of strength variability among those components which are accepted, because the proof stress, in effect, becomes a zero probability of failure stress, and specifically determines the end point on the strength distribution curve. This permits a more accurate prediction of failure probabilities greater than zero. Thus, not only is the allowable stress level for a given failure probability increased, but the confidence in the value is also improved. A later section, which presents methods for the determination of component failure probability as a function of material variability parameters, also includes methods for introducing the effect of proof testing.

Two considerations apply in the selection of the proof stress level. The first of these is the question of material damage, and limited studies which have been made, particularly with graphite, show that damage in the form of microcracks can be produced by a proof test. Test specimens are required which can be examined before and after the application of various levels of proof stress to determine a level that produces no detectable damage.

The other consideration in selecting the proof stress level is one of economics. The higher the proof stress, the higher will be the resulting allowable stress for a given failure probability, but the greater will be the proportion of components which will be destroyed. In brittle material design, optimization will probably involve the usual determination of geometric characteristics to sustain the necessary loads with minimum weight, but this will be supplemented by a study of allowable stress level and, hence, weight against cost, in terms of the type of proof test and the component rejection rate.

F. Design Criteria

The conventional practice in establishing airframe structural design criteria is to determine the maximum loads which are expected in service, and to design the airframe to function satisfactorily and repeatedly under these conditions. These loads are then increased by a safety factor, and the design is arranged so that failure does not occur under these factored loads, although permanent damage is tolerated. With structures fabricated from brittle materials, these concepts change as a result of the statistical nature of material strength. Since there is no yielding situation, there seems to be no meaning in discussing limit and ultimate loads; instead, it becomes necessary to establish an acceptable probability of failure, which should include the desired degree of conservatism.

In practice, most airframe loading conditions have an associated probability of occurrence, with the probability of occurrence decreasing as loading level increases. Hence, the probability of developing high stresses decreases as the stress level increases. The overall probability of airframe failure is the product of the probability of occurrence of a particular stress level and the probability of material failure under that stress level. Material failure probability involves, of course, the summation of failure probabilities for all brittle elements of the airframe.

Thus, the conventional limit and ultimate factors should be replaced by an acceptable failure probability for the airframe. The strength check should then involve an examination of failure probability for a number of loading conditions of different severity, each with an associated probability of occurrence and with an associated material failure probability.

One other design philosophy that can be used for brittle materials involves establishing, as a design criterion, that the material used has some strength level at which the probability of failure is zero, or that the component be proof tested to ensure some load level at which there is no probability of failure. The criterion should then require that the stresses or loads introduced during normal operation of the vehicle be limited to these zero probability-of-failure values. Consequently, the loads which occur continuously and repeatedly will not contribute to the probability of structural failure, and only the far less probable extreme loading conditions would be significant.

III. Representative Attachment Configurations

A. APPLICATIONS FOR BRITTLE MATERIALS

Before discussing brittle materials for aerospace applications, some definition of the term "brittle" is necessary, since it is conventionally used to describe the characteristics of both nonmetallic materials with zero ductility and metallic materials, such as the high strength steels, where the ductility is small but finite. In structural design, a very small amount of ductility greatly affects the degree of refinement necessary in the design and stress analysis, so that clarification of the term is necessary. The present discussion is concerned with the structural application of refractory compounds such as carbides and oxides, which are of interest because of their ability to retain useful mechanical properties at high temperature. These materials fail in a brittle manner, showing essentially zero ductility until very high temperatures are reached. In these discussions, therefore, the concepts to be presented will apply to materials of zero ductility, and it will be assumed that the stress-strain relationship is linear to failure. It should not be assumed, however, that these concepts are necessary when high strength metallic materials are used, although such structures may benefit from the application of these techniques.

Also, in this discussion, consideration will be given only to those applications where the material is used in an efficient structural manner, where the limitations of weight and requirements for high structural reliability require refined design practice. Thus, some of the common ceramic applications, such as in furnace linings, or electrical insulators, will not be considered.

In a review of aerospace applications for refractory nonmetallic materials, it can be expected that ductility is a characteristic that will always be desired by designers and one for which some compromise of the structure in other respects, such as weight, will be made. Strictly speaking, with the techniques which are presently being evolved, it should be possible to design structures with the same reliability in both metallic and non-metallic materials and to make the material selection rationally on the basis of weight, cost, etc. However, it is not expected that refractory non-metallic materials will ever match the metals in strength-to-weight ratio, particularly in view of the variability inherent in the strength characteristics of such materials and the relatively low stress levels which must be used to achieve high reliability. Refractory materials generally show high stiffness and a relatively high stiffness-to-weight ratio, which, in some instances, exceeds those of the more conventional metallic materials. It is unlikely, however, that this advantage will be sufficient to persuade a designer to sacrifice ductility and use the brittle material at temperatures where metallic materials are feasible. Consequently, applications for brittle refractories will, for the most part, be limited to those in which high temperatures are likely to be encountered.

Possible aerospace applications for refractory nonmetallic materials include small lifting surfaces, lifting surface leading edges, engine inlet leading edges, heat shield elements, insulative surface elements, nosecaps and air data sensors—all for lifting-reentry and hypersonic cruise applications. These are secondary structural applications, in the sense that the components mentioned do not support primary structural loads, although the reliability of these elements is as critical as any other aspect of the structure. In addition, it can be anticipated that refractory nonmetallic materials will find application as high temperature primary structure in thin lifting surfaces for hypersonic vehicles, where the thickness of insulation or other thermal protection which would be necessary with metallic structure, is aerodynamically undesirable. In such applications, the structure will probably consist of a strut type of frame structure with surface panels, since the conventional shell type of construction used with metallic materials requires extensive joining and very thin material cross sections, both of which are difficult to achieve with refractory nonmetallics. Nonmetallic refractory materials may also be used as primary structure for radomes and small, very-high-speed missile bodies.

In addition to the above applications for hypersonic aircraft and missiles, these materials will certainly find application as rocket nozzle inserts and possibly for the construction of complete nozzles and thrust chambers. The other application, which has already been tried a number of times unsuccessfully, involves turbine and compressor blades, both rotating and stationary, for jet engines.

B. Attachment Functional Requirements

In order to use brittle nonmetallic refractory materials, successful methods of joining will be necessary, but, nevertheless, joining will always be difficult and relatively heavy so that there will be a tendency in the application of these materials for joining to be minimized. Furthermore, although many of these materials, particularly the more refractory, are not conveniently made in sheetlike forms, they can be fabricated by hot pressing and sintering, which is convenient for complex shapes. As a consequence, it can be expected that structures or components made from refractory nonmetallics will be assembled from relatively complex, integrally stiffened, or integrally formed elements.

Joints and connections will be required to connect these elements together (since processing equipment will generally limit the size of individual elements) and also to attach elements to supporting metallic structures. Again, because of the difficulties and weight associated with joining of nonmetallic refractories, it is expected that designers will attempt to extend refractory components from maximum temperature regions into areas where temperatures permit the use of metals in a single piece. Thus, most of the joints will involve the connection of nonmetallic elements to metallic structures, permitting the actual joining elements, such as pins and bolts, to be metallic.

Among the basic functional requirements for attachments and connections are load transfer, maintenance of relative position, and sealing. Attachments generally must meet some or all of these requirements with one generally predominating in importance. With nonmetallic refractory materials, load transfer is the primary consideration, but it will generally be important that the attachments perform this function without constraint on deformation of the nonmetallic component and, particularly, that they provide freedom in every respect for thermal deformations.

Some of the specific functions for which joints will be required are as follows:

a. Attachment of leading edge segments of lifting surfaces, inlet lips, etc., to metallic or nonmetallic support structures.

b. Attachments between leading edge segments as a consequence of size limitation in element processing.

c. Attachment of ceramic radomes to metallic structures.

d. Connections between segments of large radomes where processing size limitations prevent the fabrication of a one-piece unit.

e. Attachments for electrically transparent and optically transparent windows.

f. Connections between sections of small-diameter nonmetallic refractory missile bodies.

g. Attachments between nonmetallic integrally stiffened heat shields and surface panels, and metallic or nonmetallic primary structure.

h. Joints between sections of nonmetallic integrally stiffened surface panels resulting from size limitations imposed by processing equipment.

i. Attachments for insulative surface layers for use as thermal protection for hypersonic vehicles.

j. Attachments for nonmetallic tension and compression members for truss-type primary load carrying structure.

k. Joints between sections of nonmetallic tension and compression members for truss-type primary structure as a consequence of size limitation imposed by processing equipment.

l. Attachments for nosecaps and elements forming nosecaps.

m. Attachments for liners, inserts, and complete nozzle and thrust chamber segments for rocket engines.

n. Attachments for rotating and stationary blades for jet engines, turbines, and compressors.

o. Attachments for one-piece nonmetallic refractory lifting surfaces.

C. Brittle Material Joining Methods

From a consideration of the joining and attachment requirements described in Sect. III,B, and considering also the brittle material design principles outlined in Sect. II, the joints which can be expected to find application, where brittle materials are used, can be classified into a relatively small number of types. This section describes a number of joining methods under a classification based on commonality of design characteristics, rather than on geometric or functional similarities. In each case, the joining method is described, together with its characteristics, design problems, and potential problem solutions. Specific design and analysis data are given in a subsequent section.

Most of the joints to be described are essentially standard metallic joints with a direct substitution of material. Very few joint concepts have been found which are peculiarly suited to brittle materials, and, in fact, most of the joints have some dependence on metals. This emphasizes the desirability of using integrally stiffened brittle material components extending in one piece from maximum temperature regions to points where the temperatures are low enough to permit attachments to metallic support structures. Very little practical development work has been done at this time on joints for brittle nonmetallic materials. When such work is undertaken, it can be expected that the joints to be described will be very different as geometric forms are evolved which are matched to the material characteristics, the processing limitations, and the stress distributions. Joints peculiar to brittle nonmetallic materials may, in fact, evolve in this manner.

1. *Shear Lug Connection*

The shear lug connection type of joint is illustrated in Fig. 1. It is the primary means of joining major structural components, particularly where subsequent disassembly is anticipated, or where there is a significant material change, such as from nonmetallic to metallic, or where it is necessary to isolate the nonmetallic component from the deformations of supporting metallic structures. The connection is similar geometrically to those used in metallic structures, but is generally more bulky, since it must be designed on the basis of peak stresses with all stress-concentration effects considered. In metallic construction, stress concentrations can generally be neglected, and the section dimensions based on average stresses. If, in brittle material design, weight minimization is pursued, then the various cross sections present in the lug shown in Fig. 1 could be arranged to provide the maximum amount of material in the regions where the stress concentrations exist. The extent to which this refinement is used will depend on the importance of weight in relation to the added cost of design and manufacture.

In brittle material applications, the lugs will generally be integral parts of the nonmetallic component, and the pins may be metallic or nonmetallic, depending on the local temperature and on the material used for the supporting structure. The trend in brittle material design will be to minimize splices, so that structural elements will generally be large and integrally stiffened, with connections only where the components are attached to supporting metal structure. The type of connection most useful for this purpose is that shown in Fig. 1.

The connection shown in Fig. 1 contains many sources of stress concentration which must be considered in the stress analysis. These are indicated in the figure. They include:

a.   Stress concentrations around the edge of the hole, such as at sections AA and BB.

b.   Concentrations due to eccentricities in the direction of loading, and due to offset of the load from the center of the lug as a result of tolerance buildup between the fittings.

c.   Concentrations due to pin bending, which will tend to concentrate the load at the inside edges of the hole.

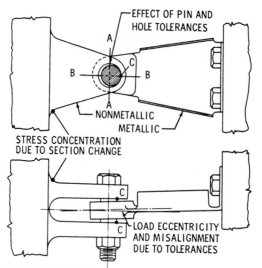

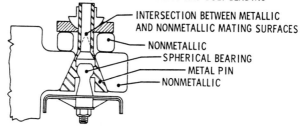

FIG. 1. Pin and lug connection.

　　d.　Concentrations due to dimensional tolerances between the bolt diameter and the hole diameter, resulting in "line" contact.

　　e.　Stress concentrations at the fillets where the lug becomes an integral part of the component.

　　f.　Stress concentrations due to thermal expansion differences where a metallic pin is used in a nonmetallic lug.

From the above discussion, it will be evident that, with materials exhibiting no yielding, a combination of practical limits of geometry and practical fabrication tolerances can lead to highly concentrated point loadings, with very high localized stresses. Combining this situation with the statistical variability of material properties and the low levels of allowable stress that might be necessary to achieve high reliability could easily result in a very large and completely impractical joint. There is not presently sufficient experimental experience to indicate whether it is indeed necessary to consider all the effects mentioned above, but a number of steps can be taken to reduce their significance. At this point, it seems reasonable to use such techniques to establish the proportions and configuration of the joint, but then to establish the absolute size optimistically and to verify the integrity experimentally.

None of these stress concentrations can be eliminated, but they can be minimized by the proper choice of lug proportions and the shape of fillets. In the next section, data are given from which the stress-concentration factors due to these various effects can be determined, and these curves can be used to obtain the best fillet size and shape, within the available space envelope, for the transition between the lug and the supported component. They can also be used to establish the bolt diameter and stiffness and the tolerances on hole and bolt diameter, which will minimize the concentrations, within the limits imposed by machining accuracy capabilities and the space available for the attachment.

In addition to the proper selection of geometry as a means of reducing or minimizing stress concentrations, there are a number of other steps which can be taken. The selection of a low modulus pin material or the use of a hollow pin to reduce the local surface stiffness should reduce the concentration of load, although methods for analyzing the effect of a hollow pin are not available. The use of a soft insert between the pin and the hole should also effect better load distribution; very likely, this could be accomplished by the use of precious metal inserts. Some of these materials offer good oxidation resistance at very high temperature, in conjunction with very low strength, permitting yielding, and, although the materials are far too costly for extensive use, their application as thin inserts may be possible. However, limited experimental work with soft inserts in holes in nonmetallic refractory lugs has not shown the expected benefits.

Where significant temperatures arise and a metal pin is used, it may be necessary to make some provision for the thermal expansion differences between the pin and the hole. With a typical combination of metal and nonmetal, a diametric clearance between two- and three-thousandths of an inch at room temperature may be necessary on a $\frac{1}{4}$-inch pin in order to provide for the thermal expansion differences over a 3000° temperature change. Such a clearance at low temperatures may be too great, and a modified lug arrangement as shown in Fig. 1 may be necessary. This uses a tapered pin and a tapered hole, and is based on the fact that although dimensional changes resulting from temperature are different for materials with different thermal expansion coefficients, angles remain unchanged. Thus, if the mating surfaces are tapered so that the projections of these surfaces meet at a single point, then the same tolerances between the pin and the hole will remain, regardless of temperature.

Where freedom from restraint to thermal deformation of the refractory component must be provided, there are at least two methods that may be employed. The simplest of these, which can be used where the component is attached to a metallic structure, involves a pin or bolt to provide rotational freedom about one axis, and flexing of appropriately designed metal support brackets to provide rotation about a second axis. A typical arrangement is shown in Fig. 1. Where the angular displacement about all three axes is significant, the necessary freedom can be provided with a spherical bearing also shown in Fig. 1. Such bearings can obviously be constructed in metal if temperatures at the attachment points permit. Evidently, this type of attachment can also be made in refractory nonmetallic materials, since successful ball bearings have been made of materials such as aluminum oxide.

2. *Tension Lug Connection*

Complementary to the lug designed to use a pin in shear as described above, is the fitting designed to attach structural components subassemblies, etc., with bolts in tension. Typical examples are shown in Fig. 2. This figure shows, in addition to the basic tension lug, variations which are similar in design and analysis. They include the angle or T-section flange attachment, and versions which are useful for connecting cylindrical sections, such as radomes or small missile body sections. As shown, various clamping devices, snap rings, etc., may be used in lieu of bolts. This type of joint provides no accommodation for relative motion between the nonmetallic component and the supporting metallic structure, such as may either be caused by deformations under load or result from temperature gradients. Accordingly, all arrangements for avoiding restraints on the deformation of the nonmetallic component must be made by building flexibility or hinges into the metallic supporting structures. Only metallic bolts or clamps are anticipated, so, again, the joint must be used where the temperature is sufficiently reduced to make an attachment between nonmetallic and metallic elements of the structure. It is considered that attempts to make nonmetallic bolts of a conventional type would be impractical, because the proportions required to reduce stress concentrations to the point where a reliable connection could be made would be impractically large.

Generally, the tension lug will also be integral with the nonmetallic component, but the close tolerance machining required in the shear lug to minimize stress concentrations is not necessary except under the bolt

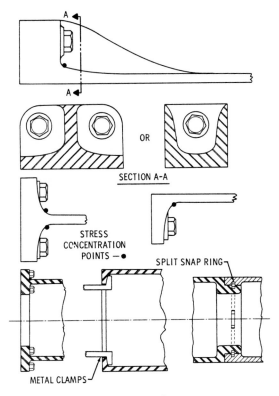

FIG. 2. Tension lugs.

head and at the face which contacts the metallic supporting structure. Soft metal inserts in these areas may be necessary to avoid load concentrations at high spots on the lug faces.

The design problem with the tension lug is again one of properly assessing and providing for the many stress concentrations which arise. No particular techniques are available for minimizing these concentrations except by the proper selection of fillet size and shape and the proper selection of thickness and thickness taper in the various elements of the joint. The use of soft metal inserts for distributing the bolthead load has been mentioned. Other possibilities include machining a narrow ridge into the underside of the bolthead, or designing a spherical surface on the underside of the bolthead in conjunction with a spherical seat in the nonmetallic fitting and an oversized hole to accommodate angular misalinement of the bolt. Careful and accurate pretensioning of the bolts may be necessary where a multiple bolt connection is used to ensure that each bolt takes its share of the load.

This type of fitting is very difficult to stress analyze by simple beam theory, not only because the fitting contains stress raisers due to changes of section and concentrated load applications, but also due to the fact that most of the elements involve beams which are too short for the simple bending stress distribution to develop. This type of fitting is common in metallic construction, but, nevertheless, accurate stress analyses are not common, since experience has shown that, with metals, the typical simple stress analysis based on beam theory is conservative. Undoubtedly, the fitting can be analyzed quite accurately by the finite element method of stress analysis described in the next section. Approximations to the stress analysis can be made with the aid of stress-concentration factor data also given in the next section. This data permits allowance to be made for the stress concentrations at the points marked in Fig. 2. These stress concentration factors must be applied to stresses calculated by simple beam theory which must include the effect of eccentricities and, in the case of the cylindrical sections, must include the hoop stresses. The next section also gives peak stresses in the elements of the fitting under the bolthead.

3. Lap Joints

Typical lap joints are shown in Fig. 3. In brittle material construction, this type of joint has application where limitations imposed by fabricating equipment, available material dimensions, or complex geometry make it impractical to fabricate the structural element in one place. Unfortunately, braze or adhesive bonding material which will match the temperature capability of the brittle refractories is not available at present, and the

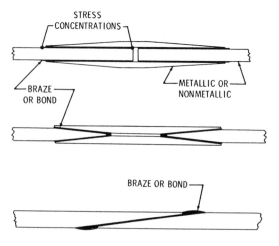

FIG. 3. Brazed or bonded lap joints.

extensive use of this type of joint is therefore not foreseen until such materials are available. The use of this type of joint as a means of attachment by brazing to a metallic support structure is also possible. This type of connection is suitable for transmitting tension, compression, shear, or a moment in the plane of the splice plates.

Even with geometric symmetry, this type of joint introduces stress concentrations in the primary members at the ends of the splice plates, and in the splice plates at the ends of the primary members, since, at these points, there is a maximum mismatch in local strain. This stress concentration can be minimized by tapering the elements of the joint and, to some extent, by choosing the stiffness characteristics and the thickness of the bond material.

Data are given in the next section from which the stress concentrations in the primary members of this type of joint can be assessed as a function of the geometry and material characteristics of the primary member, the splice plate, and the bond. These data will permit selection of the geometry which, within the available space, will minimize the stress concentrations. Note that these data differ from that available from most reference works where the concern is usually for the stresses in the bond. With brittle material applications, particularly if the joint is made by brazing, the stress concentrations in the primary members are at least of equal importance.

4. Clamp Attachments

Figure 4 shows another method of joining which, it is expected, will be frequently used with refractory nonmetallic components, although again the application is limited to the attachment of such components to metallic structures, since the joint itself involves metallic elements. The upper joint in Fig. 4 has the difficulties typical of most of these joints, which include load concentrations due to lack of perfect match between contacting surfaces and due to eccentricity in the direction of the applied loads. The former problem may require soft faces on the metal components or perhaps a metallic deposit on the ceramic. The second problem can perhaps be alleviated by using a cylindrical section in the nonmetallic component at the point where contact is made with the metal parts. This will permit some angular displacement of the metallic load application fitting. If this type of connection is used, for instance, around a cylindrical component, adjustments must be possible in the metallic components so that a reasonably equal distribution of load can be obtained. Provision must also be made to accommodate the thermal expansion differences; this may be done, as shown, by slotting the metallic rings.

Stress analysis of this type of joint is relatively simple and requires primarily a correction of the axial stress in the nonmetallic element to allow

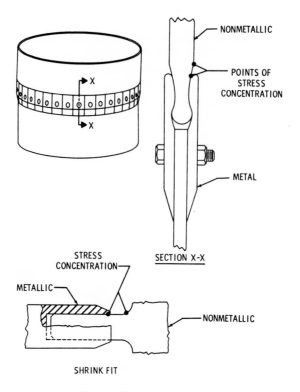

FIG. 4. Clamp connections.

for the change in cross section. Curves for making this correction are given in the next section.

The second joint shown in Fig. 4 also requires metallic elements and is based on the use of friction as the mechanism of load transmission. This type of joint introduces problems in the metallic elements of maintaining the necessary frictional forces at high temperature in the presence of thermal expansion differences and creep under sustained stress. With respect to the nonmetallic components, however the only considerations are the stress concentrations introduced adjacent to the edges of the clamps. The magnitude of these stress concentrations can be approximately assessed by means of the data for lap joints given in the next section.

5. *Surface Panel Clips*

In the use of nonmetallic refractory materials and structural components, the problem of joining nonmetallic elements to each other predominates and, as already explained, is expected to lead to the extensive use of complex integrally stiffened nonmetallic components made as large as available processing equipment will permit. Most of the joints required will then be between these components and supporting metallic structures. For these reasons, stiffened shell structures typical of metallic construction cannot be anticipated; instead, applications involving nonmetallic surface structures will use an internal metallic primary structure, made either from refractory metals or from more conventional materials and provided with internal cooling. Some temperature drop between the external surface and the internal metallic structure will be provided by insulation, and the nonmetallic surface will be constructed with relatively small integrally stiffened panels. In this situation, the surface panel clip shown in Fig. 5 is

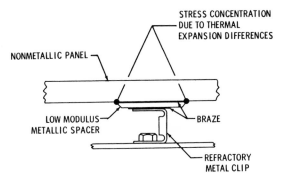

FIG. 5. Surface panel clips.

useful. It is simple and light in weight and provides both thermal expansion accommodation and a small conduction path to minimize heat flow to the vehicle interior. Such a clip will generally be brazed to the surface panel. Local thickening of the panel, together with heat flow through the clip, will keep the braze temperature at an acceptable level.

The design problems introduced with this attachment include considerations of the local stress concentrations produced in the nonmetallic material by the clip and the stresses introduced by thermal expansion mismatch between the clip and the panel. Both effects are modified considerably by the thickness and stiffness characteristics of the braze material used in the attachment and, in fact, the reduction of these stress concentrations may require the introduction of a low modulus spacer between the clip and the panel.

IV. Analytical Procedures

From the discussions of the previous sections, it will be evident that the design of attachments with brittle materials requires, in a number of areas, methods of analysis which are more refined and sophisticated than those traditionally used for conventional structural design. Such refinement is most necessary in the methods used to conduct a stress analysis of a structural component, where, for satisfactory brittle material design, it is necessary to predict very localized peak stresses such as occur at changes in cross section, points of load application, and other sources of stress concentration. Furthermore, the methods used should accommodate thick sections, where the stresses may vary through the material thickness, since brittle material components will be complex one-piece shapes of relatively bulky cross section, and the assumptions typically made for the analysis of thin shell structures will not be valid.

Analytical refinement is also necessary in determining temperature gradients within brittle material components, for the same reasons. The criticality of these materials to local stress concentrations is equally significant, with respect of thermal stresses, and requires a correspondingly refined analysis of temperature gradients. Again, the relatively bulky construction expected with brittle materials requires a "three-dimensional" analysis.

Finally, analytical refinement is necessary in establishing allowable stresses, to the extent that statistical methods, reflecting the variability in material mechanical properties, must be used. Since the probability of component failure, from which allowable stress levels can be established, depends on contributions from each element and the stresses associated with each element, the failure probability analysis must also be sufficiently refined to reflect the very detailed stress distribution.

This section discusses the analytical techniques which are presently available to meet these requirements and presents, where possible, design charts to facilitate analysis. However, those analytical techniques which offer real potential for achieving the required level of refinement are heavily dependent on computer support and require the development of a computerized analysis capability of considerable scope. Such a capability will generally be developed, over an extended period of time, to meet the general needs and match the particular facilities of an individual organization, rather than to solve individual analytical problems such as those associated with brittle material joint design. Accordingly, the discussions on this subject will be somewhat general, emphasizing the necessary characteristics of such a capability and the problems typically encountered and giving references to important works where the detail necessary to develop such a capability can be found. The computer methods suitable for the refined stress analysis of complex shapes involve: (a) a general program which solves a matrix of equations defining equilibrium and compatibility of individual elements into which the structure is divided; (b) a series of subroutines defining the loading-deformation relationships for a variety of idealized structural elements; and (c) a number of small supplemental subroutines to effect transformation of axes, and to determine internal stresses from the computed displacements. The discussions which follow will cover these general programs and will also cover those particular element relationships which are likely to be of interest in the analysis of joints in brittle materials.

In the absence of an extensive computerized analysis capability, the equations defining stress distributions, temperature distributions, failure probability, etc., must be solved directly, and design charts are given to assist with these solutions. In many respects, however, particularly in determining stress distributions in brittle components of complex shape, these methods are very inadequate. Accordingly, in the information to be presented, some very gross approximations have been made in the interests of giving the designer some working material covering all of the situations anticipated in brittle material joint design. There is some justification for such approximation at present, since, in order to predict failure, the stresses are used in conjunction with a statistical description of material strength which, at the present state of the art, is itself only approximate.

A. Determination of Failure Probability for Joints in Brittle Materials

Conventional structural design with metallic materials involves a number of basic assumptions which are normally accepted and used without question. When structural design is extended to brittle materials three of these assumptions must be reconsidered, as follows:

a. The assumption that the strength characteristics of a complex structure, subjected to a complex system of internal stresses, can be predicted from experimental data on material properties determined from small simple specimens subjected to simple stress systems.

b. The assumption that the mechanical characteristics of the material for any given set of conditions can be defined specifically by a single unique value.

c. The assumption that the strength of a structural component is determined by the stresses it is capable of withstanding at some critical point.

When brittle, nonmetallic materials are used, the same facility for determining material properties from small simple test specimens and using the information to predict the characteristics of large, complex components subjected to complex loadings must be available; otherwise, structural design with such materials becomes impractical. A material failure theory which is generally accepted for this purpose, with brittle nonmetallic materials, is the maximum stress theory, which assumes that the component will fail when the maximum principal tension stress equals the strength of the material, as determined from laboratory specimens in simple tension.

With brittle materials, however, the mechanical characteristics are not expressible as a single number. Due to the variability in any particular mechanical property, the most that can be done is to predict the probability of failure for any particular stress condition. Variability in mechanical properties is assumed to be due to the presence of flaws, which produce local stress concentrations that cannot be relieved by yielding, due to the lack of ductility. Whether a sample of material will fail under a given stress condition will depend, therefore, on the size and distribution of flaws, and, since both are random, the only statement that can be made about failure is the probability of its occurrence. Furthermore, since the probability of experiencing a flaw of critical size will increase as the size of component, or as the volume of material under consideration, increases, the strength becomes a function of component size.

The introduction of a statistical approach to the expression of mechanical characteristics, together with the dependence of failure probability on volume, also means that the strength of a component cannot be determined by the examination of a critical point. Rather, the probability of failure of the entire component must be expressed, and this involves some type of summation of the failure probabilities at all points within the component.

The variability in mechanical properties of a brittle material implies that there is a distribution function which shows the relative frequency with which a particular value of some mechanical property may be expected to occur. When plotted in normalized form, this function is typically an approximately S-shaped curve, approaching or passing through zero (absolute impossibility) at one extreme and asymptotically approaching unity (absolute certainty) at the other.

To construct a distribution curve defining a particular mechanical property for a particular material generally requires a very large number of test specimens, since the structural designer is interested in the extreme lower portion of the curve, where the probabilities of failure are very small, while, at the same time, the rareness of extreme events precludes a good definition of this part of the curve. In order to avoid extensive testing programs, it is desirable to find a general mathematical description of the distribution function, applicable to all brittle materials. At present, there is no complete agreement on the type of curve to be used, although a relationship established by Weibull is accepted as the most satisfactory to date.

The Weibull distribution function is based on the flaw theory, with the assumption that the flaws are distributed at random with a certain density per unit volume. The result is a representation of the material as a series model, or a chain, in which failure depends on the weakest link.

The Weibull distribution function is expressed as the probability of fracture which is given by

$$S = 1 - \exp\left\{-V\left(\frac{\sigma - \sigma_u}{\sigma_0}\right)^m\right\} \tag{1}$$

where V is the volume of the element under consideration, σ is the applied uniform tension stress, and σ_u, σ_0, and m are material constants. If the Weibull function is truly applicable to the material under consideration, and if the material used for small test specimens and for the structural components is truly identical, then σ_u, σ_0, and m will indeed be material constants and will not change with volume.

Equation (1) can be generalized by writing the exponent as an integral over the volume of the component, and expressing σ as a variable in terms of V. In the completely general case, a component can be divided into a large number of elements each sufficiently small for the stress within the element to be considered uniform. The above equation can be applied to each element, and, by proper summation, the probability of failure of the component can be determined. Furthermore, the method can be extended to a triaxial stress state in each element, following the method of Weibull (1939). Finally, if the material parameters σ_u, σ_0, and m are determined as a function of temperature, the values appropriate to the temperature of each element can be used.

Evidently, the variability in mechanical properties introduces a basic difficulty with brittle materials, since the infrequent but real possibility of low strength values demands low stress levels, relative to mean strength of the material, and, hence, high weight, if extremely low probability of failure is to be achieved.

A most promising method of circumventing this difficulty is to subject each component to a proof test. A proof test reveals those components which are low in strength, and the elimination of the few extreme values substantially increases the permissible stress level for a given probability of failure. It should be noted that the proof stress may be less than the applied stress, for any particular element, and still significant improvements will be produced in failure probability for a given applied stress. Maximum benefits are produced if the proof stress equals the maximum applied stress, but the selection of the proof stress level must also consider the economics of the possible component failure rate and the degree of material damage imposed on acceptable components. The effect of proof testing has been studied by Anthony et al. (1965) and Barnett et al. (1965).

The generalization of the Weibull method for predicting failure probability, involving all of the considerations mentioned above and including also the effect of proof testing, is given in the AGARD Handbook (1968). From this reference, the risk of rupture for an element experiencing uniform, mutually perpendicular triaxial principal stresses σ_x, σ_y, and σ_z is given by

$$B = V(\sigma_x{}^m/\sigma_0{}^m)[I/I_0] \tag{2}$$

where V is the volume of the element and the reference axes are selected so that σ_x is the maximum principal stress. σ_0 and m are material constants, and

$$\frac{I}{I_0} = \frac{\iint[\cos^2\phi\cos^2\Psi + (\sigma_y/\sigma_x)\cos^2\phi\sin\Psi + (\sigma_z/\sigma_x)^2\sin^2\phi - (\sigma_u/\sigma_x)]^{m-1}\cos\phi\,d\phi\,d\Psi}{\iint[\cos^2\phi\cos^2\Psi]^{m-1}\cos\phi\,d\phi\,d\Psi} \tag{3}$$

where σ_u is another material constant, and Ψ and ϕ are angles defining a point on a spherical surface of unit radius centered at the center of the element under consideration. Furthermore, the integrations extend only to positive values of the terms within the brackets.

Curves for evaluating $[I/I_0]$ have been computed (in the AGARD

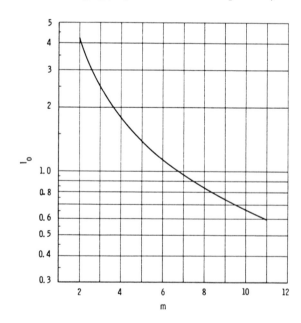

FIG. 6. Variation I_0 with m.

Handbook) for a large number of values of the parameters involved in order to facilitate the determination of the failure probability when extensive computer facilities are not available. A sample of these curves is given in Figs. 6–9.

For a complete structural component, the probability of failure is given by

$$S = \sum B \tag{4}$$

where the summation is extended to all component elements for which B is positive, and providing also that the probability of failure is small (less than 10^{-5}). (See AGARD Handbook.)

If the component is subjected to a proof stress, of any distribution, then the probability of failure is given by

$$S = \sum (B - B_P) \tag{5}$$

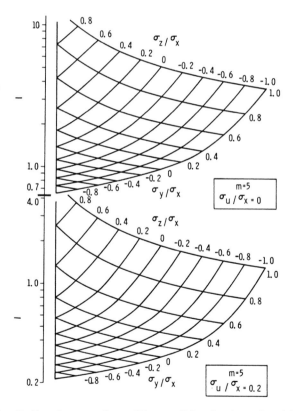

FIG. 7. Complex stress factor I for $m = 5.0$ and $\sigma_u/\sigma_x = 0$ and 0.2.

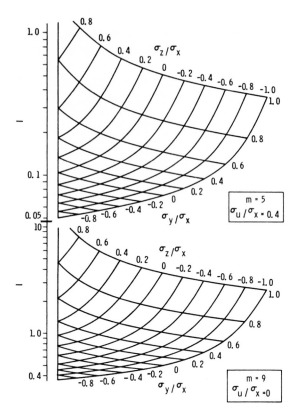

FIG. 8. Complex stress factor I for $m = 5.0$, $\sigma_u/\sigma_x = 0.4$ and $m = 9.0$, $\sigma_u/\sigma_x = 0$.

where the B values of each element are evaluated for the applied stress distribution, and the B_P values of each element are evaluated for the proof stress distribution.

In the application of brittle nonmetallic materials, it is customary to determine the material strength characteristics by conducting bending tests to failure on small bars of rectangular cross section. A four-point loading system is used so that the center portion of the bar is subjected to a constant bending moment.

Applying the Weibull expression to this condition and considering, conservatively, only the volume of material subjected to the maximum bending moment, one finds the following expression for failure probability:

$$S = 1 - \exp\left\{ -\frac{V}{2(m+1)} \left[\frac{(\sigma_b - \sigma_u)^{(m+1)}}{\sigma_0{}^m \sigma_b} \right] \right\} \qquad (6)$$

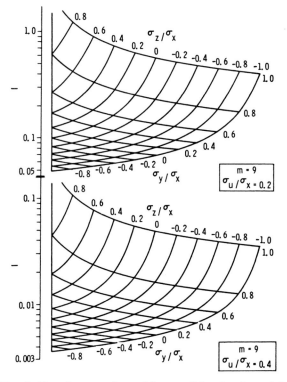

FIG. 9. Complex stress factor I for $m = 5.0$ and $\sigma_u/\sigma_x = 0.2$.

where σ_b is the maximum bending stress. If N bars are tested and are arranged in order of increasing failure stress, and if σ_{b_n} is the failure stress of the nth bar, as measured in the test, then the failure probability corresponding to the fracture stress σ_{b_n} is

$$S_n = n/(N+1) \tag{7}$$

These equations can be used to determine the Weibull constants for the material. To do this, the above equation is rewritten, for the nth test bar, as follows:

$$\log \log(1 - S_n)^{-1} + \log \sigma_{b_n} = (m+1) \log(\sigma_{b_n} - \sigma_u)$$

$$+ \log\left(\frac{V}{2(m+1)}\right) - m \log \sigma_0 \tag{8}$$

which shows that a plot of the Weibull distribution function will be linear in a system of rectangular coordinates in which $\log \log(1 - S_n)^{-1} + \log \sigma_{b_n}$ is the ordinate and $\log(\sigma_{b_n} - \sigma_u)$ the abscissa. The slope will be $(m+1)$ of the distribution function in these coordinates.

Assuming a four-point bending test, the extreme fiber stresses at failure are determined, using the simple bending stress formula

$$\sigma_b = 3Pa/bd^2 \tag{9}$$

where σ_b is the maximum bending stress at failure, P is total applied load at failure, a is the distance from the ends of the bar to the load application points, b is width of test bar, and d is depth of test bar.

For each test specimen, the value of the terms $[\log \log(1 - S_n)^{-1} + \log \sigma_{b_n}]$ and $\log \sigma_{b_n}$ are determined. Values of $[\log \log(1 - S_n)^{-1} + \log \sigma_{b_n}]$ are plotted against the corresponding values of $\log \sigma_{b_n}$. If the resulting curve is a straight line, the material does not have a finite zero strength σ_u. A concave downward curve indicates the material does have a finite zero strength; a tentative value is then taken for σ_u, $\log(\sigma_b - \sigma_u)$ is calculated and the test data replotted. If the tentative value for σ_u is too large, the resulting curve will be concaved upward and smaller values for σ_u must be taken until the resulting curve approximates a straight line. At this point, the method of least squares is used to determine the slope of the straight line and the goodness of fit of the test data to the straight line for values of σ_u above and below the graphically determined value. The value for σ_u is selected which gives the best fit of the test data to a straight line, and m is computed from

$$\text{slope} = m + 1 \tag{10}$$

With σ_u and m established, σ_0 is calculated using the intercept of the straight line on the ordinate and the volume of the test specimen which was subjected to the applied stress. The value of the intercept is equated to $\log[V/2(m + 1)] - m \log \sigma_0$ and the equation solved for σ_0.

B. General Method of Stress Analysis for Joints in Brittle Materials

The finite element analysis method is very effective for stress analysis of brittle material joints. However, it requires a large-scale, highly automated computer program, because accurate analyses of practical joint configurations in this mode necessitate the development and solution of large order ($>$100) systems of algebraic equations.

In the present discussion, it will be assumed that the analysis procedure in question is the displacement approach to finite element structural analysis. Alternative forms of finite element analysis, particularly the matrix force approach, are in fact practiced by large organizations in the aerospace industry and have been applied successfully to joint design. The range of elements employed in matrix force analysis is presently limited, however, and does not extend to the types to be described subsequently. An in-depth examination of alternative approaches to finite element structural analysis is given by Gallagher (1964).

The basis of the method is the concept that any structure, however complex, can be represented as a system of "finite elements." Each type of element needed for the representation of the classes of structures to which the capability is to be addressed is assumed to behave, under load, in an idealized manner. Thus, with an assigned simplified form of stress or displacement response, formulations can be obtained for the element which expresses the edge forces or stresses as functions of the as yet unknown edge displacements. The elements are joined together analytically through the writing of equations of joint equilibrium, resulting in a system of equations relating the applied loads to all of the defined displacements (degrees of freedom) of the system. These are algebraic equations and are solved for the displacements. Subsequent algebraic operations yield the solution for the stress state throughout the structure.

The principal features of the above-described approach include its versatility with respect to practical applications and its amenability to development in the form of the earlier-noted highly automated computer program. A representative form for such a program is described in the following.

The flow of information in this program is portrayed in Fig. 10. The input data consist simply of the geometric description of the joint, material properties, specified loads, and the definition of the finite elements which constitute the analytical model. This information is directly referred to the portion of the program containing the library of finite element formulations. Available in this library must be a sufficient number of different types of elements to represent properly the range of situations encountered in brittle material joint design. A review of elements most commonly required

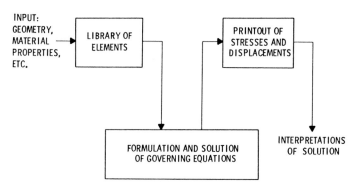

FIG. 10. General purpose program for discrete element analysis.

in this area is presented below. It should be noted, however, that modern programming concepts permit the expeditious inclusion of new element types into the analysis program system at any time in the future when the occasion arises.

Once the pertinent element formulations have been drawn from the library and numerically evaluated for each element of the total structure under analysis, the next operation is to develop and solve the systems of equations which describe the behavior of the total structure. The element formulations are combined in an automatic and straightforward procedure to yield the desired equations, and solution is accomplished through use of the more efficient of the many mathematical subroutines today available for this purpose [see Tocher (1966), for example]. The subject portion of the program extends through to the back-substitution of solved-for displacements into the element formulations to obtain the internal stress distribution.

Typically, the printout of the solution consists of a list of the predicted displacements of the joints which connect the elements, the state of stress within each element, the reactions on the boundary of the structure, and the results of various checks that are programmed to assess the validity of the results. Depending on the sophistication of the program, it is possible to include the determination of principal stresses and to develop trajectories of these in the form of graphical output.

The foregoing type of program requires implementation with the pertinent element formulations. The prevalent forms of solid element for the three-dimensional stress analysis of brittle material joints are pictured in Fig. 11; they consist of the triangular cross-section ring, the tetrahedron, and the rectangular parallelepiped.

The triangular ring element, which was formulated with the thermal stress analysis of brittle material rocket engine linings in mind, has been extensively employed in that field and can be regarded as thoroughly verified with respect to solution accuracy. The element formulations,

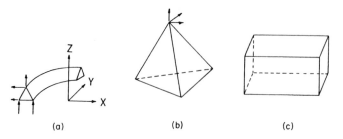

FIG. 11. Finite elements for solid structure analysis: (a) triangular cross-section ring; (b) tetrahedron; (c) rectangular prism.

presented by Wilson (1965), Clough and Rashid (1965), and Rashid (1966), are based on the assumption that the element edges sustain linear displacement modes in the deformed state (which is identical to the assumption of constant stress within the element) and axisymmetric behavior. Published formulations of this and the other cited solid elements account for orthotropic material properties.

The tetrahedron element is a basic geometric shape for complex, nonsymmetric problems, but is disadvantageous from the standpoint of defining the analytical model. Thus, the rectangular parallelepiped is preferred for representation of the major portion of the volume of a solid, with tetrahedra being employed to "fill out" the irregular portions of the analytical model. Formulations for the tetrahedron were first advanced by Gallagher et al. (1964). Subsequently, the relationships were expressed in terms of special coordinates by Argyris (1965a) and for more sophisticated assumed representations of deformational behavior by Argyris (1965b). The basic representation of Gallagher et al. (1964) employs the concept of linear displacement functions, with an associated restriction to the constant-stress case within the element.

Formulations for the rectangular parallelepiped are reported by Melosh (1963). Again, it is assumed that the element faces remain planar in the deformed state.

Certain applications can make use of two-dimensional elements (e.g., plates), either in a direct representation or modified to account for three-dimensionality, as in the case of the plane strain condition. The wide variety of available formulations for such elements places their review beyond the scope of this chapter. The reader is advised to consult Przemieniecki et al. (1965) for comprehensive summaries of the characteristics of two-dimensional element formulations.

Przemieniecki et al. (1965) have shown that the solution-accuracy and convergence characteristics of finite element representations for two-dimensional structural analysis were well established during the decade since the introduction of the analytical technique in the early 1950's. The three-dimensional formulations, however, have evolved only since 1961, and have not had, in each case, the type of thorough experience in practical applications which furnishes complete verification of solution accuracy. Nevertheless, the existing formulations are based on appropriate concepts in finite element theory and are to be regarded as correct.

Joint analysis problems often involve geometries in which one dimension (the joint thickness) is very much smaller than the others (the dimensions in the plane of the bond or contract surfaces). Yet, the stress analysis objectives require analysis gridwork requirements in all directions. The result is a tendency toward the use of elongated elements, and, in this regard, a caution must be given, since the accuracy of element formulations deteriorates as the element aspect ratios grow large. This has been shown by Taig and Kerr (1964).

The above circumstances also dictate the problem size requirements cited at the outset of this section. Large problem size is prejudicial, from the standpoint of computational cost, data interpretation, and availability of the method to a wide population of designers. These difficulties do not affect all potential users. Major aerospace firms and the larger organizations dealing with major structural engineering projects have at their disposal the type of computer and finite element program which can cope with these factors. Also, capabilities which have been specialized to deal with brittle material joint analysis are at the disposal of a far wider group of practitioners. Nevertheless, the practical value of an analytical method must be judged, to some extent, on its accessibility to any prospective user. It would appear that the latter objective is approaching fulfillment with the introduction of the highly efficient third generation class of computers and associated time-sharing concepts.

C. Stress-Concentration Method of Analysis for Local Effects

In the absence of computer methods to develop the stress analysis of a component of complex shape under complex loads, an approximation can be made by using engineering theory to compute stresses due to bending and axial load, across the principal sections, and then superimposing the effect of various stress concentrations, such as changes of cross section, points of load application, the presence of holes, etc. Stress distributions resulting from many different concentration effects such as these have been determined, either by photoelastic methods or by application of the theory of elasticity, and are available in the literature. From the discussion of brittle material joining concepts in Sect. III, the various stress-concentration effects that are likely to be of interest can be determined and, in this section, graphical data for the determination of stress concentration factors for most of these effects are given.

All of the data presented are taken from the available literature, but, in most instances, these data have been rearranged and condensed so as to produce a more compact presentation and to emphasize those aspects significant to design.

Considerable use has been made of the principle of superposition, so that many secondary effects, such as the effect of a finite component boundary on the stress distribution due to a hole, can be included as correction factors to a basic stress-concentration factor. In these instances, substantial license has been taken in the interests of convenience and simplicity, and the data is offered without proof of accuracy but with confidence that the results are conservative. These approximations are considered justified, however, in the interests of convenience, since this general method of stress analysis is approximate. Furthermore, the statistical determination of allowable stresses and the description of material variability, which are the basis of the statistics, are at present, quite approximate. Thus, while the refinement of stress analysis methods to include stress-concentration effects is necessary with brittle materials, very accurate predictions of these effects are not presently justified.

All of the stress-concentration data presented are concerned with peak stresses, since very little data are available in the literature on the stress distribution away from the point of maximum stress or on the stresses normal to the maximum. In conventional stress analysis, the peak stress is the primary consideration, since it will control static strength of the component if the material is of low ductility, or it will control fatigue strength even with ductile materials. Accordingly, it is not generally necessary to know the associated stress distribution. In order to make an analysis of the component failure probability, however, the entire stress distribution must be known. Again, recognizing the approximate nature of the failure probability analysis, the very localized effect of stress concentrations, and the limited amount of stress distribution data available, it is suggested that, for failure probability estimates only, the problem be treated by assuming a certain volume of material subjected to the peak stress. For each stress concentration effect, an approximate assessment of the magnitude of this volume can be made from the limited stress distribution data which are available. For instance, the stress distribution around a circular hole in an infinite plate under uniaxial tension is known, and the volume of material subjected to a principal stress greater than any selected ratio of the maximum principal stress can be determined. It is suggested that the same volumes be used for the effect of holes of noncircular shape, with or without reinforced edges, in the presence of component boundaries, etc. The stress level (in terms of the peak stress) at which there is no longer a significant contribution to component failure probability must be judged by the designer, based on the strength distribution curve for the particular material. Despite the gross approximations involved in the above procedure, it is easy to ensure conservative results, and the method and data are offered until more refined techniques are available.

The stress-concentration data presented in Figs. 12–23 are based on the various joint concepts presented in Sect. III and are attempts to present some useful information, for the designer, for all of the stress analysis problems presented.

Figures 12–16 present stress-concentration effects for changes in cross

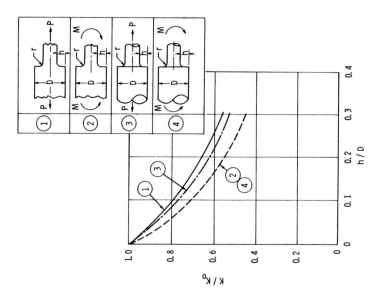

FIG. 13. Geometric stress-concentration correction factors for finite boundaries, for flat bars and rods with fillets under tension or bending.

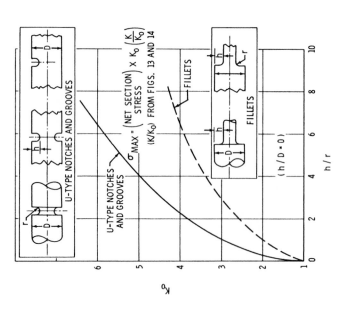

FIG. 12. Geometric stress-concentration parameters for flat bars and rods with U-type notches, grooves, and fillets under tension or bending.

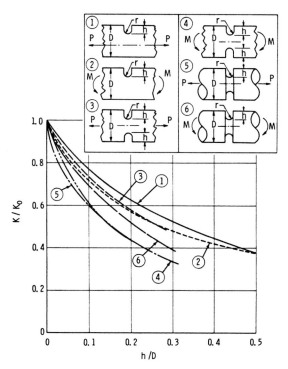

FIG. 14. Geometric stress-concentration correction factors for finite boundaries, for U-type notches and grooves for flat bars and rods under tension or bending.

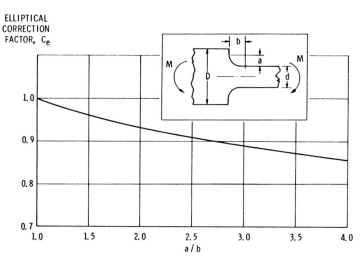

FIG. 15. Correction factors for elliptical fillets in flat bars in bending, for $D/d \sim 3$.

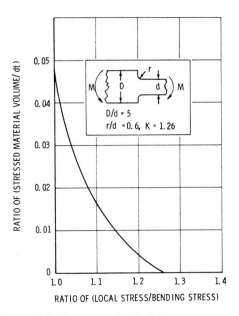

Fɪɢ. 16. Affected material volume associated with stress concentration for a circular fillet under bending.

section in the presence of a fillet. The basic curve (Fig. 12) gives the stress concentration when the change in cross section is very small, and then secondary factors are given to correct for larger section changes and for noncircular fillets. The total stress-concentration factor is the product of all of these individual factors. Torsion loadings are not included, since the effects of torsion are principally shear stresses, and, in current brittle material failure probability theory, shear stress is not considered. Figure 16 gives some data from which one can assess the volume of material affected by a fillet at a cross section change. Information on the distribution of stresses at a change in cross section is very difficult to obtain, and Fig. 16 is based on photoelastic data and is taken from a single example. The geometry associated with this example is indicated on the figure. A relatively large fillet radius is involved in this example; a smaller radius will give higher stress concentrations but a smaller volume of affected material, so the use of the figure should be conservative.

Figures 17–21 give similar data for the effect of holes. Three basic curves (Figs. 17–19) give stress concentrations for reinforced holes of any elliptical shape in an infinite plate subjected to uniaxial and biaxial stresses. Correction factors for the effect of a finite boundary are given in Fig. 20, while Fig. 21 gives data on the volume of material affected by the "disturbance."

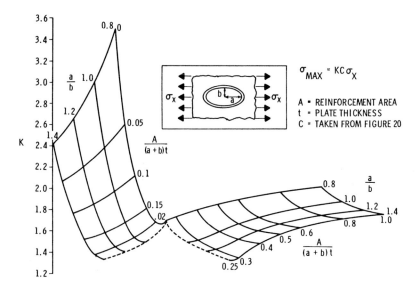

FIG. 17. Geometric stress-concentration factors for reinforced elliptical holes in infinite flat plates, uniaxial tension (based on Royal Aeronautical Society Handbook (1966)).

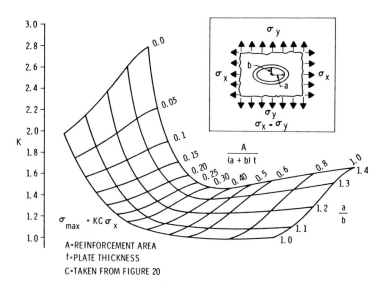

FIG. 18. Geometric stress-concentration factors for reinforced elliptical holes in infinite flat plates, biaxial tension, $\sigma_x/\sigma_y = 1.0$ (based on Royal Aeronautical Society Handbook (1966)).

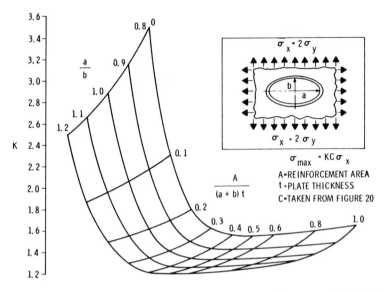

FIG. 19. Geometric stress-concentration factors for reinforced elliptical holes in infinite flat plates, biaxial tension, $\sigma_x/\sigma_y = 2.0$ (Based on Royal Aeronautical Society Handbook (1966)).

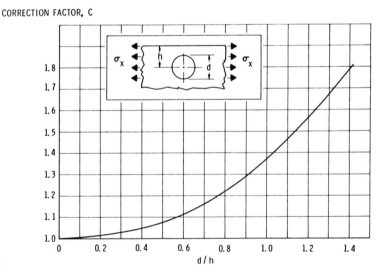

FIG. 20. Correction factor for the effect of finite boundary near a hole.

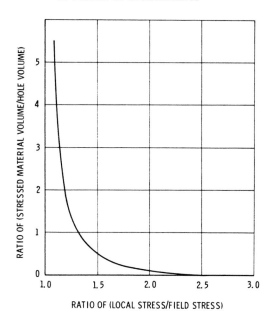

FIG. 21. Affected material volume associated with stress concentration in infinite sheet with circular hole under uniaxial stress.

Local concentration effects under the point of application of loads, specifically, bolts or pins in holes, are given in Table I. Graphical data are unnecessary in this case, since the expressions defining stresses and stress distributions are relatively simple.

Data to assist in the design of tension-type joints are given in Figs. 22 and 23, which show stress-concentration factors for T-type fittings with bolted attachment. Stress distribution data is not available for this situation, so that data on the volume of material experiencing various levels of stress are not given. However, the stress-concentration problem is similar to that which develops at a change of cross section with a fillet. It is suggested, therefore, that the information given in Fig. 16 be used as a guide to the volume of material affected by the stress concentration for the case of the tension joint.

For adhesively bonded or brazed lap joints, there are essentially no analyses available in the open literature which give stress-concentration factors for the stresses in the splice plates, although many analyses have been made of the stresses in the bond. An isolated example has been found in a survey conducted by Kutscha (1964), who quotes from a work by Goodwin in 1963. In this example, a 0.040-inch splice plate brazed to a 0.080-inch bar with a 0.003-inch braze layer is analyzed. The length of

TABLE I

CONTACT PRESSURE—CYLINDER IN A CIRCULAR GROOVE
[k VALUES]

	Pin material, D_2		
Lug material, D_1	Steel	Columbium	Molybdenum
Graphite	2660	2310	2860
Zirconia	2980	2510	3270
Aluminum oxide	3410	2750	3870
Silicon carbide	3550	2820	4070
Boron nitride	1963	1809	2040
Zirconium diboride	3410	2750	3870

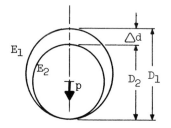

Maximum stress:

$$\sigma_c = \frac{k(p\,\Delta d)^{1/2}}{D_1}$$

Associated material volume subjected to peak stresses:

$$\text{Vol/inch} = \frac{\pi}{4K_r^2}\left(\frac{pD_1}{E_1}\right)$$

where

$$k = 0.798\left[E_1 \middle/ \left\{(1-\mu_1^2)\left[1 + \left(\frac{1-\mu_2^2}{1-\mu_1^2}\right)\left(\frac{E_1}{E_2}\right)\right]\right\}\right]^{1/2}$$

P loading (lb/inch)
μ Poisson's ratio
E modulus of elasticity
$K_r = \sigma_1/\sigma_p$
σ_1 principal stress level below which stresses do not add significantly to the probability of failure.
σ_p peak principal stress level

overlap is 0.70 inch, and the ratio of braze modulus to sheet modulus is 0.667. The joint is constrained so that bending stresses and bending deformations do not result from eccentricity of the splice plate. The splice plate is tapered in thickness and a fillet is assumed at the edge of the braze, both considerations which will minimize the stress concentration in the plates. From this study, a stress concentration of 2.25 is indicated. Again, the volume of material affected by this concentration is very small; the stress-concentration factor being reduced to 1.1 within a radius of 0.010 inch.

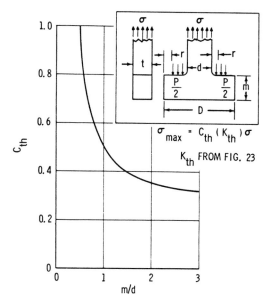

FIG. 22. Stress-concentration factor for T-head configuration.

The same reference also gives, in generalities, the results of parametric studies by Goodwin. For instance, if the joint is allowed to bend by removing constraints, such as would be the case with a single lap joint, the maximum tension stress in the sheet becomes very large. In fact, an unsupported asymmetric joint of this type should be avoided in brittle materials. Changes in braze modulus do not seem very significant, although the changes considered (55% reduction) are small, compared with a change from braze to ceramic bonds. Braze thickness also had a very small effect. Tapering of the splice plate made only slight reductions in the maximum tensile stress, compared with an untapered plate, as did increasing the length of the overlap to three times the value mentioned above. Apparently, the stress-concentration factor given above seems to be reasonably good for any practical geometry, at least for plate tension stress. Note, however, that the braze or bond shear stress is much more sensitive to the variables mentioned.

One other unpublished study has been conducted specifically for this chapter. It considered lap joints with untapered plates of equal thickness and a lap-length-to-plate-thickness ratio of 5.0. This joint was allowed to undergo bending due to the eccentricity of a single lap. Two ratios of bond-modulus-to-plate-modulus were considered, representative of a ceramic adhesive and a metallic braze, respectively, both in conjunction

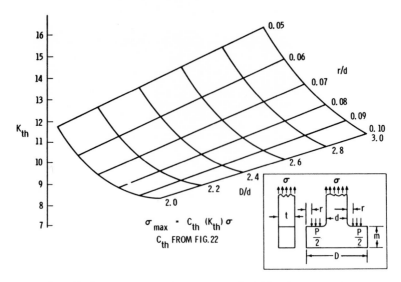

FIG. 23. Stress-concentration parameter for T-head configuration.

with brittle nonmetallic refractory plates. In both cases, the bond-thickness-to-plate-thickness ratio was 0.01. The ratio of maximum principal stress to applied stress was 3.80 for the brazed and 4.36 for a ceramic bonded joint.

V. Experimental Results

Review of the literature shows that very little experimental work has been done with brittle material joints, and the programs reviewed have not, in general, followed the approaches described in this chapter.

The experimental evaluations that have been conducted on attachment methods for brittle materials may be categorized as dealing with the following:

a.   Bolted attachments.
b.   Bonded attachments
c.   Clamped attachments
d.   Internal flanged attachments for cylinders.

All evaluations were conducted at room temperature, and, in most cases, the attachment methods did not consider all mechanical aspects of high temperature attachments; that is, the joints did not include design features to maintain tightness at elevated temperature and also during cooldown to room temperature.

The results from these experimental evaluations are summarized in the following paragraphs and, where applicable, comparisons are made with predicted values.

Bolted joints in graphite and alumina, shown in Fig. 24, were evaluated by Arnquist (1960). Tensile control specimens were used to determine the basic material strengths and the relative efficiencies of the joints. The failure stress for each of the joints was based on the gross cross-sectional area with no provision to include the stress-concentration effect of the hole.

The countersunk fasteners used for the graphite lap joint resulted in lower joint efficiencies than for the protruding head fasteners, but the differences were small. The lower joint efficiencies may have resulted from the decreased effective cross-sectional area, due to the counter-sinking for the fasteners, and from the tension stresses induced in the specimens by torquing the fasteners. A comparison of the pinned and bolted-clamped joints loaded by two straps showed substantially greater joint

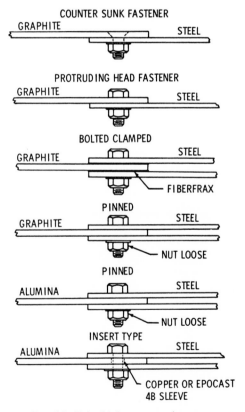

FIG. 24. Bolted joint test specimens.

efficiencies for the bolted-clamped specimens. The pinned-type joint is more susceptible to axial misalinement of loading, which may have caused bending stresses in the test joints.

For the alumina test joints, the use of Epocast inserts resulted in the highest joint efficiencies. The copper insert joint was no better than the plain pinned joint, which is somewhat surprising, since it would be expected that the local bearing stresses would be reduced by using a soft interface material.

The joint efficiencies obtained in Arnquist's studies are low, but the values in themselves are not significant in establishing the feasibility of designing reliable joints in brittle materials. Unfortunately, since a stress analysis of the joints is not given, the effectiveness of the design techniques used cannot be assessed.

Frye and Oken (1962) investigated joining methods for attaching alumina to a metallic structure. Two types of bolted joints were evaluated: (1) bolted joints with nominal holes, and (2) sleeved or potted bolts using copper and brass sleeves, Sairset cement, Presstite, and silver braze potting. The specimens were a simple rectangular shape, concentrically loaded. Before conducting tensile tests with the above specimens, the authors conducted torque-down tests with countersunk and hexhead fasteners in $\frac{1}{4}$-inch-thick alumina plate. All of the specimens containing countersunk fasteners failed during torquing, presumably due to the wedging action of the countersunk head, although the authors indicate the mismatch of the bolt head and hole taper to be the cause. For the hexhead torque-down tests, either the nut was stripped or the bolt broke. The tensile tests show large scatter in the results from simple bolted joints, significant benefit from metallic sleeves (by a factor of at least 2.0), but surprisingly poor results from the use of silver braze. Potting with cements produced various results; Presstite, for instance, produced significant improvements, but Sairset cement did not. The tensile strength of all the joint specimens, however, was substantially less than would be predicted by taking the net section strength (0.10 to 0.20 times the net area strength).

Two types of bolted attachments in ATJ graphite were evaluated by Anthony et al. (1960); the "standard lug" described in Sect. III, and the "single point" attachment for small diameter leading edges (Fig. 25). These two attachment schemes compensated for the differential expansion between the graphite and the metallic connecting members by utilizing tapers. For the "single point" attachment, in which the connection is made through two bolts, the differential axial growth between the bolt holes in both members of the joint is compensated by slotting one of the bolt holes in the metallic member of the joint. Elevated temperature tests of both joints were conducted to determine the effectiveness of the tapers to

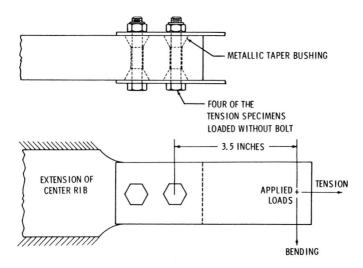

FIG. 25. Single-point attachment, bending and tension loading setup.

accommodate the differential expansion. Both joints retained "tightness" at elevated temperature, as well as during cooldown to room temperature, although it was not known whether the attachments become tighter at high temperature or had the same degree of tightness as when assembled at room temperature.

The joints were tested in tension, and the results were compared with the predicted failure loads for both attachments based on (a) the ATJ graphite strength for one failure in one hundred, and (b) the mean strength of the ATJ graphite. In addition to making predictions based on two material strength levels, two analysis methods were also used to predict the failure loads for the standard lug. The first method considered the lug as a plate loaded through a hole with a stress-concentration factor for the effect of the hole, while the second method employed the theory of elasticity. Stress-concentration factors only were used for the single point attachment stress analyses.

Two standard lugs were loaded to destruction in tension and, in both cases, the failure load was 1800 lb. One of the lug specimens had a prior loading history. This lug was subjected to 300 repeated load cycles which varied from zero to 1200 to 0 lb. Evidently, this prior loading history did not cause material damage. An additional standard lug, which had been coated with an oxidation-resistant coating, failed at 850 lb. It was noted from the material test bars, however, that the coating lowered the strength of the ATJ graphite, because the coating contained microcracks due to the differential expansion of the coating and the graphite substrate.

A comparison of the two methods of analysis indicated the failure loads predicted by the theory of elasticity method (640 lb for one failure in one hundred strength and 1050 lb based on the mean strength) and the loads predicted by the stress-concentration method for one failure in one hundred (700 lb) were conservative. The mean strength and the stress-concentration method gave good predictions (1320 lb) for the uncoated lug; for a small sample size, the mean strength should, therefore, be realized. However, the mean strength and the stress-concentration method were unconservative for the prediction of the coated lug failure load (1240 lb), even though the strength data were obtained from coated bars. It is believed that these latter results are quite questionable due to the cracks in the coating.

Five "single point" attachments were subjected to tension loads, and five specimens were loaded by differential shear loads by a loading bar, as shown in Fig. 25. Four of the tension specimens were loaded by one bolt, and one specimen was loaded through two bolts. The predicted failure load for one failure in one hundred was 914 lb, while the mean strength prediction was 1550 lb. The test failure loads ranged from 1640 to 2380 lb. Evidently, predictions including stress-concentration effects and the use of the mean strength, since only a few samples were involved, gave very satisfactory results. The highest failure load (2380 lb) was obtained by the specimen loaded through two bolts; this would be expected, since the stress-concentration factor for a multiple connection is lower. This effect was not included in the predictions. The predicted failure loads for the single point attachments loaded by differential shear loads were 340 and 580 lb, based on the one failure in one hundred strength and the mean strength, respectively. These are the predicted loads which, when applied to the loading bar 3.5 inches from the outboard hole, would cause failure. The actual failure loads ranged from 390 to 415 lb. In this case, the prediction using stress-concentration factors and the material mean strength is a little unconservative but still in remarkably good agreement.

Another series of tests were conducted by Anthony et al. (1960) to obtain experimental indications of the effect of lug proportions on load carrying capability. These specimens were essentially with lugs machined at the end of the specimen. There were four types of lugs:

a. 0.250-inch hole diameter, 1.250-inch lug diameter, 0.500-inch thick.
b. 0.500-inch hole diameter, 1.500-inch lug diameter, 0.500-inch thick.
c. 1.000-inch hole diameter, 2.000-inch lug diameter, 0.500-inch thick.
d. 0.500-inch hole diameter, 1.500-inch lug diameter, 1.000-inch thick.

All the lugs were designed with equal cross-sectional areas except type d, which had a cross-sectional area twice that of the others. Equal areas eliminated the effect of size between specimens a, b, and c. That is, the failure load should be identical for types a, b, and c if concentration factors and material variability could be neglected. With specimen d having the same geometry as specimen b, but twice the cross-sectional area, a direct indication of the effect of size was obtained. If there were no size effect, type d should have had twice the load carrying capability of type b.

Predicted failure loads were calculated, both on one failure in one hundred strength and on the mean strength, by use of the stress-concentration factor method for a flat plate loaded through a pin, and five lugs of each type were tested in tension. Both sets of predictions and the test results are shown in Table II. The predicted failure loads based on the one

TABLE II

Test Results of Lug Failure Load

| Lug type | No. | Predicted failure load, (lb) | | Average failure load (lb) |
		1 failure in 100 strength	Mean strength	
A	5	Conservative	350	434
B	5	Conservative	520	581
C	5	Conservative	730	732
D	5	Conservative	1040	813

failure in one hundred strength tended to be conservative. The predicted failure loads with the use of the mean strength, as Table II indicates, showed excellent agreement, except for lug type d. This discrepancy may have been a size effect of the ATJ graphite, which was not used in the predicted failure load.

Since the cross sectional area of specimen type a, b, and c were equal, the only variable (other than the variability of the material) was the stress-concentration factor due to the geometry of the lug. As the hole-diameter-to-lug-diameter ratio increases, the stress-concentration factor is reduced. The test results also indicate this. Type a lugs, which had the smallest ratio of hole-to-lug diameters, had the lowest average failure load, while type c lugs, with the highest ratio of hole-to-lug diameters, had the highest average failure load. The results from this series of tests provide considerable confidence in the approach of including the effects of stress concentrations in designing reliable brittle material joints.

The effectiveness of ceramic-to-ceramic joints bonded with inorganic adhesives was investigated by Hofer (1965). Aluminum oxide bend bars were cut transversely and rejoined with the inorganic adhesives. Approximately 10 different adhesives were used in this investigation. Flexure tests were conducted on these bend bars and the failure strengths were compared to the mean failure strength of aluminum oxide bend bars without joints. The bar failure strengths were only 1.3 to 5.4% of the mean failure strength of the bend bars without joints. All of the failures occurred in the joints. The test results were not very encouraging, but it is difficult to understand why such tests were conducted, since it is not considered good engineering practice to subject adhesives to tension loadings.

Frye and Oken (1962) also investigated bonded joints, but with the bond in shear, and their results are promising, but the testing was limited. Each specimen consisted essentially of an alumina plate bonded to a metal plate and loaded in tension. The alumina plate ends were either parallel or modified by machining a shoulder or a taper. Bonding was supplemented in the joints by use of a bolt or clamping. The test failures for the clamped-and-bonded shoulder end and the clamped-and-bonded tapered end specimens did not occur in the bonded area but at points of stress concentrations that were introduced into the alumina element of the specimens by the machining of the filleted shoulder or the taper. The bonded-and-bolted parallel end specimens with no bolt load attained the highest joint strength. In fact, a load capability approaching that which would be predicted from the net area strength through the bolt hole was achieved. The results from this series of tests again suggest that adhesively bonded joints designed with stress-concentration factors in mind may be satisfactory. Also, as would be expected, there is no benefit to be gained by combining bolts with a bonded joint.

Clamped joints were also studied by Hofer (1965). Specimens were fabricated in Marblette, a brittle organic substance, and also in Hydrostone plaster. The specimens were bars which had a "necked down" region at each end to receive the clamps. Approximately 100 joints in each material were tested in tension. The joint efficiencies ranged from 13.3 to 26.5% for the Hydrostone specimens, and from 18.3 to 38.1% for the Marblette specimens, based on the gross cross-sectional area. The specimens failed in the necked down area, the point of maximum stress concentration, and minimum cross-sectional area.

Frye and Oken (1962) conducted evaluations of three clamped joints in alumina. The test joints were somewhat different from Hofer's joints in that the alumina had a filleted shoulder machined at each end, and the metallic clamps butted against these shoulders. The test joint efficiencies were 14.6, 14.9 and 14.5%.

Unfortunately, these two investigations presented test results as joint efficiencies, and it is not possible to assess the effectiveness of the clamp joints, since a stress analysis of the joints is not given.

Attachments for joining cylindrical shells by internal flanges were studied by Hofer (1965). The test specimens, which simulated one-half of the joint, were cylinders 4 inches high, with an outside diameter of 4 inches and a wall thickness of $\frac{1}{4}$ inch, cast in Hydrostone plaster. The specimens were cast in three internal flange thicknesses: $\frac{1}{4}$, $\frac{3}{4}$, and $1\frac{1}{2}$ inches. The test specimens were mounted by cementing the unflanged end of the cylinder to a plate and applying an axial tension load to the cylinder by loading the internal flange through a loading disk. The results of these studies were presented as joint efficiencies, that is, the failure load was compared to the load carrying capacity of a homogeneous monolithic cylinder. Based on the mean strength, the joint efficiencies ranged from 5.7 to 14.9% and from 13.3 to 25.2%, for the $\frac{1}{4}$- and $\frac{3}{4}$-inch internal flanged cylinders, respectively. When the specimens with the $1\frac{1}{2}$-inch flange were tested in the same manner, failure of the adhesive bond at the unflanged end of the cylinder occurred. Therefore, the remaining cylinders were tested as cantilever cylindrical shells, mounted at the flanged end. Joint efficiencies were calculated on the basis of the theoretical bending stress present in a cantilever beam of the same length. Twenty-five specimens were tested with the resulting joint efficiencies ranging from 42.9 to 75.3%, based on the mean strength of the Hydrostone plaster.

The results from the internal flanged cylinders with an axial tension verified analytical studies of this joint by Hofer, in that increasing the flange thickness resulted in a substantial increase in the load carrying capacity of the joint. The higher joint efficiencies obtained for the joint in bending may have been a result of lower stress-concentration factors for bending relative to axial load, as well as a smaller volume of material subjected to the peak bending stresses.

In summary, the experimental evaluations of joints are very limited and have numerous shortcomings. Adequate support with stress analyses is generally not available, but, in the few cases where consideration of stress concentrations has been made and where adequate predictions are available for comparison with test results, there are remarkably good correlations and good indications that the methods presented in this chapter will lead to satisfactory joints.

VI. Recommended Research

The needs of brittle material joint design are most satisfactorily met, at present, with respect to stress analysis; the finite element analysis method has been developed to the point where a satisfactory stress analysis of a joint of essentially any configuration can be made. Development work here should proceed in the direction of design by computer, involving the selection of optimum geometry for a given set of load and environmental conditions, and for specified constraints. This subject is already being pursued by a number of investigators under the name of "structural synthesis," and, since this capability is required for essentially all aerospace structures, continued research can be anticipated without particular emphasis from the needs of brittle material joint design.

Another aspect of finite element analysis which needs attention is in the refinement of the available programs and procedures, so that computer time can be substantially reduced. The number of elements which must be used to represent adequately the geometric complexities of a typical structural joint, and in particular to detect adequately the localized stress concentrations, is large, and the resulting cost of problem solution is so great that extensive parametric studies are impractical. Here again, practitioners in finite element analysis are well aware of this need, since it is not unique to brittle material joint design, and continued improvement can be expected.

The next subject requiring attention is the development of statistical representation of the mechanical properties of brittle materials. Unfortunately, although considerable attention has been given to this matter, the methods in use are still limited to the Weibull representation, which has its basis in a series-type material model. Before too much effort is expended in improving this situation, however, there are two other subjects which should be pursued, since they may help to orient any work on strength variability representation.

One of the difficulties with the statistical representation of material strength is the large number of test specimens needed to define properly the strength distribution curve, particularly at the low levels of failure probability which are of practical interest. A most useful development, therefore, would be some method of conducting large numbers of mechanical property tests at low cost; possibly by multiple testing on a single specimen, or by some nondestructive method which detects material damage without specimen failure. If such methods can be developed so that a much larger quantity of data could be made available on the variability of material strength, then it should be correspondingly easier to find satisfactory mathematical descriptions of the distribution curves. In addition, the effect of many environmental and processing parameters on the distribution curves can be determined—information which at present is almost nonexistent.

It is also evident, from a few studies which have been conducted, that attempts to achieve a realistic level of structural reliability by working the structure at low stress levels are essentially impractical, at least with present materials. Accordingly, methods must be found, such as proof testing, to permit higher stress levels without reduction of reliability. The development of such methods might obviate the need for a more precise definition of the strength distribution curve than that given by the Weibull formula. For instance, proof testing establishes the lower limit of the strength distribution curve, and working stresses will generally be reasonably close to the proof test value, so that only a small section of the curve will actually be used. In this situation, an accurate definition of the curve may not be essential.

Two other aspects of material strength and its variability which need urgent attention are the mechanical properties, and their variability, under complex stress conditions; and related to this is the need for a better understanding of material failure modes, again under complex stress conditions. Essentially unknown for instance, are the effects of anisotropy, a characteristic common among many nonmetallic refractory materials.

The whole subject of attachment concepts for brittle materials needs extensive work, since virtually nothing has presently been done. Concepts for many different applications, for many loading systems, for various environmental conditions, and for many materials must be designed, developed, fabricated, and tested in order to define good and poor practice, and in order to determine how far the approach described in this chapter must be applied, where it is deficient, etc. As such work is undertaken, it will certainly involve optimum design techniques, as applied to brittle material joints. This is another subject which, to date, has received no attention, as will be evident from examination of the joint concepts presented in this chapter. Obviously, these are taken almost directly from metallic joining practices; also obvious is the fact that these will change considerably as they are optimized with respect to brittle material characteristics and as they reflect, for instance, the variability in material properties, the increased significance of stress concentrations, etc.

Research and development are also needed to establish design criteria for brittle material structures, in general, and joints, in particular. Certainly, because of strength variability, the conventional factor of safety must be replaced by an acceptable failure probability, and, possibly, this must be combined with probability of occurrence of various load levels. Criteria on acceptable material damage, redundancy, and a number of other design controlling aspects also need to be established.

VII. Summary and Conclusions

The most obvious conclusion that can be drawn from an examination of the subject of brittle material design in general, and the design of joints and attachments in particular, is the very limited amount of information and experimental work that exists. Nevertheless, the general characteristics of these materials are understood and it has been possible to assemble a rational approach to brittle material joint design which promises, on the basis of very limited tests, to be satisfactory. A considerable amount of experimental work is necessary before it can be determined whether all the steps in the proposed design procedures are necessary or, indeed, whether they are sufficient, but, nevertheless, a basis has been established which will permit the logical accumulation of data and experience, and which should lead eventually to a satisfactory technology.

It is also evident, from the data presented in this chapter, that many structural applications for brittle materials and, hence, for brittle material joints, exist chiefly in areas where the refractoriness of inorganic non-metallic compounds is necessary. An examination of these applications and an understanding, based on the characteristics of nonmetallic refractory materials, of the type of structural components which will be used has permitted a classification of joining methods into a relatively few types, and, in turn, this has permitted the definition of potential problem areas and the type of design data needed for satisfactory results.

It can also be concluded that the areas in which brittle material design differs from design with ductile materials include: the need to specify stress distributions much more accurately; the need to consider material variability and to use, as a consequence, a statistical definition of strength; the need to control material processing so that variability is minimized; the need to develop new failure theories for brittle materials; and the need to develop new design criteria, since conventional factors of safety have no meaning when the material strength is defined statistically.

With respect to these differences in design approach, it can be concluded that the techniques for achieving a sufficiently refined stress analysis are available, although there is room for development, particularly in the direction of minimizing the computer time needed for their application. Furthermore, a good approximation to the required stress distribution may be possible using the stress-concentration factor approach when extensive computer facilities are not available. Curves of stress-concentration factors particularly selected for use with joint and attachment design have been assembled, and most of the anticipated design situations have been accommodated.

It can also be concluded that a relatively large amount of work has been done in attempting to analytically define the variability of the mechanical properties of brittle materials, and, based on this work, useful graphs and charts for assessing the probability of failure of a complex component have been developed. However, this work is based primarily on a single approach to the definition of material strength, and the assumptions on which this approach is formulated are not particularly appropriate to the characteristics of structural materials, although the assumed curves for the description of strength variability do match limited experimental data quite well. It can also be concluded from the work reported in this chapter that, before too much effort is applied to the improvement of the method of describing variability in the mechanical properties of brittle materials, attention should be given to such practical matters as the stress levels and failure probability values which will be used, the techniques which will be necessary to maximize allowable stress levels for a given failure probability, and the design criteria philosophies which will define acceptable failure probabilities under various operating conditions. When these matters are examined, in conjunction with an understanding of the significance of strength variability in an actual complex component containing a wide distribution of stresses, the importance of accurately defining strength variability may change.

In all other areas where important differences in design approach can be anticipated between ductile and brittle materials, virtually no information or experience exists. This is particularly true of tests conducted on actual joints in brittle materials. The tests that have been conducted, however, can be divided into two groups: those conducted using commercial non-metallic materials and essentially conventional metallic material design approaches, where the result was generally failure; and those tests where efforts were made to select good quality materials and where some of the concepts mentioned above were applied to design. These latter, although very limited in number, show considerable success from which it can be concluded that a basis for satisfactory brittle material joint design is available.

Symbols

A	area	K_0	geometric stress-concentration parameter
B	risk of rupture		
B_P	risk of rupture, proof stress distribution	K_{th}	T-head stress-concentration parameter
C	correction factor	M	bending moment
C_e	elliptical correction factor	N	total number of bars
C_{th}	T-head stress-concentration factor	P	axial load
		S	probability of failure
D	diameter, depth	S_n	probability of failure of nth bar
E	Young's modulus of elasticity		
I	complex stress factor	V	volume
I_0	complex stress parameter	x, y, z	coordinates
K	geometric stress-concentration factor	d	depth, diameter
		Δd	diameter difference

h	height	σ_0	material characteristic stress
m	material flaw intensity	σ_p	peak principal stress level
n	rank	σ_u	stress at which there is zero
p	loading (lb/inch)		probability of failure
r	radius	μ	Poisson's ratio
t	thickness	Ψ, ϕ	angles defining a point on a
σ	stress		spherical surface of unit radius
σ_1	principal stress level		

ACKNOWLEDGMENTS

The authors wish to acknowledge the generous assistance of several individuals in the preparation of this chapter. Mr. A. Krivetsky developed all of the graphical data presented, while Mr. J. Witsil prepared all the figures. Dr. R. Gallagher prepared the discussion on finite element analysis, and Mr. A. Mistretta prepared the section on the review of experimental data on joints and attachments.

REFERENCES

AGARD (1968). "Brittle Material Design Handbook." Advisory Group for Aerospace Research and Development, Paris. (To be published.)

Anthony, F. M., Blessing, A. H., Buckley, E. H., and Dukes, W. H. (1960). "Investigation of Feasibility of Utilizing Available Heat-Resistant Materials for Hypersonic Leading Edge Applications," Technical Report No. WADC 59-744, Vol. 2. Wright Air Development Center, Wright-Patterson Air Force Base, Dayton, Ohio.

Anthony, F. M., Marcus, L., and Mistretta, A. L. (1965). "Selection Techniques for Brittle Materials," Technical Report No. 65-209, Vol. 1. Air Force Materials Laboratory, Wright-Patterson Air Force Base, Dayton, Ohio.

Argyris, J. H. (1965a). Am. Inst. Aeronaut. Astronaut. J. 3, 54–60.

Argyris, J. H. (1965b). "Continua and Discontinua: Proceedings of the Conference on Matrix Methods in Structural Mechanics," Technical Report No. AFFDL TR 66-80. Air Force Flight Dynamics Laboratory, Wright-Patterson Air Force Base, Dayton, Ohio.

Arnquist, J. L. (1960). In "Symposium on Design with Materials That Exhibit Brittle Behavior, Washington, D.C.," Vol. 1, pp. 236–263. Material Advisory Board, Washington, D.C.

Barnett, R. L., Costello, J. F., Hermann, P. C., and Hofer, K. E. (1965). "The Behavior and Design of Brittle Structures," Technical Report No. AFFDL TR 65-165. Air Force Flight Dynamics Laboratory, Wright-Patterson Air Force Base, Dayton, Ohio.

Clough, R. W., and Rashid, Y. (1965). J. Mech. Eng. Div. Am. Soc. Civil Engrs. 91, 71–85.

Frye, H., and Oken, S. (1962). "Large Ceramic Radome Manufacture by Dry-Isostatic Pressing Techniques," Final Report No. ASD TDR NR-62-967, Appendix 3. Aeronautical Systems Division, Wright-Patterson Air Force Base, Dayton, Ohio.

Gallagher, R. H. (1964). "A Correlation Study of Methods of Matrix Structural Analysis." Pergamon, Oxford.

Gallagher, R. H., Padlog, J., and Bijlaard, P. P. (1964). *Am. Rocket Soc. J.* **32**, 1152–1154.

Hofer, K. E. (1965). "Study of Attachments for Brittle Components," Final Report No. FDL-TDR-64-123, Pt. 2. *In* "Utilization of Refractory Nonmetallic Materials in Future Aerospace Vehicles," Pt. 2. Air Force Flight Dynamics Laboratory, Wright-Patterson Air Force Base, Dayton, Ohio.

Kutscha, D. (1964). "Mechanics of Adhesive Bonded Lap-Type Joints: Survey and Review." Report No. ML-TDR-64-298. Forest Products Laboratory, U.S. Department of Agriculture, Washington D.C.

Melosh, R. J. (1963). *J. Struct. Div. Am. Soc. Civil Engrs.* **89**, 205–224.

Przemieniecki, J., Bozich, W. F., Johnson, J. R., and Mykytow, W. J. (eds.) (1965). "Matrix Methods in Structural Mechanics" (Conference Proceedings), Technical Report No. AFFDL TR 66-80. Air Force Flight Dynamics Laboratory, Wright-Patterson Air Force Base, Dayton, Ohio.

Royal Aeronautical Society (1966). *Roy. Aeronaut. Soc. Eng. Sci. Data: Aeronaut. Ser. 5.* Royal Aeronautical Society, London.

Rashid, Y. (1966). *Nuclear Engineering and Design* No. 3, pp. 163–182.

Taig, I., and Kerr, R. (1964). *In* "Matrix Methods of Structural Analysis," pp. 267–315. Pergamon, London.

Tocher, J. L. (1966). *J. Struct. Div. Am. Soc. Civil Engrs.* **92**, 75–88.

Weibull, W. (1939). *Ing. Vetenskaps Akad.* **151**, 1–45.

Wilson, E. L. (1965). *Am. Inst. Aeronaut. Astronaut. J.* **3** (12), 2269–2274.

CHAPTER 7

EFFECTS OF RESIDUAL STRESS ON BRITTLE FRACTURE

A. A. Wells

Abstract: The usual definitions of applied stresses and residual stresses, arising from incompatibilities of strain in a body, are considered to depend on arbitrary definition of the boundaries of the body, from which it is argued that the fracture response of the material must be the same for each. Examples of residual stress systems are described, such as bolted, riveted, and welded joints, shrink fits, lack of fit in assembly, and rolled, peened, and differentially hardened surfaces, illustrating the extent to which residual stresses are susceptible to control and are often beneficial. The mechanisms of residual and reaction stress accumulation in welded joints are described in a semiquantitative manner to show, in particular, the influence of the equalization temperature and plastic yielding. The effects of residual stress on brittle fracture in casualties are illustrated in terms of nucleating defects and spontaneous cracking. The Fawley oil storage tank is identified as a model casualty, susceptible to exact analysis, and providing the key to laboratory study by notched and welded wide plate tests. The results of those summarized also contribute to knowledge of the effects of furnace and mechanical stress relief and of multirun welds in thick plates, and show that local damage at the nucleating flaw from thermal strain activated plastic flow is at least as important as elastic residual stress in producing spontaneous or low stress fractures. The methods of linear fracture mechanics are used to study crack propagation and arrest in low-stress fractures of notched and welded wide plates, such that the applied and residual elastic stress contributions to fracture are quantitatively compared; and the metallurgical nature of the local embrittlement is identified, and its influence on toughness estimated. It is shown that critical fracture conditions depend on balance between the static loading toughness in the damaged region and the propagation resistances, as affected by strain rate in the undamaged material beyond. Optimum conditions for furnace, mechanical, and local thermal stress relief are quantitatively described. It is considered that the topic of welding residual stresses is now of waning research interest, having been overtaken by a demand for investigation of the morphology of defect growth and local thermal damage in low alloy steels of structural quality.

I. Introduction

A. Stresses from External Loads and Residual Stresses

The physical concept of stress, defined as load transmitted over unit cross section, with normal and shear components, remains as a comparative abstraction, since there are very few situations in which it can be measured directly. The load suspended on a wire is one of these, but it is necessary to show, even in this simple case, that the load is uniformly distributed over the cross section of the wire. In order to do this, the associated concept of strain is introduced, and it is argued that the uniform distribution of stress follows, first, from the uniformity of extensional strain, and second, from the elastic relationship between stress and strain. This example epitomizes one of the difficulties associated with stress, strain, and fracture, in that stress can normally be inferred only from strain, yet the source of the strain may be in loading external to the body, or the body may be strained internally from some lack of fit in its members. Applied and residual stresses arise from these two sources of strain. As if the complexity were insufficient, a further uncertainty arises from relationships between stress and strain other than linear-elastic and, typically, the effects of yielding in ductile metals. It is not surprising, therefore, in the context of welding residual stresses, with which this paper will be much concerned, that there can have been authoritative statements in the past as contradictory as the following:

> Locked-in stresses do not contribute materially to failure (Ship Structure Committee, 1947);

> ...The hypothesis that residual stresses lead to failure in fabrication has been of great utility in that modified practices based on the validity of this hypothesis have been proved successful over many years of development in this field of activity (Osgood, 1954).

For practical purposes, most engineers recognize examples of residual stresses such as the riveted or bolted joint. Without such residual stresses, the joint would be slack and unfit for service. Residual stresses arising from thermal shrinkage in glass represent another example, where the associated distributions of strain are also made more readily apparent by photoelastic observation. Nevertheless, the definition of residual stress that depends on incompatibility of strains allows the acceptance of a hydraulic press under load as an example of residual stress, if the whole press is considered as a discrete body. Consequently, the distinction between applied and residual stresses must be considered as relative and subject entirely to arbitrary definition of the boundaries of the body under consideration. It is then but a slight step to the conclusion that elements of the material respond in the same way to the components of stress to which they are subjected, and will not distinguish the source of the stress, be it applied or residual.

A more important distinction arises from the ability of the deformation to "follow through" or be sustained in the presence of the stresses, whatever their source. This has much to do with the length of and compliance along the load path, or stress trajectory, and a load suspended on a wire, on the one hand, and a riveted joint, on the other hand, represent extreme examples. (Compliance is defined, in engineering terms, as the reciprocal of stiffness.) Yet another distinction arises from the triaxial stress state, since the stress conditions for both yielding and fracture require the definition of the components on all three orthogonal principal planes at a point. The combination of three tensile components favors tensile fracture; if one or more is compressive, shear deformation or fracture is a likely substitute. It is necessary, then, to see whether a triaxial tensile stress state is more likely to be induced by residual than by applied stresses. It will appear that this condition is more frequently produced by notching than by any particular configuration of applied or residual stresses. Finally, there is the aspect of embrittlement by the same agency that gives rise, in particular, to the residual stress system, which is likely to introduce confusion between cause and effect.

To the question as to whether residual stresses cause brittle fracture there can therefore be no clear-cut answer. Many factors must be considered in particular cases, and the best enlightenment that can be expected will issue from separating the effects of each recognizable variable.

B. Sources of Residual Stress

In the most general sense, states of residual stress may be divided into those produced by mere mechanical movement and those produced by permanent set of the material of construction. The second group can then be subdivided according to the mechanism producing permanent set.

Two such mechanisms involve differential plastic deformations from mechanical working and the application of heat, and a third arises from differential phase transformations. Although not necessarily exclusive, the number of cited systems will serve to illustrate the ubiquity of residual stresses.

The bolted joint is perhaps the best example of a mechanical system of residual stress, preserved by friction, but otherwise reversible in application. It is also an example in which it is patently obvious that fractures can be produced by the action of residual stresses alone, and one in which the combination of residual and applied stresses is of engineering importance in, for instance, the case of bolted pipe flanges with internal pressure. This case has given rise to the paradox of attenuation of load variation in flange bolts due to the action of pulsating pressure, the explanation being associated with the compressive preload on the gasket, which is merely relieved when the pressure rises. The degree of attenuation depends on the relative compliances of the components, and increases, in particular, with the ratio of the bolt to the gasket compliance, which is naturally high. Were it not for this fortunate characteristic, there might be many more fatigue failures in flange bolts associated with pressure vessels.

Residual tensile stress is induced in rivets as a result of precompression beyond the elastic limit, whether applied statically or by impact. In a simple analysis of this system, it can be assumed that the rivet deforms during compression at constant stress equal to the yield stress, until such time as the heads bear on the plates being joined, around the edges of the hole on both sides, to develop axial compressive stresses in the plate material that are limited to elastic magnitudes. On removal of the upsetting force, both sets of forces relax, and the interesting conclusion is that there can be no residual stress unless the compliance of the plates under the rivet heads exceeds that of the rivet. This compliance in cold riveting may be provided by washers, by the elastic spring of random corrugations in the plates, or by the effects of radial compressive stresses when the rivet fills the hole. In hot riveting, differential thermal contraction is deliberately provided to induce residual tension in the rivets, and this is more directly effective.

Rolling loads, or loads applied over limited areas, whether singly or in combination as peening, are capable of inducing residual surface compressive stresses on the surfaces of bodies, if sufficient in the first instance to cause yielding. An explanation of this effect is to be found in nonuniform stress distribution, as well as the influence of Poisson's ratio on elastic recovery. The local compression produces in the first instance a state of nearly hydrostatic, or nearly equal triaxial compressive stress near the surface, but the horizontal components must be reacted by parallel components of tensile stress in the regions below. The tensile stresses persist at diminished magnitude when the local surface compression is removed, as is made clearly evident when a railway line bows upward on being removed from the track after heavy duty. Residual surface compression is often beneficially employed to improve the fatigue resistance of engineering parts, but at least part of the improvement must be attributed to the closing of surface pores and microcracks, and favorable alinement of subsurface defects produced by the mechanical treatment, since the effect of compressive mean stress *per se* on fatigue performance is not always significantly large.

Most cold-working operations, insofar as they introduce nonuniform stress distributions and plastic deformation, also leave the object in a state of residual stress. This is sometimes conducive to delayed fracture, as in the season cracking of brass cartridge cases from the stress corrosion mechanism.

Shrink fitting of engineering parts represents one of the simplest and most useful applications of residual stress arising from differential heating and expansion, but there are at least two others of similar value. In the shrinking of buckled automobile panels to counteract distortion arising from manufacture or collision damage, use is made of one or a succession of heated spots from a blow torch. The heated spot, which should not be too great compared with the panel thickness, is restrained from radial expansion by surrounding material, and yields prematurely in compression at the high peak temperature corresponding to red heat. It accordingly contracts during cooling and may approach a state of yield point radial tension. Nevertheless, the surrounding area is induced into a state of circumferential compression. This process, in unskilled hands, may merely change the pattern of buckling, but is effective if used with experience and understanding. Heat spotting in thicker materials may be used to improve the fatigue resistance at susceptible design details of high stress concentration, such as exist at the ends of fillet weld attachments. Under these conditions, the residual compression circumferential to the heated spot is placed over the stress concentration. The mechanism of improvement in this instance may not be completely understood, especially when it is recognized that a comparable improvement of fatigue strength may be induced by a substantial coating of the stress-concentration area by plastic or paint, without heat spotting. However, the heat spotting is thought to be fairly permanent in its improving effect, whereas the painting may be only transient.

Finally, the process of surface hardening by local heating may be considered in relation to carbon and alloy steels, where the rate of cooling induced by metallic heat conduction and water quenching is sufficient to produce transformation to martensite. This microstructure is recognized to be hard and wear-resistant, and the process is successfully applied to rolls, cams, rocker arms, and other engineering parts. Certain hard martensites can also be brittle, and it is therefore important to note that the phase transformation also involves a small lattice volume expansion compared with the underlying pearlite, which has the effect of inducing surface compressive stresses. The presence of these compressive stresses has been demonstrated in X-ray studies of lattice displacements at hardened surfaces compared with those in the same microstructure in the free state, and their effect on suppressing surface cracking has mainly been demonstrated as a result of collective experience.

It will be appreciated in all these cases that the effect of residual stresses is best understood where it is concerned with induction of frictional grip effects in simple assemblies of parts, and somewhat less well understood where the stress distributions are complicated by yielding effects. The effect is least understood where fracture intervenes. Nevertheless, this introductory review may perhaps be concluded with a quotation from Oliver Heaviside, who is credited with discovering the use of, but not proving the validity of, the operational calculus. "Shall I refuse my dinner because I do not understand the processes of digestion?"

II. Welding Residual Stresses

It has been seen that a riveted joint functions efficiently with benefit from residual stress. Most engineering structures are also residually stressed to some degree from lack of fit of the components, but welded joints in particular are known to have substantial residual stress distributions arising from the differential thermal expansions in welding. The qualitative effect is similar to that at a heated spot, and the main component of stress is yield point tensile along the weld. Weld distortion is another feature associated with the local heating during welding. These two effects were exhaustively studied in breadth in the early days of welding (Spraragen and Cordovi, 1944; Okerblom, 1958), but a completely quantitative analysis of the distributions of deformation and stress of thermal origin in fusion welding has seemingly never been attempted, owing to the grave difficulties in taking into account the effects of yielding. A restricted treatment adds to understanding, nevertheless.

The transient temperature distribution in a thin plate of infinite extent due to a moving line heat source has been given by Rosenthal (1946). The present author (Wells, 1952) demonstrated from this that the maximum temperature T_m above that of the surroundings was given by

$$T_m = Q/8k\left(\frac{1}{5} + \frac{vx}{2\alpha}\right) \tag{1}$$

where Q (cal/cm thickness-sec) is the strength of the heat source, k is thermal conductivity (cal/cm-°C-sec), α is thermal diffusivity (cm²/sec), x (cm) is the transverse distance from the plane of motion of the heat source, and v (cm/sec) is the velocity of the latter. Clearly, when $vx/2\alpha > 1$, as it is often found to be outside the fused zone under practical conditions, the peak temperature is approximately inversely proportional to transverse distance from the weld center plane, with the reference temperature of melting at the edge of the fused zone. This relation is applicable to peak temperatures which occur at an intermediate distance from the source also in plates of finite extent, the associated heat flow characteristic of which is a transverse equalization of temperatures some time after passage of the heat source at values T_e greater than the initial temperature to the extent of the total heat of welding distributed over the whole plate volume (Roberts and Wells, 1954). The time scale of metallic conduction is generally much more rapid than that of the subsequent overall cooling by atmospheric convection, and the generation of residual stresses is virtually completed at the time of temperature equalization.

For the computation of longitudinal components of residual stress, taking yielding into account in the same direction, the crude assumption may be made that the plate consists of an assembly of unconnected longitudinal strips of invariant length during welding. The associated elastic thermal stress is then, very nearly, $(T_m - T_e)\beta/E$, where β is the expansion coefficient and E the elastic modulus, and is limited by compressive yielding during heating, and then by tensile yielding during cooling, in the manner of Fig. 1a. The result of applying this simple analysis to results of experimental measurements by De Garmo et al. (1946) and Rodgers and Fetcher (1938), is shown in Fig. 1b. In the former case, the surface measurements on the comparatively thin plate are somewhat affected by bending, from the asymmetry through the thickness of the heat source distribution. The yield strength of the weld metal has also been underestimated in the analysis. The second group of investigators adopted the expedient, for purposes of laboratory control and ease of analysis, of making a Thermit weld, which may be considered as a fusion weld laid at unspecified high velocity. They also used a thicker plate of relatively small length and width, with a correspondingly higher equalization temperature. In this case, the inadequacy is clear of the assumption in the analysis of invariant length during the thermal cycle. The plate appears to shorten to relax the tensile stresses along the weld, and vice versa at the outer edge.

The latter effect is accompanied by the generation of transverse compressive stresses at the ends of the weld, balanced by tensile stresses in the middle portion, and the generation of these has been studied analytically by Cotterell (1961), with reference to local stress relieving. Further reference is made to the latter work in Sect. VI.

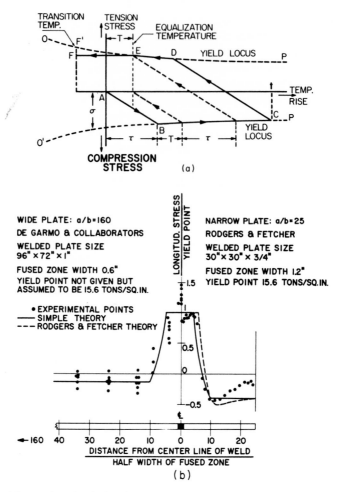

FIG. 1. Measured and calculated longitudinal residual stresses at butt welds (Wells, 1953).

Another source of tensile welding stresses, known as reaction stresses, has been studied by Weck (1947) and these are generated in the transverse direction when a pair of rectangular plates, rigidly fixed at their parallel extreme edges, is joined by means of a butt weld. Such conditions arise at the closing welds in structures of a rigid, highly restrained type. Weck demonstrated, as a result of many experiments, that the transverse tensile reaction *elastic strain* throughout the plates is equal to the fractional expansion at the equalization temperature. Evidently, the expansion takes place freely into the molten pool as the weld is laid, and the freezing of the latter induces tension during cooling. Whereas residual stresses are formed prior to the equalization of welding temperature distributions, it may be argued that reaction stresses reach their full values after equalization. This corresponds with the comparatively greater range beyond the welded joint in which they are formed. Under normal conditions, however, it is difficult to create a structure that is sufficiently rigid to incur full yield point values of reaction stresses, and their greater range is compensated by smaller magnitudes. Thus, it is more usual to consider the free transverse contractions arising at butt welds. These are observed with remarkable consistency, and are often of the order of 0.03 inch at manual welds, and several times greater at electroslag welds of large cross section.

So far, the comparatively simple conditions at single run welds have been considered, but many more joints in practice are deposited using multirun techniques. The temperature distribution arising from any one of these runs is likely to correspond more with conditions of axial symmetry than plane heat flow. As such, the features of the two distributions resemble one another, although the transverse temperature gradients at any given time are somewhat higher in the former case. When one run is super-imposed on another, it would be possible to calculate the aggregate temperature distribution, also by superposition, but doubtful whether the result could be used in association with known yielding properties to calculate residual stresses in a meaningful way.

It is also somewhat difficult to measure residual stresses within the interior of a body, since some method involving strain relaxation must usually be employed, such that it is difficult to reach the interior to place gage marks prior to the destructive process of elastic strain relaxation by subdivision. Some success has been achieved with the use of transducers placed in drilled holes of size sufficiently small to minimize disturbance of the original residual stress distribution. This method has apparently been used, but only in conjunction with electroslag welds.

An important characteristic of the residual stress distributions in multi-run butt welds, involving the relaxation of longitudinal tensions in under-lying runs, from the stretching during cooling of those placed on top, was, nevertheless, fortuitously discovered through the observation of differing cracking susceptibilities at surface and midthickness. Further reference is made to this in Sect. III,B. A weld in 3-inch-thick mild steel plate was made with a balanced double-V preparation of 30° included angle, and $\frac{1}{8}$-inch root face and gap. It was deposited in balanced fashion downhand, using about 60 runs of weld metal. The squared ends of a 36-inch length were then carefully machined, and the overall length accurately measured, after which a 3-inch width enclosing the weld was cut out and subdivided into nine equal square section strips, whose relaxed lengths could be remeasured. While it was not possible to measure all components of residual stress by this procedure, equivalent longitudinal components could be inferred, and it was found that there had been complete relaxation before subdivision within the interior, leaving the yield point components of residual stress only at the weld and plate surfaces. It was also determined in other experiments that the width of cross section with high tensile residual stresses was a much smaller multiple of the fused cross section width when multirun deposits were laid as compared with single run deposits of equivalent aggregate area, such as electroslag welds. Yet again, the distribution of longitudinal residual stresses acquired the same characteristic of maxima at the plate surfaces and minima within the interior when multiruns were deposited from one side only in a single-V preparation. In this case, however, there was more accompanying bending distortion in the longitudinal and transverse directions associated with contraction of the last layers of weld to be completed.

III. Residual Stress Effects on Brittle Fracture in Welded Structures

A. As Seen from Casualty Data

Distortion of plated structures resulting from fusion welded joints can often be seen with the naked eye, particularly when it takes the form of bending or buckling. As such, it is clearly activated by material deformation and, hence, stress; and it is, therefore, evident that residual stress problems were faced and sometimes overcome at the inception of welding as a productive joining process. Electric arc welding, by the time of the decade from 1930 to 1940, had made possible the joining of steel plates of 1-inch thickness and greater, and isolated cases of brittle fracture, sometimes almost spontaneous in character, began to arise. Such fractures had also been experienced sporadically in riveted structures over many earlier years, as described later by Shank (1954), but the thread of association of one with another had not yet been spun. The brittle fracture problem broke upon an unsuspecting world with the spectacular failures of welded ships, although never more than a tiny fraction of the vast total constructed for the prosecution of World War II was ever affected. It is natural in this setting, without assimilation of past lessons from casualties involving brittle fracture, scattered as they were in the literature, that the scapegoat should first have been discovered in the effects of residual stress. It is even more plausible, when the pattern is inspected, of many of the short arrested brittle fractures that were experienced, such that the evidence was not totally destroyed with the structures, as it was with some of the more extensive fractures. An interesting characteristic was that few of these short cracks traveled along welds, except at some distance away in a parallel direction. Many more were transverse to welds, arresting at a distance of a few inches away on both sides, as described by Adam (1945) with respect to ship bottom plating. These are just the circumstances where fractures would be expected to be driven by the effects of reaction and residual tensile stresses, respectively. Moreover, a high proportion of these short fractures were spontaneous, i.e., they arose during construction, or in the presence of loading much less than that assumed for the purposes of design.

It is perhaps remarkable, in this light, that the official report in 1946 of the Ship Structure Committee (1947) should contain such a clearly stated denial of the effects of residual stress as that quoted in Sect. I,A. But that report must be considered in the context of the almost emotionally charged situation then obtaining. Residual stresses were inseparable from welding, and could be effectively removed only by large-scale furnace treatment, utterly impracticable in shipbuilding. Welding, moreover, was an immensely productive joining process with a great future, and that future could not be compromised. There was, furthermore, a much more satisfactory solution to the fracture problem in terms of improving the notch ductility of steel, and it is true indeed that, if a material is notch ductile, which is to say that it will not crack, it will no more crack as a result of residual stresses than of applied stresses. Absolute truth is sacrificed to expediency in official inquiries on important matters in most countries, and this was no exception. However, the result was highly successful, in that the steel industry quickly rose to the occasion and produced the required qualities of steel. It is now of interest to reexamine the second and later statement in Sect. I,A, by Dr. H. Harris (Osgood, 1954) whose considerable experience had been with welded mild steel pressure vessels, all of which in the highest qualities and large plate thicknesses were, and still are, stress relieved by furnace treatment. The motive to discount residual stresses was absent here, and the perspective clearer.

There is no better casualty on which to study the effects of residual stress on brittle fracture than that of the Fawley cylindrical oil storage tank with vertical axis, which was a simple butt welded shell of $1\frac{1}{4}$-inch maximum plate thickness resting on a flat base and having a separate floating roof (Shank, 1954; Anon., 1955). Two fractures were successively experienced, both of which commenced in the horizontal butt weld above the first course of plating, one before and one during water test. Both fractures propagated across the weld and into the plating above and below in the vertical direction. The first was arrested, so that the tank could be repaired. The second occurred later in the middle of a quiet night, when the tank had been filled with water to satisfy the test conditions. The tank was then completely ruptured. Both fractures were initiated at cavities filled with weld metal to replace sections of welding withdrawn for inspection. Ample evidence arose that the cavities had not been filled so as to obviate weld defects under the difficult deposition conditions, and the use of weld probe sampling for inspection was discontinued after this occurrence. The two fractures were nucleated, as in so many other cases, at these small weld defects. The applied hoop stress at which the casualty occurred was about 11,000 lb/inch², and the temperature about 40° F. The welded joints were, of course, not stress relieved, and no driving force other than longitudinal tensile residual stress can be adduced for the first crack in the empty tank. The apparent difference between this and the second crack, driven additionally by applied tensile hoop stress, lay in the extent of propagation.

B. In Laboratory Tests on Wide Plates

One of the questions posed by the Fawley tank casualty related to the ability of a brittle crack to initiate in a statically loaded plate subject only to a steady reduction of temperature. Weld reaction stresses in an internally notched rectangular plate attached along opposite edges to a heavy steel "window frame" were employed by Weck (1952) as a means to study this possibility. The fabrications were cooled slowly in a chamber, and two of three in which the test plate was a coarse-grained notch brittle steel cracked spontaneously, although the temperature of the plate in both cases was found at the instant of fracture to be 6° F below that of the frame, so that the stresses had slightly increased during cooling. A test plate of fine-grained notch tough steel did not fail at a much lower temperature, even after receiving blows from a hammer. Although recognizing that reaction stresses motivated the fractures, Weck concluded that there was no evidence that these stresses had rendered the material more brittle, with respect to transition temperature, than would have been evident in a straightforward notched tensile test.

The Fawley fractures encouraged the repetition in the laboratory of fractures assisted by residual tensile stresses using wide test plates with simulated weld defects. Such tests on pairs of plates each $30 \times 18 \times \frac{3}{4}$ inch, joined by butt welding on the long edges after placing jeweler's sawcut notches in the prepared edges, had earlier been performed in bending by Greene (1949), who had demonstrated short arrested fractures spontaneously or at low applied stresses in as-welded specimens. The fracture stresses were much greater in similarly prepared plates which had been stress relieved either at 1200° F in a furnace or by a mechanical method. Spontaneous short fractures were produced in a repetition of the experiment by Warren and Vaughan (1953), and under the influence of residual stresses and cooling in notched and welded disks by Hebrant *et al.* (1957) and Vinckier (1959).

The present author (Wells, 1956) repeated Greene's experiment with substitution of slowly applied direct tension, and, in one of several specimens, obtained a through fracture at an applied stress of 21,000 lb/inch^2, and, in another, an arrested crack of 12 inches length at a stress of 11,000 lb/inch^2. Five shorter cracks were obtained at lower applied stresses, and one was spontaneous. All the test temperatures lay between 43° and 22° F. This behavior closely paralleled that in the Fawley tank, with the qualitative indication of a limiting applied stress for distinguishing crack propagation and arrest.

Attempts were then made to reduce the longitudinal tensile residual stresses in four remaining identical test plates by warming each to a temperature above the notch brittle transition temperature identified for the material in a Charpy V-notch test and prestretching to the yield point of 34,000 lb/inch^2. This had the effect of increasing the strengths of each specimen when reloaded in the former temperature range or just below it to values equal to or in excess of the prestress. It was concluded that the increase in strength could be attributed to loss of residual stress.

Kihara *et al.* (1959) amplified these results in repeat tests in which the notch configuration was varied, and several different prestress levels were adopted (Table I). The effect in each case was to produce a low-temperature fracture stress somewhat in excess of the prestress. It could thus be concluded additionally that the fracture initiation condition in these tests was that the sum of the applied and residual stress components near the notch should reach or exceed the yield stress.

Meanwhile, Kennedy (1957) reported notched and welded wide plate test results, relating to various forms of weld treatment, on specimens otherwise comparable with those tested by Wells (1956). Furnace stress relief at 1200° F was confirmed to be efficacious in restoring yield point strengths, with substantially more than the negligible elongation that could be conferred by prestretching. Nevertheless, the fractures were still brittle in the same temperature range as adopted for the as-welded tests. Specimens mechanically stress relieved by the Linde low-temperature process gave no improvement in strengths, but it was afterwards discovered that the method had been misapplied, and subsequent correctly treated specimens reached the expected high fracture strengths. An interesting series of tests, in which the welds were locally flame heated to 1200° F to simulate the temperature cycle in a furnace treatment, gave disastrously low fracture strengths, from which it could be concluded that the weakening effects of the residual stresses and associated plastic strains arising from the local heat treatment outweighed those even from welding.

TABLE I

STRENGTHS OF NOTCHED AND WELDED PLATES, FULLY AND PARTIALLY STRESS
RELIEVED BY PRETENSION

Condition	Specimen No.	Test temp. (°C)	Pre-tension, 1000 psi	Fracture stress, 1000 psi	Elonga-tion (%)	Mode of fracture[a]
Pretension after welding	M 5	−28	7.6	14.2	0.05	S
and notching	10	−28	15.0	24.1	0.07	S
	15	−27	22.0	23.5	0.07	S
	20	−26	29.2	33.9	0.11	H
	5	−54.5	7.2	6.7	0.03	S
	15	−48	21.9	23.1	0.10	S
	10	−49	14.6	21.8	0.06	S
	23	−28	33.6	37.8	0.11	H
	15	0	22.0	36.6	0.19	H
Pretensioned after welding	M′ 5	−33	7.7	9.1		
and before notching	10	−29	14.6	19.3		
	15	−29	22.5	26.8		
	20	−28	30.3	36.2		

[a] S: Single stage fracture at low-stress level (no plastic deformation); H: fracture at high-stress level (after plastic deformation).

These results collectively demonstrate the effects of residual stresses, singly and in combination, on brittle fracture in welded specimens, but it is obvious, even from the contrasting fracture elongations in furnace and mechanically stress relieved specimens, that other factors are involved. In particular, the notch root material adjacent to the weld would appear to have been damaged by heat and plastic deformation from welding, making fracture initiation somewhat easier than in material restored by isothermal heat treatment. The latter restoration would not be destroyed during subsequent isothermal cooling, as it would be by repetition of the plastic strain cycle in the locally heat-treated specimens. These effects are discussed at greater length in Sect. V, but it is appropriate at this point to recall experiments conducted by Soete (1960) with the object of separating the thermal cycle from the notch effect. Three mild steel specimens were prepared, of cross section 5.4 × 1.34 × 39 inches long, with symmetrically disposed longitudinal slits 22 inches long and 2.9 inches apart. The center of the three ligaments so created in each specimen was then reduced to a thickness of 0.6 inch. Transverse fatigue cracks of 0.4-inch length were then developed from small drilled holes in the central ligaments by cyclic loading each specimen, after which the specimens were aged at 250° C for 1 hour.

The cracked central ligaments were then cut transversely near each end and rewelded so as to create longitudinal tensile reaction stresses, the magnitudes of which could be gaged accurately by the elastic strains of the outer ligaments of each whole specimen. The specimens were then each cooled to $-8°$ F and broken in tension, the average applied tensile stress (whole cross section) to fracture varying only between 10,000 and 19,000 lb/inch^2. However, the reaction stress in each central ligament before external loading application was already between 62,000 and 69,000 lb/inch^2. Since the fracture stresses were still higher than these values, the absence of notch root damage from thermal cycling must be confirmed as significant.

Of the many notched and welded wide plate tests that have since been conducted, with the object of exploring the properties of various types of steel and other variants, mention may be made of the series conducted at the University of Illinois (Nordell and Hall, 1965), in which six types of notch were explored, and thick plate tests at the British Welding Research Association (Wells, 1961b; Wakefield and Wells, 1962). The tests on 3-inch-thick plates of silicon killed mild steel at the British Welding Research Association used the weld preparation described in Sect. II, with jeweler's saw notches cut into the nose of each prepared edge over the middle third of thickness. Such specimens gave unexpectedly high fracture strengths in the as-welded condition, and the effect was traced as described to relief of residual stresses near midthickness by the balanced multirun welding technique. Alternative specimens prepared with sawcuts of equal area, but placed across the four outside corners of the preparation, gave a significantly higher proportion of low applied stress fractures. Further tests, on plates of similar thicknesses, were conducted on a Mn-Cr-Mo low alloy steel (Burdekin and Wells, 1966) with similar weld preparations combined with the center notch. The specimens were heat treated at various temperatures before fracture test. Curious longitudinal secondary fractures near the fusion plane were set off by the main transverse fractures in two of the specimens. It is likely that the driving stresses for these secondary fractures were of residual character, in association with the end welds by means of which the specimens were attached to the testing equipment.

IV. Analysis of Residual Stress Effects in Notched and Welded Wide Plates by Fracture Mechanics

It is generally recognized, with regard to brittle fractures in low-strength or mild steels, and strongly apparent in casualty fractures, that they are difficult to start, but that they run comparatively easily and at high speed.

Qualitatively, it would appear that a specimen or structure must be loaded to general yield if presented with a sharp notch of small area in virgin material, or to a local stress of yield magnitude with damaged material at the notch, if the initiation barrier is to be overcome. Thereafter, propagation continues until the stress field declines to about one-third yield point magnitude. These ideas had brief currency, the former being argued by the present author (Wells, 1953) the latter by Robertson (1953). But neither concept takes account of crack length, and the arrest stress hypothesis also ignores the observed phenomena of stress redistribution during cracking, which are inevitable with cracks whose velocities do not exceed the comparatively low limit of Rayleigh elastic surface waves.

The mainly accepted reason for the differing resistances to crack initiation and propagation is held to lie with the effect of rate of loading on yield point in low-carbon steels. The yield point is lowest with slow loading, and vice versa, so that high rates of loading would be more likely to produce clouds of cleavage microcracks in the vicinities of crack tips. The production of these disconnected microcracks would precipitate complete fracture. A similar effect on yield point is known to be produced by change of temperature. Thus, the effects of temperature and loading rate must be considered in any measurement of cracking resistance.

First successes in the exploitation of linear fracture mechanics with regard to mild steels were achieved with regard to crack propagation and arrest at low applied stresses in as-welded specimens (Wells, 1956), since yielding effects during fracture could be substantially discounted. In Wells (1956) the G contribution from longitudinal residual tensile stresses was synthesized, in an ancillary welded tested plate, by incrementally slitting the plate symmetrically along the cracking path and measuring the relaxation displacement distribution across the slit for each new slit length. From these measurements, the strain energy liberated by slitting could be determined and related to slit extension. Several subsequent developments in analytical technique, relating to the effects of both applied and residual stresses, simplified the approach and improved its scope. These may be enumerated:

1.   Change from the crack extension force (G) to stress intensity (K) treatments facilitated direct summation of the effects of residual and applied stresses.

2.   Improved stress analysis permitted plate edge boundary effects to be considered.

3.   Development of calculated relationships between values of G, K, and notched specimen compliance values (C) permitted the effect of plate length on stress attentuation during cracking to be considered.

4. Dynamic photoelastic analysis of cracking in transparent plastic plates (Wells and Post, 1958) confirmed the completeness of stress redistribution at observed cracking velocities, so permitting the use of static stress distributions in approximating the calculation of crack propagation and arrest situations, subject only to the attenuation conditions noted at item 3 above.

The most recent analysis (Wells, 1965a) recognizes for summation the stress-intensity contributions from applied stresses (K_σ) and residual stresses (K_r) as follows (Irwin, 1957):

$$K_\sigma = \sigma[W \tan(\pi a/W)]^{1/2} \tag{2}$$

$$K_r = 2\left(\frac{a}{\pi}\right)^{1/2} \int_0^a \frac{\sigma_r \, dx}{(a^2 - x^2)^{1/2}} \tag{3}$$

W in Eq. (2) is plate total width and a is the half length of a central crack, and σ is the applied stress. Equation (3) relates to a similar geometry, with the reservation that plate edge boundary effects are ignored, in the sense that $a < W/2$. σ_r is the pressure on the crack face at distances x from the center of the crack or, as in this case, the residual stress existing before the crack was created. Both situations may be shown to be identical in their influence on K_r by the simple expedient of superimposing an equivalent negative pressure distribution at the crack, whereby the crack will be just closed and the original residual stress distribution restored. The drop of σ [Eq. (2)] that occurs, as the plate is progressively severed, depends on the lengthwise span L at which the plate grips are fixed in space during fracture, the resulting compliance of the whole plate, and its change during cracking. By use of Eq. (2) in terms of G $(EG = K^2)$, and the basic equation of strain energy release in terms of compliance (for two symmetrical cracks, expanding equally),

$$G = \tfrac{1}{2}P^2 \, dC/(2 \, da) \tag{4}$$

where P is the load per unit thickness, it may be shown that the stress-reduction factor equal to the cracked and uncracked compliance ratios is

$$1 + (4W/\pi L) \ln \sec(\pi a/W) \tag{5}$$

The actual length L of the plate may be adjusted upward in calculation to include the testing machine stiffness effect, if the cracking is sufficiently slow for such to be felt. For the more usual fast cracking in long specimens, it may be necessary to adjust L downward to take into account the limiting distance to which elastic relaxation waves could have traveled from the source of the crack. In the wide plate experiments to be considered, where the length L and width W of specimen were equal, the effective length was taken to be $8L/\pi$ to conform with the best condition for analysis established in the earlier dynamic photoelastic tests.

Distributions of stress intensity for a typical welded wide plate configuration are shown in Fig. 2. With regard to K_r, the favorable comparison may be noted between the measured distribution from the slitting technique (Wells, 1956), and that calculated from Eq. (3). Summation of K_σ and K_r contributions is seen to give rise to a declining curve consistent with crack arrest conditions for applied stresses less than about 12,000 lb/inch².

In Table II, 37 values of crack arrest K values estimated in the above manner are shown for welded and notched wide plates of six steels of different types and thicknesses. The results are reasonably consistent, bearing in mind the wide variety of conditions represented, embracing cracks arrested at lengths from 8 to 94% of plate width, and applied stresses from 0 to 37% of yield point. The two largest sources of variability are considered to have been the residual stress distributions, which would have reflected the vagaries of manual welding, and local yielding near the welds. The results, nevertheless, indicate with increased precision the extent to which the fracture strengths were diminished, or the cracks lengthened by the residual stress components.

Recent static loading tests on full thickness unwelded wide plates of steel W (Table II), with symmetrical 3-inch-deep edge notches, revealed low-stress fractures and closely comparable crack initiation K values at similar temperatures (Wells, 1965b). The notches were finished with a 0.006-inch saw blade. Such easy crack initiations had not previously been obtained from many examples of arrested cracks of similar length, and this may have been due to the gathered shear lips and comparatively rough textures of the latter. Thus, it would appear that most of these running brittle cracks in mild steels were manifestations of plane strain fracture,

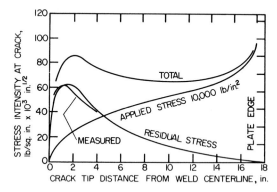

Fig. 2. Crack stress-intensity values during propagation in welded wide plate (Wells, 1965a).

TABLE II

CALCULATED CRACK-STRESS INTENSITY VALUES AT ARREST IN WELDED AND NOTCHED
WIDE PLATES

Material	Test temp. (°C)	Applied stress at fracture (lb/in² × 10³)	Half crack length at arrest (in.)	Stress intensity $(K)^a$ (lb/in.² $\sqrt{\text{in.}}$ × 10³)		
				Residual stress	Applied stress	At arrest
Steel F	−5	0	2.6	56	0	56
1 in. thick Y.P.,	−4	0.7	2.15	60	2	62
36 lb/in² × 10³	−1	2.7	2.9	52	8	60
	6	2.9	1.95	61	7	68
	−8	6.5	2.85	53	19	72
	−5	6.5	3.05	50	20	70
	−4	11.4	4	42	41	83
			8	18	57	75
Steel P	−28	7.8	14	5	51	56
1 in. thick Y.P.,	−25	5.2	3.9	43	19	62
36 lb/in² × 10³	−25	4.3	4.4	38	17	55
	−8	3.4	2.6	55	9	64
	−8	6.1	4.7	36	24	60
	−8	9.9	3.05	46	30	76
	−8	13.4	5.25	33	55	88
	−7	4.0	3.6	45	14	59
	0	9.4	3.3	48	31	79
	1	0	2.0	61	0	61
	4	9.6	3.65	45	33	78
	10	10.5	2.25	59	62	121
Steel Q	−27	5.1	12.6	8	31	39
1 in. thick Y.P.,	−25	8.5	17.0	1	76	77
40 lb/in² × 10³	−22	1.8	4.0	47	6	53
	−15	7.0	2.9	59	21	80
Steel S	−56	5.6	4.0	50	20	70
1 in. thick Y.P.,	−40	7.6	8.4	20	38	58
43 lb/in² × 10³	−40	8.7	4.0	50	31	81
	−30	2.5	2.9	62	7	69
	−24	6.3	5.6	36	27	63
Steel T	−65	14.6	9.0	21	77	98
1 in. thick Y.P.,	−50	7.4	2.6	77	21	98
49 lb/in² × 10³						
Steel W	−45	5.2	2.3	63	14	77
3 in. thick Y.P.,	−20	8.5	2.45	61	23	84
38 lb/in² × 10³	−10	13.7	3.25	52	66	118
	−10	8.5	2.55	60	14	74
	−8	0	1.5	66	0	66
		12.9	7.0	24	61	85

^{a} K_r corrected for yield-point changes from one steel to another. K_r not corrected for yielding when external stress is applied.

the arrests being reversals on the time scale of plane strain crack initiations. This is not always so, since Japanese investigators have shown, by progressively thinning plates subjected to crack arrest tests, that toughness values at arrest at particular temperatures become subject to transitional increases at about $\frac{1}{2}$-inch thickness. The latter can be interpreted as progression toward plane stress fracture conditions.

V. Separation of Residual Stress and Metallurgical Damage Effects at Crack Initiation

It will have been gathered from the discussion in Sect. I,A and from Weck's conclusions (1952) referenced in Sect. III,B that an attractive early hypothesis was that materials were embrittled by the presence of residual stresses. The substance of this hypothesis, which was favored by many continental engineers, was that residual stress systems were of a triaxial tension character. A convincing demonstration of the hypothesis would be found in the "clinking" (sound of cracking) of ingots, since it is common knowledge that the interior of an ingot cools last and therefore finishes in a state of hydrostatic residual tension. There is one physical objection; namely, that the interior stresses, although uniformly triaxial, cannot exceed magnitudes comparable with those at uniaxial yield because of shearing yield alternatively induced in the outer shell. A triaxial stress condition can be embrittling only when it is also a means of stress intensification through the suppression of yield, and this dual requirement is apparently found only in nature at the root of a notch or reentrant boundary. The triaxiality hypothesis totally ignored the presence of internal defects and cracks, and these would have been nucleated in the clinking ingot, not so much by inordinately high stress of triaxial character as by the segregation of impurities at the pipe or core and at interpenetrating dendrites. This example exposes the kernel of the large-scale fracture problem in welded or cast structures in that the first defects are formed in zones of metallurgical heterogeneity under the influence of stress and deformation alone. It is only subsequently that they coalesce and become cracklike, acquiring the power to penetrate neighboring material of higher quality by virtue of increased stress intensification and defect size. Hence, the fracture problem is likely to be perpetuated by initiation and growth in regions of metallurgical damage. Moreover, since the process of nucleation is so transient and sometimes confined to so small a volume, it will often be preferable to control fracture at a stage of early growth of a crack than at or before nucleation.

Although residual stresses in the absence of notch effects may be limited by yielding in contiguous volumes to only moderate values, they may be associated with plastic strains that are large compared with elastic values at yield by five times or more. Such plastic strains, particularly at slightly elevated temperatures, are well able to produce strain aging, although insufficient to cause strain hardening. The mechanism of strain aging is thought to involve the pinning of dislocation movement by thermally activated diffusion of carbon and nitrogen atoms into sites in the slightly expanded lattice near the latter; that of strain hardening to impede the dislocation movement by the sheer number of dislocations produced. The strain aging effect, which is that of yield elevation, is powerful and capable of the stress intensification required for enhanced embrittlement.

Embrittlement by plastic strains from local heating near sawcut notches is characteristically revealed in Charpy specimens extracted from welded and notched wide plates to preserve intact the original notches, as shown in Fig. 3. Energy absorptions are reduced to as little as one-quarter of the reference values for virgin plate, and the effect is substantially greater than that of a standard strain-aging treatment, after which the notches are cut.

Considerable local embrittlement is also produced, even when strain aging is partly suppressed by subsequent refrigeration, by compressive prior plastic deformation at notches, as demonstrated by Mylonas (Mylonas *et al.* 1958; Mylonas, 1959). In $\frac{3}{4}$-inch-thick mild steel specimens 10 inches wide with 1.5-inch-deep sharp edge notches, Mylonas was able to produce through fractures at net area stresses as small as $\overline{40\%}$ of yield, corresponding to K values of 25,000 lb/inch^2 $\sqrt{\text{inch}}$, by plastic precompression, and short arrested fractures from the notch roots at even lower applied stresses.

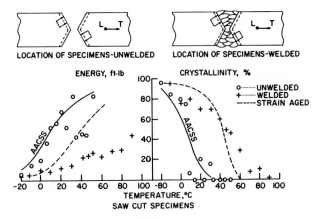

FIG. 3. Charpy energy absorption and crystallinities for specimens extracted from a notched and welded wide plate (Wells, 1961b).

Below-yield fractures were also obtained by Turner (1968) by precompression of 3-inch-wide notched specimens, but not by Spence (1959) on circumferentially notched specimens of $\frac{1}{2}$-inch diameter. These graded results would appear to support the fracture mechanics conception of the effect of specimen size on fracture strengths at given toughness levels. Moreover, the attribution of a K value for fracture initiation in Mylonas' specimens enables the relative contributions of elastic residual stresses and locally embrittled crack initiators to be seen in clear perspective with regard to low stress fracture. The function of local damage is apparently to depress the K values at static loading initiation to levels comparable with those for crack propagation in undamaged material. If the damage is overdone, the prematurely initiated running crack is quickly arrested, and reinitiation from this point in undamaged material may be quite difficult. Something of the statistical uncertainty of fracture in welded structures of poor quality can be seen from this required coordination of fracture mechanisms.

Although strain aging may be a dominant mechanism in the local embrittlement of mild steels, it would appear to be less important in some low-alloy steels, which, nevertheless, exhibit damage mechanisms peculiar to themselves. Insofar as they are formed by agencies other than thermal plastic strains and may be evident in welded joints heat treated after welding, they cannot be considered as residual stress effects.

VI. Function and Conduct of Stress Relief Treatments

Stress relief heat treatment was practiced as an adjunct to cold forming operations in mild steels long before the advent of welding, and the implication of the name is that its unquestionably beneficial effect on ductility was attributed to the relief by creep relaxation of accumulated residual stresses. Further study, as will be described, has shown that strain-aging effects are also neutralized by furnace treatment at about 1200° F, in a manner probably inseparable from relief of residual stresses.

Further reasons were added in favor of stress relief in fusion welded structures; namely, the restoration of dimensional stability in assemblies requiring to be machined, the beneficiation of weld metal mechanical properties, the improvement of resistance to stress corrosion under hostile chemical conditions, and the improvement of brittle fracture resistance. The popularity of furnace stress relief grew largely with the manufacture of welded pressure vessels, which often required the treatment at intermediate stages in fabrication in order to suppress spontaneous cracking as more welding was added. The sequel is that no cases of brittle fracture in service in completely stress relieved welded constructions were experienced over very many years, even in quite thick constructions.

The efficacy of furnace stress relief, with slow, almost isothermal heating and cooling of the whole structure, has been explained in terms of the freedom from differential plastic straining at stress concentrations and defects during cooling after heat treatment. There have been cases, nevertheless, of brittle cracking in the furnace due to thermal stress induction at the commencement of too fast a rate of heating. Interest also centers on desirable thermal cycles for furnace stress relief.

Notwithstanding the existing empirical rules that heating rates should be limited to stipulated values, it is useful to consider the results of plane transient heat flow calculations in a plate of thickness, t, heated equally at both faces and subject to a uniform rate of temperature rise T' throughout. When such heating is fully established, there will be a difference of temperature between inside and outside, of magnitude sufficient to cause the thermal stress difference σ',

$$\sigma' = \frac{T't^2\beta E}{8\alpha} \tag{6}$$

where β is expansion coefficient, E is Young's modulus, and α is thermal diffusivity. It will be observed, realistically, that the heating rate should be inversely proportional to the square of thickness of the maximum section. This limitation may be quite important in thick fabrications, where a very slow heating rate would be to some extent incompatible with metallurgical requirements, particularly those concerned with resistance to high-temperature creep.

With regard to relaxation of residual stress in mild steels at various temperatures, many tests have been performed with specimens elastically prestrained in tension or torsion in rigid frames, which have then been placed in a furnace for various lengths of time (Tummers, 1963; Wells and Burdekin, 1963). In the case of heavy constructions, the rate of heating is relatively slow, for reasons of heat transfer and thermal stress limitation, and stress relaxation progressively takes place during the heating period, so that further relaxation tests have been performed (Roberts et al., 1963). Results from these tests are presented in Figs. 4a and 4b. It is evident, for the wide range of British steels there exhibited, that stress relaxation is quickly and effectively completed at 1200° F. The empirical rule of 1 hour at peak temperature per inch of thickness is, in fact, a reflection both of stress relaxation requirements and those of temperature gradient and thermal stress activation during heating, typified by Eq. (6).

The results of a number of notched and welded wide plate tests on 1- and 3-inch-thick mild steels (Wells and Burdekin, 1963) show in

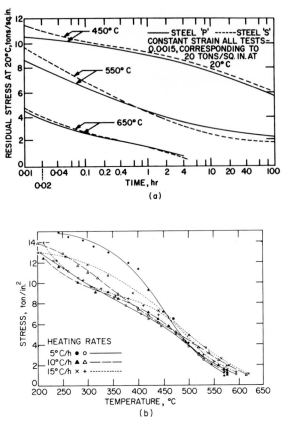

FIG. 4. Stress-relaxation data for British mild steels under uniform conditions of (a) temperature and (b) heating rate (Wells and Burdekin, 1963; Roberts et al., 1963).

Figs. 5a and 5b the effects of furnace stress relief on notch ductility at various temperatures. The overall fracture strain ordinate in these plots emphasizes that no low-stress fractures were obtained in the tests. The remarkable ductilities shown, even at very low temperatures in 1-inch plates, also parallel the results of stress relaxation tests shown in Fig. 4a, but this should not be interpreted as a conclusion that relief of elastic residual stresses is solely responsible for the improvement. It is simply a recognition that stress relaxation and recovery from strain aging are inseparable aspects of the heat treatment process. Similarly, the less effective results of 1200° F treatment on the thicker plate notch ductilities should not be misconstrued as resulting from a 3-hour, as opposed to a 1-hour, treatment.

Two additional factors intervened to influence these results. First,

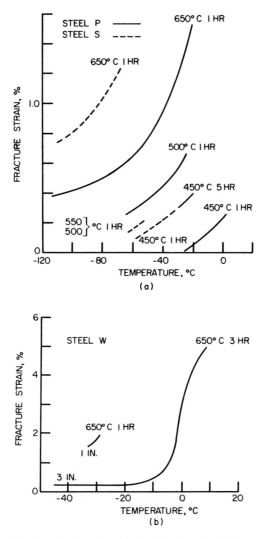

FIG. 5. Stress relieved, welded, and notched wide plate tensile test results for 1- and 3-inch thick mild steel plates (Wells and Burdekin, 1963; Wakefield and Wells, 1962).

the increased plate thickness caused a significant progression toward plane strain fracture conditions where plane stress was clearly shown in the thinner plates by the transverse plate contractions. Second, the thicker plates were, of necessity, provided with larger artificial defects. Moreover, the majority of these extended into the weld metal during welding and heat treatment, so as to increase the aggregate area by natural cracking.

The reason for this defect extension is now known to be associated with the rutile coated electrodes which were used, which deposit weld metal of inferior high-temperature creep ductility (Taylor, 1968) as compared with basic low hydrogen weld metal. Greatly different propensities of the two weld metals to exhibit slow hot crack extension in notched and welded wide plate specimens was demonstrated in an earlier investigation (Wells, 1961a), such that the brittle strengths below yield in the as-welded condition were significantly affected by the increased aggregate flaw sizes. These results contribute overwhelming evidence of the dangers of employing rutile-coated electrodes in heavy stress relieved constructions, or those to be used at elevated temperatures, however attractive may be their properties in control of deposition, or freedom from fume.

Warm prestretching, whose beneficial effects on fracture strength were discussed in Sect. III,B, is a form of mechanical stress relief, whose counterpart is a byproduct of the test loading of welded steel structures. Such test loading is practiced to a diminishing extent with building and civil engineering structures, owing to the increasing costs and impracticability of doing so. However, it is customarily performed on all pressure vessels, including site welded storage vessels too large to be furnace stress relieved. It is a philosophical point as to whether such a preload or hydrostatic test is performed to show that the structure is safe for service, or to improve its resistance to brittle fracture. But the dichotomy of views increases in importance if the structure is deliberately warmed to achieve safe performance of the test. Evidence from the wide plate tests would indicate that this is a rational course of action, based on the protection from low-stress fracture subsequently conferred at lower temperatures. However, it has also been shown that the margin of safety obtained from mechanical stress relief is slender, because there may be no post yield ductility arising from it, and it has recently been suggested by Harris that if the hydrostatic test be performed under warm conditions it should subsequently be repeated at the lowest service temperature, to establish it as a performance test as well as a conditioning treatment.

The slender margins against fracture in service arising from dependence on the hydrostatic test, with little or no associated control of the notch ductility of the structural material, are shown in two examples. The Schenectady hydrogen sphere of wartime mild steel construction burst violently from weld defects at a fabricated manway (Shank, 1954). It had been pressure tested as a concession to only 1.15 times the design pressure. The failure occurred soon after installation, during bright sunlight on a morning after a cold night, and it is possible that the pressure stresses were thereby supplemented by thermal stresses. The welded carbon dioxide liquefier (Burdekin, 1963) was pressurized to destruction because of interest in its history. Having been 24 years in service at temperatures down to −40° F without benefit of thermal treatment, after which it was condemned because of observed internal defects, it was necessary to know the residual strength, above the test value of 375 lb/inch², to which it had been repeatedly subjected at room temperature. Failure took place at 500 lb/inch² in spite of extensive precracks revealed at the nozzle stress concentration where the fracture originated. These precracks were covered with black high-temperature oxide, indicating that they arose at the time of welding. They extended to 90% of the full plate thickness of ½-inch. Others in the main seams of the vessel occupied the middle third of plate thickness over long lengths. The Charpy V-notch energy absorption at the test temperature of 18° F was 7 ft-lb. It cannot be doubted that this vessel would have failed at 375 lb/inch² at the beginning of its life, if it had also been at −40° F, and the long safe life must be attributed to the prior hydrostatic test at room temperature. The example shows that defect propagation rates by fatigue through pressure fluctuation can be negligibly low under low stress operating conditions, but they would not necessarily be so for multiple applications of full design pressure. Thus, mechanical stress relief as a fracture palliative may possess only a limited life in terms of numbers of possible service load applications before repetition is desirable or necessary.

Much recent work has been conducted on the elastic and plastic behavior at nozzles in cylindrical and spherical pressure vessels (Leckie and Payne, 1965) since these represent the most important sources of stress concentration. This work has largely confirmed the value of a simple concept by means of which the shakedown pressure can be calculated. At shakedown pressure and below there is no reversed yield when the pressure is relaxed to zero, hence, no incremental collapse. The shakedown pressure is thus the obvious choice for performance of the hydrostatic test, and is that at which the hoop stress in the vessel is approximately $2\sigma_y/j$, $j > 2$, being the stress-concentration factor. If the design stress is $m\sigma_y$, the overpressure factor, based on shakedown, is

$$2/jm \tag{7}$$

This is a condition relating to fracture protection in service for hydrostatically tested vessels, whether or not they have been furnace stress relieved, that designers would do well to consider.

All the limitations that apply to mechanical stress relief as a means of fracture protection apply to the Linde low-temperature process for treatment of long fusion welds. In order to be efficacious, it must be performed with precision, as indicated in notched and welded wide plate test results described in Sect. III,B. Although the concept is elegant, the process has been little used, except for the protection of storage vessels from stress corrosion. Here, it is only necessary to ensure that the heated bands have the correct temperature at the exposed surface, and there is more latitude in control.

Local thermal stress relief has, however, been applied with great success in the treatment of closing circumferential butt welded joints in cylindrical pressure vessels of great length, pipes assembled on site, and, in certain instances, in the site attachment of nozzles to spherical storage vessels. The associated temperature gradients chosen to minimize the growth of thermal stresses were first governed by empirical rules and subsequently by stress analysis. The object of the latter is to produce a prearranged temperature time cycle within the relevant part of the structure while differential temperatures, and particularly the component thermal strains arising from them, are limited to values that will not themselves produce yielding at any stage of the process. It is not necessary for thermal stresses to be avoided altogether. These disappear once cooling is completed unless yielding has previously occurred, in which case fresh residual stresses are left behind. For simple situations, these residual stresses (with an upper limit of yield point value) are roughly equal to the difference between the maximum thermal stresses that would have occurred without yielding, and the yield point stress, both at the temperature when yielding ceased. If the thermal yielding is avoided, the local heat treatment of a welded structure is as effective as an isothermal treatment in neutralizing residual stress and plastic strain effects.

The usual means of local heating employ a uniform heat flux over a circumferential band or a disk embracing the welded area, with lagging to minimize losses and diminish the temperature gradient outside the heated area. Calculated thermal cycles which were also checked experimentally have been collectively presented (Burdekin and Wells, 1962), and the recommended widths of heated bands or disk diameters for use on mild steels are summarized as follows:

Cylinder of radius r, thickness t, and length l
    Circumferential —4 to 6 $(rt)^{1/2}$
    Longitudinal   —l
Flat plate of width l
    Transverse   —l
Sphere of radius r and thickness t —6 $(rt)^{1/2}$

The degrees of relief of residual stresses from welds on flat plates and cylinders locally heat treated in this way have been checked experimentally and found to be virtually as complete as in furnace treatments at the same peak temperatures.

VII. Recommended Research

Although many mild steel constructions are still, and will long continue to be, fabricated by welding, many of the mysteries of brittle fracture in these constructions have been resolved during the past 30 years. Some necessary investigation remains, notably with regard both to mild steels made by new processes and to new welding processes as they emerge, but the principal task of today is to assimilate the wealth of experience and research data already accumulated. The problem of residual stresses and their influence on brittle fracture has been left behind, probably for two compelling reasons.

First, at least partial satisfaction of the demand for mild steels of greater notch ductility, and a simultaneous increase in permissible design stresses, has imbued engineers with dissatisfaction with a toughness level at which low-stress fracture is a possibility. It is recognized in design, at least in knowledgeable quarters, that most economically proportioned structures must sustain local yield in service at design stress concentrations without evidence of distress, and this implies that the elastic residual stresses will have been relieved mechanically to a greater extent than heretofore on the first application of load. Put in another way, such are the disadvantages of relatively poor notch ductility and of restraint in fabrication of thick steels, and such the advantages of intrinsically better notch ductility and of economy in using thin sections, that it has been recognized as preferable to use the latter at high stress levels in comparatively expensive notch tough versions than to use thick sections at low toughness at conservative stress levels.

Second, the same trend has encouraged the more extensive employment of stronger low-alloy steels in welded structures. Such steels incur residual stresses but they do not, to the same extent as mild steels, exhibit either strain-aging damage or strain-rate dependence of yield and fracture, nor do they respond in the same degree to stress relief heat treatments. They may, nevertheless, benefit from heat treatments optimized on purely metallurgical considerations. In spite of much accomplished, this field appears still to possess great development potential, but the residual stress aspects of the required research are probably insignificant. Notch toughness aspects, and the morphology of the steels with regard to metallurgical damage and generation of defects, will both require exhaustive study, but these are beyond the present topic. One minor aspect of research that should be considered at the present juncture is the calculation of residual stress-and-strain fields by means of the finite element and other methods of digital computation that have quite recently become available. It is likely that the results of such calculations on the much investigated common welded joints would contribute little of technological value, but experience of the methods might enable situations of greater complexity to be investigated analytically, with corresponding growth of insight.

VIII. Summary

Since the concept of stress is an abstraction, with the possibility of experimental measurement almost exclusively through the associated strains, the difficulties of recognizing residual stress distributions are emphasized. It is shown that the definition of a residual stress system depends partly on arbitrary definition of the boundaries of the body in which they are contained and, inferred from this, that the fracture response of the material of construction cannot permit distinction between sources of stress, whether externally applied or residual. Early hypotheses on the effect of residual stresses on brittle fracture in welded structures are described in the light of the evidence then existing, and the opinion offered that the present understanding, although largely sufficient for technological control, must still be considered empirical rather than quantitatively scientific, due to the complex effects of yield activated by thermal stresses.

Several widely occurring systems of residual stress are described, including those in bolted and riveted joints, shrink fits, and at rolled, peened, and differentially hardened surfaces, as well as in welded joints. It is noted that many of these systems are beneficial and deliberately cultivated, although their fundamental bases may not yet be thoroughly understood. They illustrate that residual stress distributions are present in most structures.

Distributions of residual and reaction stress associated with fusion welded joints are qualitatively described and their origins are then traced successively from calculated temperature distributions arising from moving line sources of heat, the longitudinal thermal stresses which they produce on a one-dimensional basis, and uniaxial yielding, taking into account the effect of temperature on yield point. The concept of equalization temperature is introduced with regard to plates of finite size, and shown to be useful in assessing the balance between compressive and tensile residual stresses, and in computing reaction stresses. The mechanism for generating transverse components of residual stress is also described. The generation of distributions of residual stress in multirun butt welds is qualitatively introduced, whereby the transverse spread of temperature is relatively smaller for each run of weld metal, but the cumulative effects involve stress relaxation of runs of weld metal below the last applied. The relation between residual stress generation and distortion is mentioned.

The effects of residual stress on brittle fracture are inferred from the broad pattern of casualty behavior as experience was accumulated, and it is demonstrated that the most conclusive positive evidence arose from spontaneous or low-stress fractures of short extent occurring during fabrication. This is best illustrated in terms of the Fawley oil storage tank— a model casualty in which the simplicity of the structure and cracking pattern were combined with certain knowledge of the static loading conditions at fracture. The negative, seemingly erroneous conclusions of the Ship Structure Committee report of 1946 are explained in terms of the desired and expedient course of action to improve steel notch ductility, which was rapidly attained.

Laboratory reproductions of brittle fractures motivated by residual stresses are traced from those in which spontaneous fractures were induced during cooling of rigid welded mild steel assemblies, to the development of the welded and notched wide plate tension test, whose original objective was to repeat the Fawley-tank-type fracture in a controlled manner. The importance of the initial cracklike defect is emphasized, and the significance of notch root local damage due to heat and plastic strain is introduced. The conditions for crack arrest or through fracture are described as they were first elucidated, and the results of subsequent explorations of mechanical and furnace stress relief described. Differing patterns of behavior in multirun, manually welded, and notched thick plate specimens are noted in comparison with those in thinner plates welded with few runs.

Absence of yielding effects during crack propagation and arrest in welded and notched tension tests, with initiation at low applied stresses, created an early opportunity for analysis of the behavior in terms of linear fracture mechanics. Description of the early work is supplemented by consideration of additional factors in more refined treatments, namely, plate side boundary effects, applied stress attenuation due to plate length effects, and stress redistribution during fracture. Fracture toughness values at arrest in many wide plate tests are tabulated and discussed, and the extent to which these analyses show the quantitative effects of the residual stresses in precipitating low applied stress fractures is assessed. The relationships between plane strain and plane stress conditions at running cracks are mentioned.

Metallurgical damage effects at crack initiation from weld defects are discussed in terms of the early hypothesis that residual stresses induce embrittlement by virtue of high triaxiality. It is suggested that the best evidence was found in the clinking of cooling ingots, but that the hypothesis was untenable because it neglected the consideration that high stress intensifications are not attained in triaxial stress states unless notches are also present. The latter exist in ingots as a result of the effects of segregation and interdendritic growth. The alternative current hypothesis is described, whereby fracture nucleation is a result of thermal plastic stresses and strains superimposed on metallurgical heterogeneities, and brittle fracture is subsequently conditioned by instability of crack extension. The importance, in crack initiation, is described of local plastic strain damage due to strain aging and precompression in terms of the lowering of fracture toughness so obtained in local regions at the notch root. It is shown that the most critical conditions for unstable crack propagation into undamaged material depend on a match between the fracture toughnesses at the damaged region relative to static loading and, in the undamaged region, at the high rates of strain associated with crack propagation. It is also pointed out that different damage mechanisms are more likely in certain low-alloy steel constructions.

Early opinions on the influence of residual stresses on fracture, opposite to those expressed in the 1946 Ship Structure Committee Report, and then held by many fabricators of pressure vessels, are explained in terms of the facility with which the latter are furnace stress relieved, in contrast to ship structures, and the beneficial experience that had been accumulated with stress relief in suppressing fabrication cracks in thick constructions. Improvements in both strength and ductility, consistently exhibited in tests of notched and welded wide plate specimens subjected to furnace stress relief, are contrasted with the improvements in strength alone following mechanical stress relief by stretching, and by carefully controlled Linde low-temperature mechanical stress relief. They are further contrasted with the disastrous effect on strengths of reproducing a stress relief temperature cycle along the welded joint by very local heating. It is shown that these effects are satisfactorily explained in terms of the neutralization of strain-aging damage as well as by stress relaxation in heating to $1200°$ F, if they are not both reintroduced by plastic straining during nonuniform cooling. Optimum conditions for heating rates, residual stress relaxation, and brittle strength improvement are summarized for furnace treatments of certain mild steels and for overstress ratios in mechanical stress relief of pressure vessels. The extent to which the latter operation conducted as a proof test may also be relied on as a fabrication treatment to improve fracture resistance is debated. Finally, the optimum ranges are summarized of conditions in which fusion welded joints in cylindrical and spherical pressure vessel shells and flat plates may be satisfactorily thermally stress relieved by means of uniformly heated local areas.

With regard to recommended research, it is considered that the residual stress topic has now been systematically worked out for the purposes of mild steel welding technology, although the tools have recently become available in digital computation techniques for rigorous calculation of fields of residual stress and strain, and some attention should perhaps be devoted to this. Attention is now increasingly being given to fracture conditions in alloy steels, under the conditions of greater ductility now being demanded by engineers. Under such conditions, the effects of residual stress on fracture diminish in relative terms, but much remains to be investigated with regard to defect growth and local damage mechanisms.

Symbols

T_m	temperature of melting above that of surroundings	σ_r	residual stress component normal to crack at distance x from origin
T_e	temperature of welded plate above that of surroundings after equalization by conduction	W	plate width
		a	crack half-width
		x	distance from origin along crack path
T'	rate of change with time of temperature of plate	L	effective or actual plate length between fixed grips during fracture
k	thermal conductivity	G	crack extension force ($K^2 = EG$)
α	thermal diffusivity, $= k/\rho c$, where ρ and c are density and specific heat, respectively	C	compliance (reciprocal of stiffness) of cracked plate (per unit thickness)
Q	time rate of heat supply per unit thickness for concentrated source	σ'	center to surface thermal stress component difference parallel to plate surface
v	velocity of heat source		
β	coefficient of linear expansion	t	plate thickness
E	Young's elastic modulus	r	mean radius of curvature of cylindrical or spherical shell
K	stress intensity at crack, or stress field parameter		
K_σ	component stress intensity from applied stress σ	l	width of plate locally stress relieved by heated band
K_r	component stress intensity from residual stress (σ_r) distribution	j	elastic stress-concentration factor at nozzle design detail
σ	externally applied stress	m	ratio of design hoop stress to uniaxial yield

REFERENCES

Adam, J. L. (1945). *In* "Proceedings of the Conference on Brittle Fracture in Mild Steel Plates," p. 55. BISRA, London.
Anon. (1955). *Brit. Welding J.* **2**, 254.
Burdekin, F. M. (1963). *Brit. Welding J.* **10**, 183.
Burdekin, F. M., and Wells, A. A. (1962). *Bulletin*, September and November. British Welding Research Association, London.
Burdekin, F. M., and Wells, A. A. (1966). *Brit. Welding J.* **13**, 88.
Cotterell, B. (1961). *Brit. Welding J.* **8**, 485.
De Garmo, E. P., *et al.* (1946). *Welding J.* (*N.Y.*) *Res. Suppl.* **25**, 541s.
Greene, T. W. (1949). *Welding J.* (*N.Y.*) *Res. Suppl.* **14**, 193s.

Hebrant, F., *et al.* (1957). *Rev. Soudure (Brussels)* **13**. (Also available as Document No. IX-181-56. International Institute of Welding.)

Irwin, G. R. (1957). *J. Appl. Mech.* **24**, 361.

Kennedy, R. (1957). *Brit. Welding J.* **4**, 529.

Kihara, H., *et al.* (1958). Document Nos. X-218-58 and X-258-60. International Institute of Welding.

Leckie, F. A., and Payne, D. J. (1965). *Proc. Inst. Mech. Eng. (London)* **180**, 145.

Mylonas, C. (1959). *Welding J. (N. Y.) Res. Suppl.* **24**, 414s.

Mylonas, C., *et al.* (1958). *Welding J. (N. Y.) Res. Suppl.* **23**, 47s.

Nordell, W. J., and Hall, W. J. (1965). *Welding J. (N. Y.) Res. Suppl.* **30**, 124s.

Okerblom, N. (1958). Deformations of welded structures, translated from Russian, DSIR. H.M. Stationery Office, London.

Osgood, W. R. (1954). "Residual Stresses in Metals and Metal Construction," p. 23. Reinhold, New York.

Roberts, D. F. T., *et al.* (1963). Paper No. 63. Presented at the Joint ASME-ASTM-IME International Conference on Creep.

Roberts, D. K., and Wells, A. A. (1954). *Brit. Welding J.* **1**, 553.

Robertson, T. S. (1953). *J. Iron Steel Inst. (London)* **175**, 361.

Rogers, O. E., and Fetcher, J. R. (1938). *Welding J. (N. Y.) Res. Suppl.* **17**, 1s.

Rosenthal, D. (1946). *Trans. ASME* **68**, 849.

Shank, M. E. (1954). STP 158, p. 45. ASTM, Philadelphia.

Ship Structure Committee (1947). *Welding J. (N. Y.) Res. Suppl.* **25**, 451s.

Soete, W. (1960). *Rev. Soudure (Brussels)* **16**, 165.

Spence, J. (1959). Thesis. Department of Applied Mechanics, Sheffield University, Sheffield, England.

Spraragen, W., and Cordovi, M. A. (1944). *Welding J. (N. Y.) Res. Suppl.* **23**, 209s.

Taylor, T. E. (1968). "Creep Tests on Welded Pressure Vessels." Report. British Welding Research Association, London. (To be published).

Tummers, G. E. (1963). *Brit. Welding J.* **10**, 292. (Also see Document Nos. X-229-59, X-244-60, X-249-60, X-251-60, X-273-61, and X-318-63. International Institute of Welding.)

Turner, C. E. (1968). Report No. RP163. Admiralty Advisory Committee on Structural Steel. (To be published.)

Vinckier, A. (1959). *Welding J. (N. Y.) Res. Suppl.* **24**, 354s.

Wakefield, B. A., and Wells, A. A. (1962). *Brit. Welding J.* **9**, 29.

Warren, W. G., and Vaughan, H. G. (1953). *Trans. Inst. Welding* **16**, 127.

Weck, R. (1947). Report No. R4 (Prepared by the Admiralty Ship Welding Committee). H.M. Stationery Office, London.

Weck, R. (1952). *Welding Research* **6**, 70r.

Wells, A. A. (1952). *Welding J. (N. Y.) Res. Suppl.* **17**, 263s.

Wells, A. A. (1953). *Welding Research* **7**, 34r.

Wells, A. A. (1956). *Trans. Roy. Inst. Naval Architects* **98**, 296.

Wells, A. A. (1961a). *Brit. Welding J.* **8**, 259.

Wells, A. A. (1961b). *Brit. Welding J.* **8**, 389.

Wells, A. A. (1961c). *Welding J. (N. Y.) Res. Suppl.* **40**, 182s.

Wells, A. A. (1965a). *Brit. Welding J.* **12**, 2.

Wells, A. A. (1965b). *Proc. Roy. Soc. (London) Ser. A* **285**, 40.

Wells, A. A., and Burdekin, F. M. (1963). *Brit. Welding J.* **10**, 270.

Wells, A. A., and Post, D. (1958). *Proc. Soc. Exptl. Stress Anal.* **16**, 69.

CHAPTER 8

BRITTLE FRACTURE IN WELDMENTS

W. H. Munse

Abstract: An analysis is presented in this paper of the problem of brittle fracture
in weldments. Welding, when it was introduced, made possible many improvements
in the fabrication of metal structures; however, it increased also the frequency with
which brittle fractures have occurred in such structures. As a result, a great need
has existed for a better understanding of the basic factors that determine when a
brittle fracture will or will not initiate.

    Consideration is given primarily to the problem of low-stress fracture and the
conditions necessary for such fractures. In brittle fractures of weldments, weld
quality, residual welding stresses, and the weld properties are important factors and
must be examined in detail. The weld itself, and the fusion zone, the heat-affected
zone, the thermally affected zone, and the base metal are considered with respect
to their toughness. In addition, consideration is given to the various ways in which
these regions or zones in a weldment may be embrittled or affected by various welding processes, procedures, and treatments. Finally, the question of designing to protect against brittle fracture is discussed.

I. Introduction

In the laboratory as well as in the field, welds, weldments, and welded
structures are found to fracture either in a ductile or brittle manner. The
brittle failures, where negligible plastic flow has taken place, have in many
instances occurred at nominal stresses well below the yield point or those
stresses for which the structures were designed. Such failures have often
been catastrophic in that they have resulted in the loss of life or structure
(see Fig. 1). Consequently, the question of brittle fracture in weldments
and welded structures is of great concern and importance to engineers and
to the engineering profession.

In mild steels, brittle fractures are generally of a cleavage type, with a
granular or crystalline texture, and usually exhibit a herringbone appearance, such as that shown in Fig. 2. The chevrons of the herringbone
pattern point to the source of the fracture initiation and provide an indication of the direction in which the crack propagated. Another characteristic
of these fractures is the speed with which they propagate. Velocities as
high as 6000 ft/sec are reported in the literature. This is in excellent
agreement with the limiting crack velocity predicted by Wells (1959).

FIG. 1. Brittle fracture of welded ship. (Board of Investigation, 1947).

The low-stress brittle fractures have occurred when there has been (a) a cracklike defect, (b) high residual tensile stresses in the region of the defect, and (c) the temperature of the structure has been below the transition temperature of the material (Weck, 1966). In welded structures, the fractures generally start at points of high stress concentration such as cracks, weld defects, metallurgical imperfections, or at points of high restraint. Obviously, many interrelated factors are involved in the problem.

FIG. 2. Fracture surface of low-stress failure.

A. Welds and Weldments

Much has been written about low-stress brittle fractures in weldments, often suggesting that the welding was responsible for the failures. However, Shank (1954) has reported that brittle fractures occurred long before the advent of welded construction. Nevertheless, the evidence strongly implicates welding.

Welding has been a most important fabrication tool for many of the structures in which brittle fractures have occurred. These include such structures as ships, bridges, pressure vessels, water and oil storage tanks, power shovels, penstocks, gas transmission pipelines, earth moving equipment and, more recently, the rocket-motor cases for space vehicles. Obviously, the question of brittle fracture is of great importance to many engineers and scientists and involves not only mild steels but also the ultra-high-strength steels as well as some of the nonferrous metals.

B. Service Failures

Numerous reports of brittle fractures in welded structures are presented in the literature. Although these structures failed in a brittle manner, there are many similar structures in service that have not failed. Apparently, the conditions necessary for such failures do not exist in all of the structures.

One of the principal types of welded structures prone to fracture in a brittle manner has been the large ship. Without welding, the enormous fleet of ships used during World War II could not have been built within the short time available (Board of Investigation, 1947). However, the introduction of welding into the shipbuilding industry also introduced the brittle fracture problem. Initially, these ship failures were attributed to such factors as welding defects, residual stresses, or the metallurgical changes associated with welding (Williams, 1954). Although other factors were soon related to the ship failures, it is reported that welds have been associated with every fracture origin observed in these structures (Acker, 1953). Furthermore, in no case did fractures start in sound welds. Those cracks which started in the welds were found to soon propagate into the base metal, where the resistance to propagation was apparently not as great as in the weld metal itself. In some instances, these failures were observed to propagate for long distances and, on occasion, to fracture a ship completely in two (Fig. 1).

On March 14, 1938, a few years before the first World War II ship failures, the Albert Canal Bridge at Hasselt, Belgium, failed in a brittle manner (Shank, 1954). More recently (July 10, 1962), the welded King Street Bridge in Melbourne, Australia, failed in a brittle manner (Royal Commission, 1963). Upon examination, it was found that numerous locations in the King Street Bridge contained cracks of the type thought to have been responsible for the failure of the bridge. Thus, welded bridges as well as ships are susceptible to fracture in a brittle manner.

Other recent fractures of welded structures include pressure vessels in both thick and thin material, vessels fabricated of mild steels as well as of high-strength materials (Pellini and Puzak, 1963a; Board of Inquiry, 1967; British Welding Research Association, 1966). In one of the pressure vessel failures, a 2-ton section of the vessel was catapulted 152 ft (Fig. 3). This provides an indication of the large amount of energy that is released when such failures occur. The failure in this instance appears to have initiated from two small flaws in the heat-affected zone of the structure. The initial stages of the cracking appear to have been in the weld, while most of the failure took place in the plating. Furthermore, the failure occurred at a pressure only 70% as great as the hydrostatic test pressure specified for the vessel and was thus a low-stress brittle fracture.

In another instance, a 260-inch-diameter solid-propellant rocket-motor case is reported to have failed during a hydrostatic test. In this instance, the material was a ¾-inch-thick 18 Ni (250) grade maraging steel. Each fracture origin in this structure was related to a tungsten-inert gas (TIG) repair weld (Baker *et al.*, 1965). Thus, some of the newer ultra-high-strength steels are also susceptible to brittle fracturing when employed in welded structures.

Although the service failures described above are concerned with welded structures, brittle fractures were reported as early as 1879, long before welding was employed for steel structures. Furthermore, riveted ships as

FIG. 3. Two-ton segment of thick walled pressure vessel thrown 152 ft on failure (British Welding Research Association, 1966).

well as bolted structures have on occasion been known to fail in a brittle manner. However, the introduction of welding and, recently, many new metals appears to have accentuated the problem in many such structures.

C. SERVICE REQUIREMENTS

Welded structures must withstand many different types of loads and loading conditions. Factors of safety are employed to increase the load carrying capacity to a level considered safe for these conditions. In addition, these structures must be capable of withstanding the loads at various temperatures and occasionally under various environmental conditions. In some instances, the structures may even be required to withstand dynamic loadings. Thus, a broad range of service conditions exists for the welded structures, making brittle fractures a distinct possibility in many cases.

In order to study this problem, laboratory investigations have been initiated on various types of specimens and weldments. However, in such tests it is extremely difficult to simulate fully the loading and environmental conditions encountered in service. Nevertheless, the results of the numerous laboratory studies have been most helpful and have served as a basis for the development of design procedures to protect against brittle fractures.

D. BRITTLE FRACTURE STUDIES

The catastrophic service failures define a most important problem for welded structures. In the following sections, an attempt will be made to show the relationships that exist between the many factors that affect the brittle fracturing process in weldments. The problem will be defined and the role of welding analyzed in detail. This can be done only through a detailed examination of the materials involved, both the base metals and the weld metals, as well as the factors responsible for the embrittlement of these materials. Included will be discussions of mild steel weldments as well as high-strength steel and nonferrous weldments. Then, because of the importance of the welding process and the geometry of the structures, fabrication will be considered as well as the loading and environmental conditions. Finally, consideration will be given to the procedures currently available for design against brittle fracture.

II. Phenomonological Aspects of Brittle Fracture in Weldments

Least understood of the brittle fractures in welded structures are those which initiate at low nominal stresses. In some instances, the stress levels at which the failures have initiated are so low that one may even question whether it is possible to protect against brittle fracture initiation in these structures. A better understanding of the role of the welds and welding in these fractures is needed.

A. Low-Stress Fractures

Many of the catastrophic failures reported in the literature have occurred at nominal stresses of 10,000 to 15,000 psi, and have caused grave concern in the engineering profession. For many years, only service failures provided low-stress fractures; laboratory tests generally required the application of high stresses to produce brittle fractures. However, in recent years, several types of tests have been developed which appear to simulate the low-stress fracture behavior observed in service. To achieve these low-stress fractures requires severe notches, high residual tensile stresses, and low temperatures.

Data from one of the early laboratory examples of low-stress fracture are presented in Fig. 4. In this instance, relatively long flaws were placed in the test section which was then welded into a 9-foot-diameter sphere (Sopher *et al.*, 1958). Although the sphere was used primarily as a vehicle for testing, it provided the restraint necessary to develop the desired residual tensile stresses. In other instances, notched-and-welded test members have produced low-stress brittle fractures (Kihara and Masubuchi, 1959;

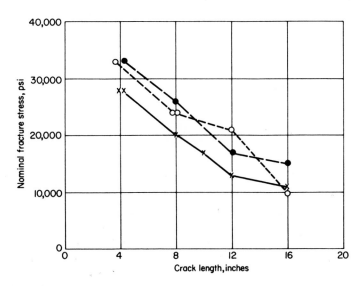

FIG. 4. Relation between crack length, crack depth, and nominal stress required to initiate brittle fracture. (Sopher *et al.*, 1958). KEY: —, $\frac{3}{4}$ in. deep; - - -, $\frac{9}{16}$ in. deep; --, $\frac{3}{8}$ in. deep.

Hall *et al.*, 1962; Greene, 1949; Wells, 1956). Both of these weldments apparently provide the three conditions necessary and sufficient to achieve low-stress brittle fractures.

In his 1960 Houdremont lecture, Soete (1960) noted that residual stresses are necessary for low-stress brittle fractures but not sufficient to alone initiate the fractures. Flaws, located in a region where the ductility will be exhausted by the welding operation, and a temperature below the transition temperature of the material are necessary also. In mild steels, the elimination of any one of these three factors appears to eliminate the initiation of low-stress fractures.

Other examples of low-stress fractures are found in the ultra-high-strength steel rocket-motor cases. In one instance, a test member 156 inches in diameter and fabricated of H-11, a hot-worked die steel, failed in a brittle manner at a stress of approximately 77,000 psi (Kies *et al.*, 1965). In this instance, the failure stress was less than 40% of the yield strength of the material, and failure initiated from a flaw which had a depth of only 0.13 inch and a length of 0.50 inch. The material in this member was only 0.38 inch thick. Thus, low-stress fractures can be found in thin weldments of ultra-high-strength steels as well as in heavy weldments of mild steels, a most discouraging condition.

B. Initiation, Propagation, and Arrest

The brittle fracturing process is often considered in terms of initiation, propagation, and arrest. In weldments, weld defects or flaws are always associated with the fracture initiation; in no case has a brittle fracture started from a sound weld (Acker, 1953). However, the weld flaw alone is not sufficient to provide the initiation in mild steel structures (Carpenter and Linsenmeyer, 1958).

A second important factor in the initiation process is the fracture stress. Both theoretical studies and laboratory experiments indicate that a critical fracture stress of approximately 200,000 psi exists for mild steel (Wright *et al.*, 1965). However, since low-stress brittle fractures initiate at nominal stresses of approximately 10,000 psi, other factors must be involved to justify this large amplification of stress.

Propagation as well as initiation may be influenced by the flaws that exist along the path of a propagating crack. However, the stress in the member is the most important parameter. Wright *et al.* (1965) report the propagation of brittle fractures at stresses as low as 5.7 ksi (see Fig. 5) but, at the same time, show that the critical stress at which these high-speed brittle fractures propagate depends on the type of steel employed, also.

The fracture propagation velocities, as noted previously, may be as high

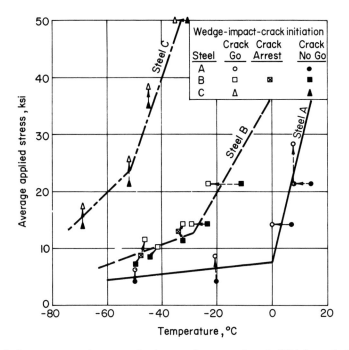

FIG. 5. Low-stress crack propagation in several structural steels (Wright *et al.*, 1965).

as 6000 ft/sec. However, in weld metal, the velocity is generally much lower than that reported for the more common structural steels (Van Elst *et al.*, 1964). Another factor that markedly affects the rate of propagation is the residual stress in the member. High residual tensile stresses will tend to increase the velocity of the crack while residual compressive stresses will tend to arrest a propagating crack. Consequently, cracks propagating across a weld, unless the weld is in a ductile state, will generally speed up. As a propagating crack reaches zones of compressive residual stress, it will slow down and even come to arrest if sufficient restraint is placed in its path. In Fig. 6, for example, an indication is presented of the effect of a residual compressive stress on the propagation of a brittle crack initially traveling at a high speed. In this instance, the velocity of the crack was reduced to a value of approximately 100 ft/sec when it reached the zone of compression, at which time the loads in the test member were redistributed and the crack forced to continue (still in a brittle manner). Initially, the crack in this member propagated at a speed of approximately 4500 ft/sec. Thus, a very wide range of crack velocities is possible during the propagation of brittle fractures in structural steels.

The third stage of the fracturing process often examined is that of arrest.

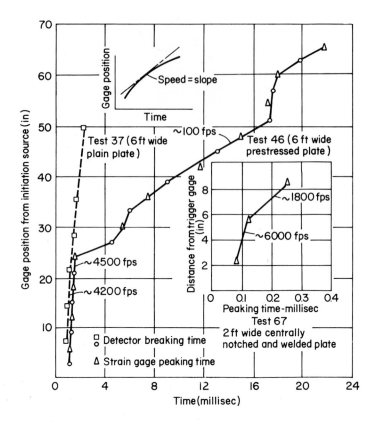

FIG. 6. Crack propagation in wide flat plates (Hall *et al.*, 1967).

This may be provided by a change in temperature of the material, a change in toughness of the material, the introduction of the tougher material in the path of the crack, or possibly the introduction of an additional energy absorbing device. In the Robertson thermal gradient test, the arresting temperature for a propagating crack is obtained. Kihara (Kihara *et al.*, 1959c), has suggested that this temperature may be related to the transition temperature obtained in the Tipper test. In other test members, such as the notched-and-welded specimen, a crack may be initiated in a high residual stress field and then be arrested as it encounters a much lower stress or a residual compressive stress. This has often resulted in the development of two stage fractures in laboratory tests and helps to explain the many arrested brittle fractures observed in actual structures. The fracture surface of a two-stage fracture may be seen in Fig. 7. In this instance, a stress approaching the yield strength of the material was necessary to propagate

FIG. 7. Two-stage fracture of structural steel weldment.

the second portion of the fracture. However, the initial cracking developed at a nominal stress of only 4000 psi.

Another means of arresting a brittle fracture is by the insertion of a strake of tough material or tough weld strength in the path of a propagating crack (Mosborg *et al.*, 1957). In the photograph of Fig. 8, the change in fracture mode of the crack is readily evident at the weld. In this instance, a long propagating crack was changed from a brittle to a ductile (shear) mode by the weld and then arrested in the tough adjacent base metal. Although such devices appear to be relatively effective in laboratory tests, the matter of designing such devices for a large structure, such as a ship, would be much more complicated.

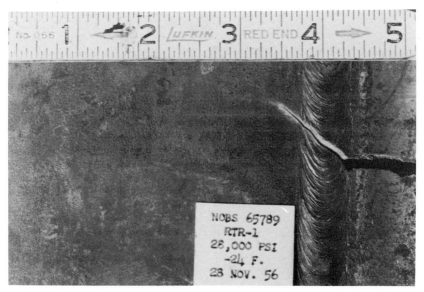

FIG. 8. Arrest of 3-foot long crack by a 12-inches wide strake of tough steel (Mosborg *et al.*, 1957).

In other instances, overlays of notch-tough welds have been employed to provide increased fracture resistance in mild steels. However, the weld used for this type of application must be considerably tougher than the base metal for the conditions under which it must operate (Puzak and Pellini, 1955).

When weld is introduced into a structure it affects markedly the state of stress in the structure and can be expected also to affect markedly the path of any brittle fracture in the structure. Four fracture paths are possible: in the weld, along the fusion line, in the heat-affected zone, or in the base plate itself (see Fig. 9). The particular crack path selected will depend on the relative toughness of these various regions and the state of stress existing in the member. Except in the case of very poor welds, brittle fractures in mild steel structures generally propagate through the welds and in the adjacent material in a direction perpendicular to the direction of maximum principal tensile stress. Because of high residual tensile stresses in welds, cracks will seldom, if ever, propagate in a weld or in its heat-affected zone. This has been verified by the International Institute of Welding whose failure investigations have been carried on over a period of several years with no failures being reported to have propagated in welds (International Institute of Welding, 1964).

In tests reported by Kihara *et al.* (1959c), a study was made of the propagation of cracks along welds (Fig. 10). For the lower-stress fractures, approximately 7000 psi, the cracks propagated parallel to the weld but at a distance of approximately 8 inches. Thus, the residual stress in the weld forced the crack away from the weld; it had a major effect on the manner in which the crack propagated in the weldment. If the weld was placed diagonally across the crack path, the fracture again tended to propagate in an irregular pattern and in a direction perpendicular to the maximum principal tensile stress; an illustration of this condition is presented in Fig. 11.

It is evident that much insight can be gained into the fracturing process through an understanding of the initiation, propagation, and arrest of brittle fractures. However, it is equally important to realize that if one can

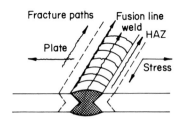

Fig. 9. Possible paths of brittle fracture in weldments (Pellini, 1956).

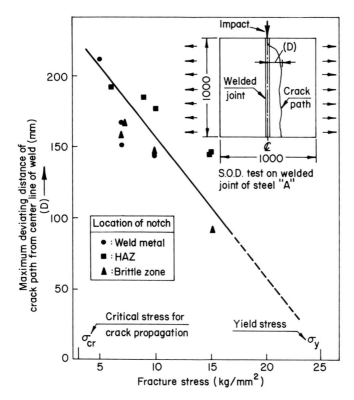

FIG. 10. Relation between fracture stress and deviation of crack from notch line (Kihara *et al.*, 1959c).

prohibit the initiation of a brittle fracture, then the problems of propagation and arrest need not be considered.

C. Role of Welding

The factors associated with the effects of welding on brittle fracture can be divided into three categories: (a) metallurgical effects; (b) geometrical effects; and (c) stress effects. With a sound weld, the possibility of brittle fracture is relatively low. However, defects in welds and their metallurgical and geometrical effects have been responsible for, or involved in, most brittle fractures. Obviously, the role of welding in brittle fracture is extremely important.

The metallurgical effects introduced by welding include such factors as changes in metallurgical structure of the parent material, hardening, strain

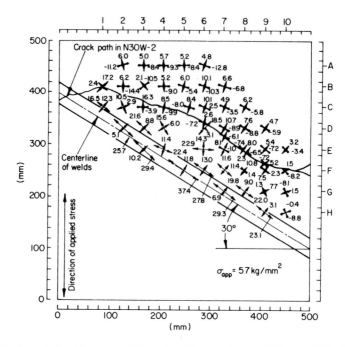

Fig. 11. Effect of residual stress field and weld on crack path (Kihara, 1961). Outward arrows indicate tensile stresses; inward arrows indicate compressive stresses.

aging, and grain growth. In a recent study, Rosenstein and Lubahn (1967) suggest that the metallurgical damage of welding provides only a minor effect on the low-stress fracturing of weldments. However, as discussed later in detail, the metallurgical effects in combination with the geometrical and stress effects can and do play a major role.

The residual stresses resulting from welding have often been observed to have a significant effect on the initiation and propagation of brittle fractures (Barton and Hall, 1960; Rolfe et al., 1959). As noted by Boyd (1955), residual stresses per se do not cause brittle fracture in a ductile material; however, in a brittle material they can produce failure in the same way as other stresses. Thus, residual stresses are neither the entire answer nor can they be neglected.

D. Tests of Weldments and Materials

More than 50 types of brittle fracture tests are reported in the literature (Hall et al., 1967). Some of the tests are used to obtain an indication of the basic mechanisms of brittle fracture, others are used for the selection of materials, and some are designed to provide an indication of the behavior of welded structures. However, there is no single test that will predict the transition temperature or behavior of a specific structure (Johnson and Stout, 1960).

A brief listing of some of the principal brittle fracture tests is presented in Table I. In most of these tests, the behavior is evaluated in terms of a transition temperature. Although several definitions may be employed for transition temperature, it in general is defined as the temperature at which there is a change from ductile to brittle behavior. Variations in the transition temperatures obtained in the laboratory often vary markedly with the type of test (see Fig. 12) and also with the thickness of the material (see Fig. 13). Consequently, the application of such information in the evaluation of the brittle behavior of an actual structure is extremely difficult.

For the higher strength materials, notched, tensile or bend specimens are generally employed to establish the fracture toughness of the materials. Such tests are employed to evaluate the toughness of the base metal as well as of the weld metals used with such materials (ASTM, 1960–1964). Once determined, the fracture toughness of the weld, fusion zone, heat-affected zone, and base metal can be used to evaluate the effect of flaws on the fracture stress in these various regions of the material (Wessel *et al.*, 1966). Such a procedure provides an effective means of evaluating the behavior of high-strength brittle materials. However, much more study and development is necessary before this type of analysis can be used effectively for the mild steels in which extensive plastic deformation occurs.

In a number of tests, welds have been introduced to include to a certain

TABLE I

PRINCIPAL BRITTLE FRACTURE TESTS[a]

Charpy impact tests: Charpy-V, keyhole, Izod
Slow-bend tests: van der Veen, Lehigh, Kinzel
Drop-weight tests: Pellini and Puzak
Explosion crack-starter test: Pellini and Puzak
Tear tests: drop-weight, explosion, Navy
Robertson thermal gradient test
ESSO notch impact test
Notched-and-welded plates (Greene or Wells notch)
Wide-plate tests (centrally notched plates)
Exhaustion of ductility tests (prestrain, temperature, ductility)
Fracture mechanics tests (notched tensile or bend)

---

[a] Hall (1968).

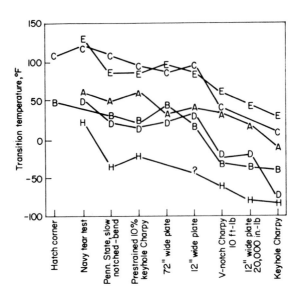

Fig. 12. Transition temperature of various steels as determined from various types of tests (Parker 1957).

extent the metallurgical as well as geometrical effects of welding. These include such tests as the drop-weight test, the explosion crack-starter test, and the notched-and-welded test. In the last few years, the notched-and-welded specimen (Kihara and Masubuchi, 1959; Hall et al., 1962; Hall and Chamberlain, 1966) has found extensive use. It has provided low-stress fractures, includes a notch as well as residual stresses, and in many ways appears to simulate the low-stress brittle behavior observed in many welded structures.

Investigators have long sought a simple laboratory test that would behave in the same manner as a welded structure in service. The notched-and-welded flat plate test begins to approach this condition, but still does not provide the full state of stress that exists in most structures nor does it provide the continuity and restraint of the structure. It would appear that the actual structure is the only test member that can fully duplicate its behavior. It is the only structure that has the proper materials, the proper state of stress, the required flaws or discontinuities, and introduces the appropriate previous stress history. This, then, suggests that much more effort is needed in the evaluation of brittle failures in welded structures. Such information, in combination with the data obtained in the many existing laboratory tests, would provide a better means of presenting a more complete brittle fracture hypothesis.

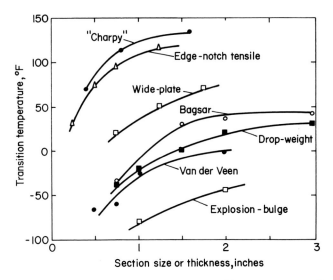

FIG. 13. Effect of specimen size or thickness on transition temperature (Roper *et al.*, 1967).

E. FRACTURE ANALYSIS

In the analysis of brittle fractures, use is often made of either a fracture mechanics or engineering fracture evaluation, or a transition temperature evaluation. In recent years, much effort has been directed toward the use of fracture mechanics or engineering fracture analysis. Such evaluations provide not only an indication of the critical stress but also an indication of the magnitude of cracks or flaws that will correspond to this critical stress.

Linear fracture mechanics is being applied widely in the evaluation of ultra-high-strength materials for which plastic zones are relatively small (Wessel *et al.*, 1966). In this application, the plane-strain fracture toughness provides a measure of the fracture resistance of the materials and, when used with the principles of fracture mechanics, provides a basis for the selection of materials as well as an indication of the limiting design stresses that may be employed with flaws of various sizes (Campbell, 1964; Johnson, 1965). However, to apply such information properly one must conduct studies to evaluate the fracture toughness of the material and welds in question. Obviously, since these properties may vary considerably as a result of fabrication and material selection, the task of evaluating fracture toughness becomes very laborious (Brown and Srawley, 1967).

An indication of some of the factors that affect the fracture toughness of a material is presented in Fig. 14. Here, it may be seen that the fracture toughness of a steel of a given yield strength may vary considerably from

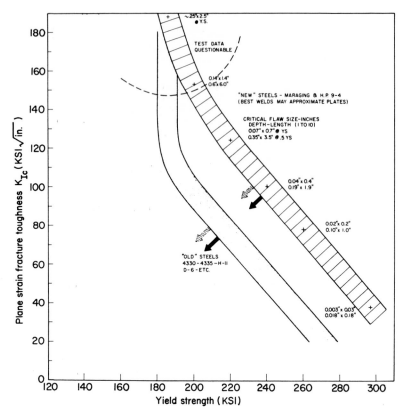

FIG. 14. Upper bound limits or plane strain fracture toughness (K_{Ic}) for $\frac{1}{2}$- to 1- inch plates of high-strength steels (Pellini *et al.*, 1965). Solid arrow: expect decrease with increased thickness; hatched arrow: expect decrease in presence of moisture (stress corrosion cracking).

one material to another and that values for the lower strength steels may be questionable. Furthermore, thickness as well as moisture, flaw size, and other variables will also affect this behavior.

Additional factors must be brought into play in evaluating the behavior of the lower strength steels in which extensive yielding may occur. For this purpose, diagrams of the type presented in Fig. 15 by Kihara (1961) provide an excellent indication of the overall picture of brittle fracture behavior, with particular reference to tension tests. In this diagram, five regions of behavior are identified. These are as follows:

I. This is the region in which brittle fracture will occur, in a structure which is free of residual stresses, only after a stress greater than the yield strength of the material has been applied.

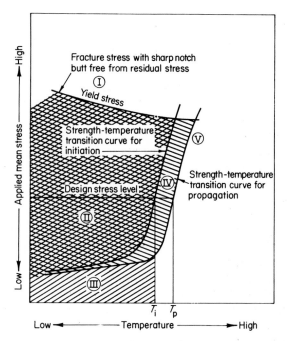

FIG. 15. Schematic representation of fracture behavior of a weldment (Hall *et al.*, 1967). Note: critical temperature for initiation (T_i) and propagation (T_p) at design stress level.

II. In this region, a complete brittle fracture of the member can be expected under low applied tensile stress. Within this region, high localized residual tensile stresses exist at the point of initiation.

III. In this region, short partial cracks may initiate in the member. However, the applied stress is not sufficient to sustain propagation. The residual stress associated with the initiation will generally have been reduced by the cracking to the extent that further propagation will require the application of yield point stress or higher.

VI. This is a region in which one would not normally expect a brittle fracture to initiate. However, if special forces are applied to initiate the fracture, it can be expected to propagate fully to failure.

V. In this region, the structure would be free from both initiation and propagation of brittle cracks.

Also included in Fig. 15 is an indication of the design or working stress. Thus, this representation provides an indication of the relationship between temperature, applied stress, and many of the other factors involved in the brittle fracture process. It does not, however, provide an indication of the importance of flaws.

On the basis of their evaluation of brittle fractures and fracture toughness of many structural steels, Pellini *et al.* (1965) have introduced flaw size into the representation of Fig. 15. In addition, the behavior of the material is related to the NDT, FTP, and FTE transitions. (NDT is the nil ductility transition, FTP is the fracture transition plastic, and FTE is the fracture transition elastic.) This provides a very effective means of evaluating the more ductile materials and structures for engineering applications (see Fig. 16). Also included is an indication of the shift in behavior produced by a variation in the toughness (tear energy) of the material; the shift is shown for low energy tear materials that do not exhibit a definite transition temperature.

The fracture analysis diagram can be used also to demonstrate why small flaws initiate brittle fractures at low stress levels when residual stresses exist in the region of the flaws. In Fig. 17, for example, complete fractures are possible at temperatures below the NDT temperature and at any stress above the "minimum crack propagation level." The reason for the initiation and propagation from small flaws, in region II of Fig. 15, is the presence of high residual stresses which, when added to the applied stress level, provide the necessary initiating stresses. In Fig. 17, the curve of "fracture for small flaws" is, in effect, shifted downward by the introduction of residual stresses, and failure may occur at any point between the

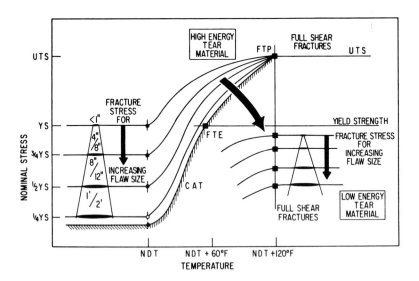

Fig. 16. Fracture analysis diagram and conceptual modifications for steels of decreasing levels of fracture toughness in the fully ductile mode—noted as "low energy tear" for the low levels (Pellini *et al.*, 1965).

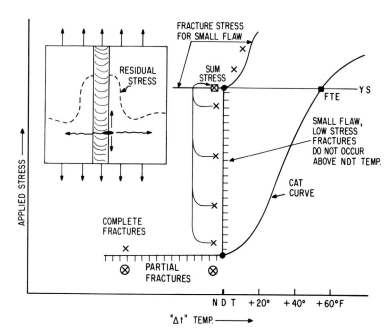

FIG. 17. Illustrating the fracture analysis diagram prediction of "low stress" fractures in the presence of high residual stress fields (Pellini and Puzak, 1963a).

original curve and the lower curve of "minimum stress for propagation," depending on the magnitude of the residual stress. Thus, the diagram makes possible consideration of the residual stresses as well as the temperature, flaw size, applied stress, and material properties.

F. PARAMETERS AFFECTING BRITTLE FRACTURE IN WELDMENTS

Many parameters, in addition to those discussed above, are known to affect the brittle behavior of weldments. The base metal, the weld metal, the fusion zone, the heat-affected zone, and the thermally affected zone generally exhibit different toughness properties, and consequently must be considered in terms of fracture resistance. Another important aspect is the welding; variations in the welding process, the welding materials, and the welding procedures affect the properties of the several zones noted. Finally, the fabrication and the loading and environmental conditions to which a structure is subjected will affect its susceptibility to fracture in a brittle manner. Further discussions of these factors will be presented in the following sections.

III. Materials and Weldments

Notch toughness, as defined by the Charpy impact tests, and fracture toughness, as established by means of notch tensile or bend tests, are often used to provide an indication of the tendency for a material to fracture in a brittle manner. Consequently, the base metal, the weld metal, the fusion zone, the heat-affected zone, and the thermally affected zone of weldments have generally been evaluated with one or the other of these tests.

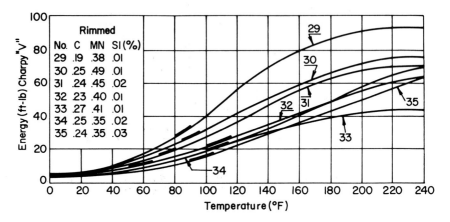

Fig. 18a

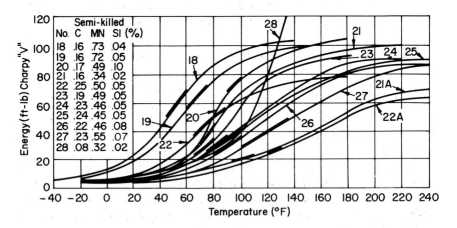

Fig. 18b

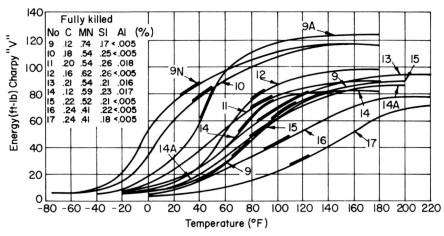

Fig. 18c

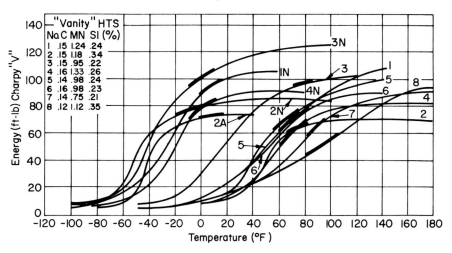

Fig. 18d

FIG. 18. Bulge fracture transitions as related to Charpy-V transition curves of structural steels (Pellini, 1952).

A. BASE METAL

The notch toughness of structural steels varies widely. Figure 18, for example, shows the Charpy-V transition curves reported by Pellini (1952) for a variety of steels. Such relationships are a function of the chemistry of the materials as well as their manufacture, heat treatment, grain size, etc.

(Shank, 1957). The effect of alloying elements on the 15 ft-lb Charpy transition temperature, according to Boulger and Hanson (1962), may be predicted by the following:

$$Tr_{15}(^\circ F) = 168 + 333\,C - 66.6\,Mn - 269\,Si + 210\,Si^2$$

$$+ 116\,Si\,Mn - 512\,Al + 2849\,Al^2 + 367\,Al\,Si$$

$$- 18.1\ \text{ferrite grain-size number.}$$

With the introduction of the many new high-strength steels, it is found that, ac the tensile strengths increase, the notch toughness generally tends to decrease (Battelle Memorial Institute, 1964). This is evident in Fig. 19 where the notch toughness of steels with yield strengths as high as 300,000 psi are presented. For a given yield strength, a considerable variation in toughness is obtained from the various steels, thereby demonstrating that not only the strength of the material but also other parameters affect its toughness. The upper curve in this diagram presents the optimum materials trend line.

A further indication of the differences obtained in the behavior of some of the steels is presented in Fig. 20. Here, it may be seen that both the

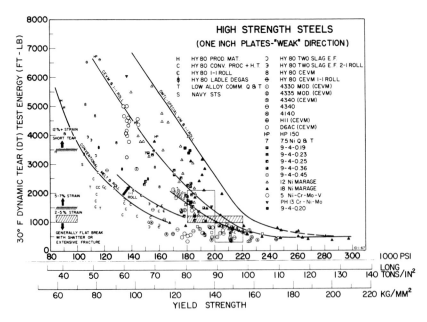

FIG. 19. Spectrum of C_v test data for high-strength steels as a function of yield strength and of processing practices (Pellini *et al.*, 1965).

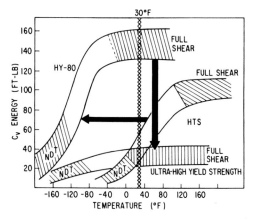

Fig. 20. Representative C_v test energy transition curves for HTS and HY-80 steels compared to those of ultra-high-strength (180–200 ksi yield) steels (Pellini and Puzak, 1963c).

transition temperature (NDT) and the energy absorption for ductile failure were improved by changing from the 50,000-psi yield strength HTS steel to the 80,000-psi yield strength quenched and tempered HY-80 steel. In changing to an ultra-high-strength steel, the notch toughness, as indicated by the NDT, was again excellent. However, the energy shelf was extremely low, indicating a low level of energy absorption in the tearing mode. Such a condition generally identifies a material that is highly susceptible to low-stress failure from notches or flaws. Behaviors of this type are the reason restrictions must be placed on the size of flaws tolerated in the ultra-high-strength materials used for such structures as rocket-motor cases. The controls on weld quality in these materials will of necessity also need to be rigidly enforced.

A general indication of the variation in notch toughness of titanium alloy plate is shown in Fig. 21. Again, it is evident that the energy absorbing capacity of the material markedly decreases as the yield strength is increased. Thus, this material also, when of high strength levels, must be welded with great care.

The variations in notch toughness indicated by the transition curves for various materials are evident also in the fracture toughness data reported in the literature. Values of K_{Ic}, the plain-strain fracture toughness for aluminum, titanium, and steel of various strengths, are presented in Fig. 22. The fracture toughness of each material decreased as the strength of the materials increased. More extensive detailed data on the fracture toughness for these materials, as well as many other materials, will be found in the literature (Wessel *et al.*, 1966; ASTM, 1965; Peck and Gerken, 1966;

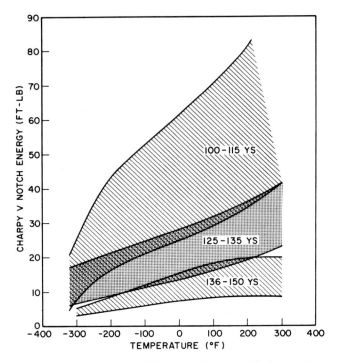

FIG. 21. Generalized relationships of C_v energy decrease with decreased temperature, representing various broad ranges of yield strength for 1-inch-thick titanium alloy plate (Pellini *et al.*, 1965).

Randall, 1966; Davis *et al.*, 1965). These fracture toughness data may be used to establish critical flaw sizes for these materials through application of fracture mechanics and thus help to provide a more rational basis for the establishment of suitable design and inspection requirements.

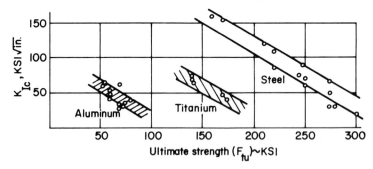

FIG. 22. General relationship between fracture toughness and ultimate strength of various materials (Tiffany and Masters, 1965).

B. WELD METAL

The weld metal is the second portion of the weldment to be considered. In general, flaws reducing the cross-sectional area of a butt weld in mild steel by 5 to 7% will not reduce the static strength of the joint (Bradley and McCauley, 1964). However, this does not apply to the notch toughness of the weld metal. The notch toughness is a function of metallurgical and chemical variations as well as of geometry.

Numerous tests are reported in the literature on the notch toughness of weld metals deposited with various types of covered electrodes (Masubuchi *et al.*, 1966). An indication of the range in transition temperature determined in NDT drop-weight tests and Charpy tests for various electrodes is shown in Fig. 23. Here, just as with the base metals, it appears that an increase in strength of the weld metal tends to decrease the energy absorbing capacity of the weld. However, this effect will be affected by the base metal and heat treatments that are employed. As a result, many of the curves cross.

Chemical composition of the weld metal as well as its grain size are known to affect the transition temperature obtained in Charpy tests. An indication of these effects is evident in the following relationship established on the

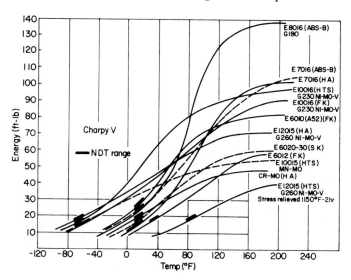

FIG. 23. General correlation of drop-weight test nil ductility transition to Charpy-V transition curves for various weld metals. The bands indicate the nil ductility transition temperature of welds and corresponding Charpy-V energies developed at these temperatures (Pellini, 1956).

basis of studies of a number of multilayer weld metals (Masubuchi *et al.*, 1966).

$$Tr_{15}(^\circ \text{F}) = 435\,\text{C} - 54\,\text{Mn} + 14\,\text{Si} + 286\,\text{P} + 819\,\text{S}$$
$$- 61\,\text{Cu} - 29\,\text{Ni} + 13\,\text{Cr} + 23\,\text{Mo} + 355\,\text{V}$$
$$- 112\,\text{Al} + 1138\,\text{N} + 380\,\text{O} + 1.08(d \times 10^4)$$
$$- 203 \pm 22.$$

Thus, the principal elements affecting the toughness of the material appear to be nitrogen, sulfur, carbon, oxygen, vanadium, and phosphorus. All of these elements tend to increase the transition temperature of the weld.

One of the newer welding processes used for the welding of thick materials is the electroslag process. In general, the notch toughness of electroslag weld metal deposits has been relatively poor (Masubuchi *et al.*, 1966) (see Fig. 24). Some improvement in the toughness can be realized through proper heat treatment; however, much further study of this problem is necessary.

The introduction of the new ultra-high-strength steels has resulted in many new welding problems. In general, they have been considered to be

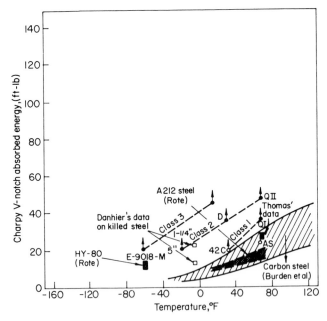

FIG. 24. Notch toughness of electroslag-deposited metals in as-welded condition (Masubuchi *et al.*, 1966).

weldable materials; however, the achievement of high levels of notch toughness in weldments has been extremely difficult. The welding process as well as the welding procedure has a significant effect on the toughness obtained.

In some instances, it has been possible to use covered electrodes for the welding of the higher strength materials (Rolnick, 1964). However, the type of coating may have an effect on the level of energy absorbing capacity developed in the welds. For example, in the case of a 5% nickel steel (Fig. 25), iron powder electrodes provided a greater toughness than did those with titania or lime coatings. In all three instances, however, it would appear that the electrodes provided relatively low temperatures for a 15 ft-lb energy level.

With the ultra-high-strength materials, such as the maraging steels, the MIG and TIG welding processes have been employed extensively. The weld metals in these materials have generally had lower levels of notch toughness than the base metal (Knoth and Petersen, 1965). As shown in Fig. 26, the welds generally tend to have a toughness that approaches the lower levels of toughness obtained for the base metal. In some instances, this reduced toughness has been related to the microstructure of the welds, in that coarse-grained weld deposits with dendrites alined along the direction of fracture gave lower toughness levels than did those weldments with more homogeneous weld metal (Kies *et al.*, 1965).

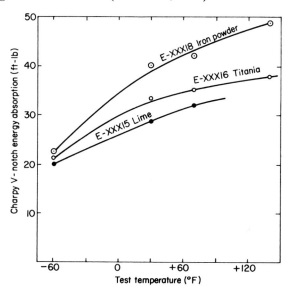

Fig. 25. Impact properties of weld metals deposited with three covered-electrode systems (Rolnick, 1964).

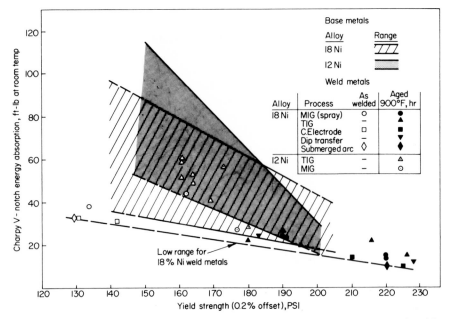

FIG. 26. Notch toughness-yield strength relation for maraging steel plate and weld metals (Fragetta *et al.*, 1964).

A further indication of the degradation in toughness produced by welding of the ultra-high-strength steels is presented in Table II. The average plain-strain fracture toughness values for the weld metal are generally well below that of the base metal. Nevertheless, at present, brittle welds must be accepted if welded structures are required in materials having yield strengths greater than 250,000 psi (Kammer and Martin, 1966).

Since some of the fracture toughness values begin to approach the fracture toughness of the base metal, it would appear that further research may help to develop suitable weld metal toughness. However, producing the desired quality of welding in the ultra-high-strength materials will require great care in welding. In addition, since hydrogen is known to cause certain of the weld metal defects, moisture and the resulting hydrogen pickup must be protected against (Rogers, 1959). Some of the recent studies reported by Meitzner and Stout (1966) clearly demonstrate the importance of hydrogen.

Although most of the discussion presented here has been concerned with steel weldments, the toughness of welds in some of the nonferrous materials is also of importance. Weldments in several titanium alloys have exhibited relatively high transition temperatures (Daley and Hartbower, 1956). These are shown in Fig. 27. Although the toughness of the weld metal appears to

TABLE II

FRACTURE TOUGHNESS OF WELD METAL

| Base metal | Welding process | K_{Ic} ($ksi \sqrt{in.}$) | | | Reference |
		Base metal	Weld	HAZ	
18 Ni (250)	TIG	80	68		Masubuchi and Martin (1966)
18 Ni (250)	SA	80	40		Masubuchi and Martin, (1966)
18 Ni (250)	TIG	77–84[a]	70–84[a]	75–95[a]	Kies et al. (1965), p. 347
18 Ni (250)	MIG	77–84[a]	74–78[a]	94–91[a]	Kies et al. (1965), p. 347
18 Ni (250)	Short arc	77–84[a]	57–73[a]	90–107	Kies et al. (1965), p. 347
HP 9–4–25	TIG	120–140	118		Pascover et al. (1965), p. 321
HP 9–4–25 ($\frac{1}{4}$ in.).	TIG	88–104	74–88	—	Peck and Gerken (1966), p. 80
HP 9–4–25 ($\frac{1}{2}$ in.)	MIG	75–96	70–118	70–120	Peck and Gerken (1966), p. 100
HP 9–4–25	TIG	99–101	85–106	80–108	Peck and Gerken (1966), p. 58
D–6ac (210)	TIG	116–120	80–97	94–97	Clark and Privoznik (1965)

[a] Test bars perpendicular or parallel to direction of rolling, respectively.

match that of the base metal reasonably well, Daley and Hartbower (1956) note that the toughness of the heat-affected zone was relatively poor. Thus, if titanium alloys are used where low temperatures and high notch toughness are required, the soundness of the weld metal may be extremely important.

In the case of aluminum alloys and their welds, the question of brittle fracture can generally be neglected. In most instances, the toughness or tear resistance of the welds and base metals are generally higher at low temperatures than at high temperatures (Meister and Martin, 1967). Nevertheless, even in aluminum, the notch-tensile ratio (the ratio of notched to unnotched strength) decreases as the yield strength of the material is increased and thus is not insensitive to the effects of sharp notches.

C. HEAT-AFFECTED ZONE

In the heat-affected zone (HAZ) of a weldment, that zone where the microstructure of the base metal is altered by the welding, significant variations in notch toughness appear to take place. This variation is influenced by such parameters as heat input, weld length, and other welding parameters (Dekker, 1962). Consequently, suitable quality controls and weld qualification evaluations are necessary to ensure the properties desired in this region. An indication of the significant variation obtained in the HAZ of several structural steels is shown in Fig. 28. This diagram also

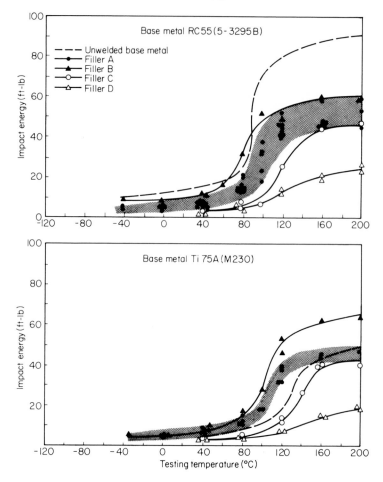

FIG. 27. Notch toughness of weld deposits formed by depositing several heats of unalloyed titanium filler material in two heats of unalloyed base metal (Daley and Hartbower, 1956).

shows the high level of notch toughness obtained in the weld metal, as compared to that originally provided by the base metal.

In a review of the welding of high-strength steels, Kammer and Martin (1966) have indicated that the low-alloy martensitic steels and the bainitic steels may possess heat-affected zones that are more susceptible to cracking than are the medium-alloy martensitic steels and the nickel maraging steels. Suitable treatments may be required after welding to improve the heat-affected zones in the low-alloy martensitic and the bainitic steels if they are to be used where high notch toughness is essential.

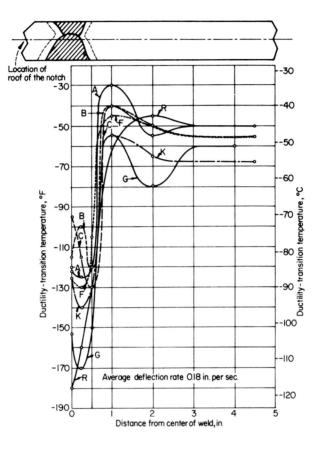

Fig. 28. Variation of the ductility-transition temperature from the center of a butt weld to the unaffected base metal for several low-carbon steels (Stout and Doty, 1953).

Code	Type of steel	C	Mn	Si	V	Ti
A	C(semikilled)	0.23	0.48	0.05	—	—
B	C-Mn	0.18	1.09	0.16	—	—
C	Mn-V-Ti	0.11	1.03	0.26	0.03	0.01
F	C (fully killed)	0.23	0.53	0.19	—	—
G	C (fully killed)	0.20	0.61	0.21	—	—
K	C (fully killed)	0.13	0.42	0.22	—	—
R	C (rimmed)	0.23	0.47	0.004	—	—

TABLE III

RESULTS OF CRACK-NOTCH TENSILE TESTS OF HIGH-STRENGTH WELDABLE STEELS[a]

	K_{Ic} stress-intensity factor (ksi $\sqrt{in.}$) for various steels[b]				
	T–1	STS	HY–80L	HY–80H	QT35
Q & T, as produced	80	113	56	118	50.5
	(−300)	(−320)	(−320)	(−320)	(−320)
Quenched: Approximates the	81.5	48.7	74.5	98.5	86
HAZ of rapidly cooled weld	(−200)	(−200)	(−320)	(−200)	(−200)
Furnace cooled: Approximates	56	32	33	69	107
HAZ of slowly cooled weld	(−100)	(−200)	(−200)	(−200)	(−100)

[a] Wessel and Hays (1963).
[b] Number in parentheses indicates testing temperature, °F.

An indication of the degradation that can be expected in the heat-affected zone of some of the lower strength quenched and tempered steels is shown in Table III. The local heat treatments performed to simulate conditions in the heat-affected zone apparently affect the various materials in different ways. In most instances, however, the slow cooling rate apparently decreases markedly the fracture toughness of the material.

D. THERMALLY AFFECTED ZONE

The fourth zone of a weldment, one often neglected in brittle fracture considerations, is that sometimes referred to as a thermally affected zone (TAZ). This is the region beyond that normally considered as the heat-affected zone where noticeable microstructural changes take place. Nevertheless, some of the mild structural steels have shown significant increases in transition temperature (decrease in toughness) in this region. This is readily evident in the data of Fig. 28 for steel A. The transition temperature of the material in the TAZ is shown to be 20 degrees above that of the base metal. Most of the other steels also show a reduction in toughness in this region, but to a lesser extent.

Although a thermally affected zone develops in mild structural steels, this condition should not be expected for all materials. For example, in stainless steel weldments (Mishler and Nichols, 1961), the weld metal itself generally provides the lowest notch toughness.

In summary, then, it is evident that, in any consideration of brittle fracture in weldments, account must be taken of the properties of not only the weld metal, but also the heat-affected and the thermally affected zones.

And, for most effective use of the weldments, suitable welding processes and procedures should be developed to provide sound welds and toughnesses in the HAZ and TAZ, as well as in the weld metal, to at least match the toughness of the base metal itself, particularly for the ultra-high-strength materials.

IV. Embrittlement in Weldments

The catastrophic low-stress fractures in welded structures and the many low-stress laboratory failures in weldments suggest that embrittling effects are introduced by welding. Consequently, many investigators have studied in detail some of the factors responsible for this embrittlement. Included have been such parameters as thermal and strain cycling, strain aging, exhaustion of ductility as a result of straining, and nuclear radiation. Although much needs to be learned in each of these areas, brief discussions will be presented to demonstrate their importance in the studies of brittle fracture in weldments.

A. THERMAL AND STRAIN CYCLING

The entire strain and thermal history to which a material and its weld are subjected must be considered in evaluating a weldment that is susceptible to brittle fracture. Several investigations have clearly shown that local embrittlement due to hot straining concentrated at defects can play a most significant part in the initiation of low-stress brittle fractures in weldments (Kiefner and Munse, 1967; Burdekin, 1967). Thus, the welding not only introduces a flaw in a region of high residual stress but also reduces the toughness of the material through a thermal and strain cycling process. The process by which this embrittlement is produced and the extent to which it takes place is still not understood; however, the realization of its existence has helped greatly in explaining the low-stress brittle fractures in welded structures.

Since the embrittlement discussed above is located near the weld and caused by the weld, it would appear that an appropriate heat treatment might restore the ductility and toughness of the material in the embrittled regions. However, any such treatments must be used with care in order that the adjacent material is not further embrittled. Stress relief treatments, for example, may improve the properties at or near the weld but, at the same time, may cause grain growth in other regions of the material and thus produce a reduction in toughness in these other regions.

B. Strain Aging

Another phenomenon which can be expected to affect the ductility and toughness of the weldment is that of strain aging. Strain aging not only affects the yield strength of certain materials, but also its ductile-brittle transition temperature, high-temperature strength, fatigue strength, and electrical and magnetic properties. This effect occurs principally when carbon and/or nitrogen are present in the steels, and is thought to be due primarily to migration of carbon and nitrogen atoms to dislocations (Baird, 1963). Again, the chemistry of the steels appears to to be an important factor.

C. Exhaustion of Ductility

At Brown University, numerous tests have been conducted to study the exhaustion of ductility in structural steels. Mylonas (1959) has reported static fractures in structural steel at stresses as low as 12% of the virgin yield point of the material. However, such failures have been observed only after the ductility has been exhausted by the application of large compressive strains. This contradicts to some extent the philosophy that residual stresses play a major role in the initiation and propagation of the low-stress brittle fractures. Typical results reported by Mylonas and his co-workers (1965) are shown in Fig. 29. Here, it may be seen that at a

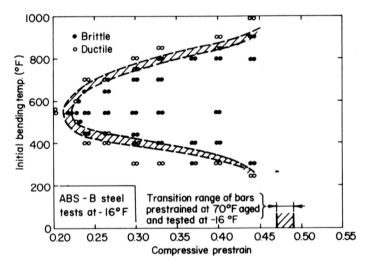

Fig. 29. Exhaustion of ductility produced by hot bending (Mylonas and Beaulieu, 1965).

bending temperature of approximately 500 to 600° F, a temperature readily realized in welding, a relatively small compressive prestrain can produce a significant embrittling effect. Only one steel is represented in this diagram; however, other steels, ranging from low-strength rimmed steels to quenched and tempered steels having yield strengths of 100,000 psi, provide a similar behavior. Furthermore, it is found that aging at 300° F for $1\frac{1}{2}$ hours tended to increase further the embrittlement of the steels (Rockey *et al.*, 1962). This effect was greater for the mild steels than for the quenched and tempered steels. Recent studies by Armenkas and Mylonas (1967) show the reduction in ductility for a maraging steel and two titanium alloys.

A restoration of the ductility in members that have been severely hot strained in compression to exhaust their ductility can be achieved by heating to temperatures of approximately 1050° F. Restoration of some ductility appears to occur even at temperatures as low as 700° F; however, higher temperatures were necessary to restore the ductility in members which had been cold strained (Mylonas and Beaulieu, 1965).

D. IRRADIATION

Radiation environments are found to embrittle steels seriously. The extent to which the materials are embrittled depends not only on the type of steel but also on the temperature during irradiation and the total neutron exposure (Pellini *et al.*, 1962). An indication of the marked increase in transition temperature resulting from irradiation is shown in Fig. 30. Included in this study were a weld metal and various other metals. This phenomenon is extremely important in the application of welding in nuclear power plants.

Although neutron exposure embrittles steels, it is found that increased exposure temperatures tend to produce some self-healing effects. Obviously many unknowns still exist in this area and further research and study concerning the interrelationships between temperature, stress, crack size, and exposure are necessary to better define the effects of irradiation on notch toughness.

E. STATE OF STRESS

In most laboratory studies, the geometry and the uniaxial state of stress provided in the members has been such that general yielding occurs at the nominal tensile yield strength of the material. The introduction of a biaxial stress field will raise the yield strength of the material and also the ease with which a brittle fracture can initiate. A triaxial state of stress can be expected to affect this condition further. In addition, the study reported by

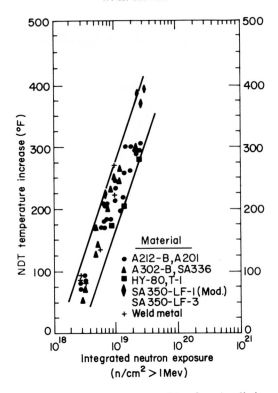

Fig. 30. Increase in the NDT temperature resulting from irradiation at temperatures below 450° F (Pellini *et al.*, 1962).

Cannon and Munse (1966) indicates that the local stress concentration near the tip of the crack in notched-and-welded members may approach a value of 13 or 14. Thus, it appears that the geometry, the state of stress, and the extremely high stress concentrations provided in the embrittled region of the notched-and-welded specimens make it possible for the material near the tip of the notch to reach the critical fracture stress as a result of the addition of the residual stresses and only a small applied stress. However, further study of this question is necessary before this hypothesis for low-stress fracture behavior can be justified.

V. Fabrication of Weldments

Any evaluation of the behavior of weldments requires an understanding of the effects of fabrication on this behavior. Consideration must be given to the welding process and procedures as well as to weld flaws and residual stresses that result from these procedures. In some instances, special weld treatments may be employed to overcome the effects of flaws and residual stresses. However, the effects of these treatments on behavior of the entire structure must be considered. Thus, fabrication and weld treatment play an important role in providing structures which will resist brittle fracturing.

A. WELDING PROCESSES AND PROCEDURES

The most common welding process used for mild steels is shielded metal-arc welding where covered electrodes are used. However, the notch toughness of the weld metals obtained from the various mild steel electrodes can vary markedly (Armstrong and Warner, 1958). The poor notch toughness of some of these electrodes is readily apparent in Fig. 31. It is evident that brittle fractures could be expected in the plates and weld metal of the World War II ships at their normal operating temperatures. In fact, with the poor toughness exhibited for these materials, it is surprising that more vessels did not fail in a catastrophic manner.

Some improvement in weld metal notch toughness can be realized by using low hydrogen electrodes. The toughness of the low hydrogen weld

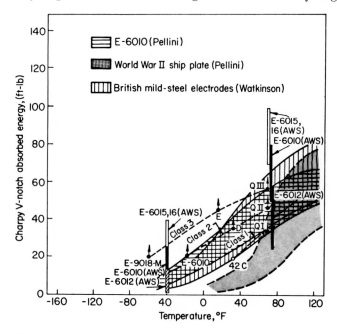

FIG. 31. Notch toughness data of weld metals of mild-steel electrodes (Masubuchi *et al.*, 1966).

metal is presented in Fig. 32 and, in general, shows a significant improvement in behavior. The materials have a much improved energy absorbing capacity at the higher temperatures and also an improvement in their low-temperature behavior or transition temperature. However, if these low hydrogen electrodes are applied to higher strength materials, there is again a tendency for a decrease in notch toughness. This is similar to the effect discussed earlier with regard to the base metal properties and is shown in Fig. 33. Nevertheless, even though there is a reduction in the energy absorbing capacity of the low hydrogen high-strength welds, they still provide considerably better notch toughness than do the mild steel electrodes shown in Fig. 31. Thus, control of the hydrogen in the welding electrode provides improved weld metal notch toughness, providing the electrodes are properly dried (Zapffe and Worden, 1949).

Attempts have been made to continue the use of covered electrodes for the welding of the higher strength steels. They may be adequate for some of the steels but, in general, other welding processes and procedures are necessary to weld properly the ultra-high-strength steels.

With the introduction of the ultra-high-strength steels, the use of inert gas welding has increased. However, other new welding processes are being

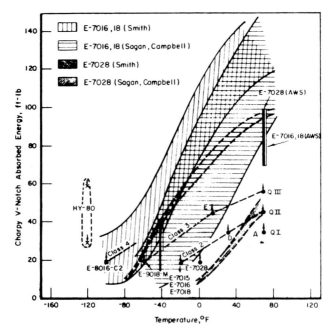

FIG. 32. Notch toughness of weld metals of low-hydrogen E-70XX electrodes (Masubuchi et al., 1966).

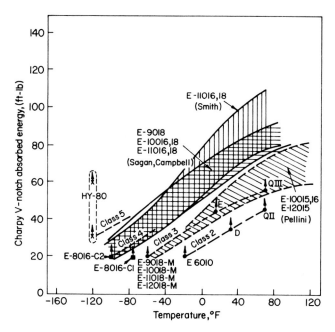

FIG. 33. Notch toughness of weld metals of low-hydrogen high-strength steel electrodes (Masubuchi *et al.*, 1966).

studied, also. These include: (1) narrow-gap welding; (2) electron-beam welding; (3) plasma-arc welding; (4) high-frequency resistance welding; (5) electroslag welding; (6) laser welding; and (7) interrupted-arc welding (Evans and Martin, 1965). A number of these processes have been used to prepare weldments in 18 Ni maraging steels, and a general comparison of these weldments is presented in Table IV. Apparently, the TIG welding process has been most successful for the welding of this steel; some of the other processes appear to be more difficult to apply and much less flexible in their application.

In addition to the proper selection of the welding process for each material, the details of the welding procedure must be properly selected, also. In the case of maraging steels, for example, the aging characteristics of the material require that the procedures take into account the following recommendations (Evans and Monroe, 1963):

(1)   Avoid prolonged times at elevated temperatures,
(2)   do not preheat; keep interpass temperature below 250° F,
(3)   use minimum possible weld energy input,
(4)   avoid other conditions causing low cooling rate.

TABLE IV

GENERAL COMPARISON OF WELDING METHODS FOR 18 Ni MARAGING STEEL[a]

Method	Types of defects found	Distortion	Weld-nugget structures	Weld-tensile properties	Weld toughness
TIG	Porosity, tungsten inclusion, lack-of fusion zones	Medium	Excellent	95% plate	Equal or better than plate
Excelco ¼ TIG	Minor porosity, minor lack-of-fusion zones	Minimum	Excellent	95% plate	10% better than plate
Sub arc	Cracks and longitudinal cracks, lack of fusion, undercut	Severe	Poor; large grain	Erratic, depends on Ti loss	Usually less than 50% of plate
MIG	Porosity and undercut	Medium	Fair	90% plate	90% plate
Short arc	Porosity, lack of fusion	Minimum	Excellent	90% plate	Equal to plate
Plasma arc	Porosity and longitudinal cracks	Medium	Fair	Not known	Not known
Electron beam	Lack of fusion	Minimum	Not known	Not known	Not known

[a] Details of the welding procedure are found in the review prepared by Evans (1966).

These guidelines will help to maintain the initial properties in the base metal.

Also of considerable importance in the welding of high-strength steels is the chemical composition of the welding wire. For example, in the MIG welding of materials such as the HY-80, HY-100, and HY-150 steels, guidelines such as the following should be considered (Dorschu, 1963; Telford and Enis, 1965). Carbon content should be minimized for maximum toughness, ductility, and cracking resistance. The carbon should generally be retained at a level of approximately 0.10% or less. The manganese content should be in the range 1.6–2%. This element serves as a mild deoxidizer but also provides the necessary strength and improves the weld bead shape. However, if too much manganese is included, it will cause cracking and brittleness problems. A nickel content in the range 2–3% is generally preferred. The higher level of nickel content helps to provide a strengthening effect but, if placed at too high a level, will tend to promote cold cracking. A fourth element, chromium, will also aid in providing increased strength but at the expense of notch toughness. It is a very strong carbide former, and consequently enhances the formation of bainite at slow cooling rates. If provided in amounts greater than 1%, it might provide cold laps in the joints. The chromium content should be related to the manganese and nickel contents of the weld. Another element which is generally included is molybdenum, and at levels between 0.4 and 0.6%. This element also is a strong carbide former and, consequently, if added in greater quantity, will adversely affect the toughness of the weld. In addition, the usual controls of phosphorus and sulfur are necessary. Obviously, the chemical composition of welding wires used for inert gas welding is extremely important if high toughness is to be achieved.

Another variable in the inert gas welding process is the shielding gas. Its composition, purity, and moisture content may also affect the toughness of the weld metal. An indication of weld toughness obtained with various shielding gases is presented in Figs. 34 and 35. It appears that some of the materials and procedures provide toughnesses equal to or better than that of the mild steel electrodes shown in Fig. 31. However, they are far from providing the high notch toughness shown in Fig. 32 for some of the low hydrogen electrodes.

Another of the welding processes commonly used for structural steels is the submerged arc welding process. This process, as shown in Fig. 36, may provide a relatively low notch toughness. However, the toughness can be improved by changes in the welding procedure and also changes in chemistry of the welding wire. Additions of nickel and manganese are generally beneficial, and additions of vanadium, carbon, molybdenum, chromium, and silicon harmful (Dorschu and Stout, 1961). Reducing the welding heat

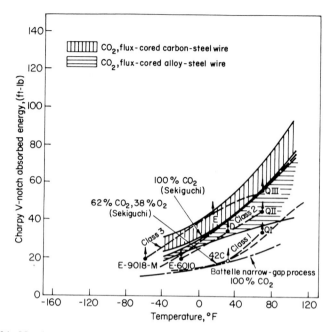

FIG. 34. Notch toughness of CO₂ and CO₂-O₂ metal-arc deposited weld metals (Masubuchi *et al.*, 1966).

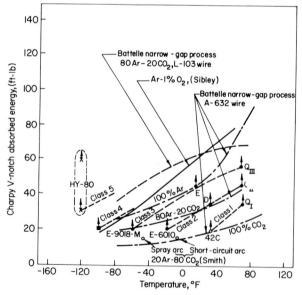

FIG. 35. Notch toughness of argon and argon-CO₂ metal-arc deposited metal (Masubuchi *et al.*, 1966).

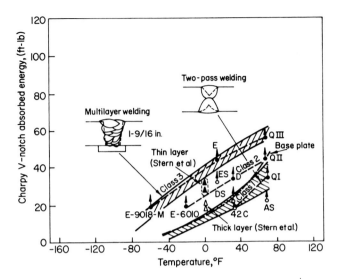

FIG. 36. Notch toughness of submerged-arc weld metals, two-pass and multilayer welding (Masubuchi *et al.*, 1966).

input and the restraint during welding can also be beneficial. However, there are limits to the extent to which these steps can be pursued in obtaining the desired weld toughness, and so they must be used with care.

Some of the welding procedure parameters affecting submerged arc welds produce similar effects in welds produced by the other welding processes. For example, increases in heat input and the accompanying reduction in cooling rate generally decrease the strength of a weldment and also its notch toughness in the low-carbon low-alloy quenched and tempered steels. An indication of the effect of a variation in heat input on notch toughness is shown in Fig. 37. As the heat or energy input was increased, a marked shift in transition temperature occurred in the grain-coarsened material. Improvements in the notch toughness can also be obtained in some weldments by increasing the number of weld passes. As the number of weld passes increases, a lower heat input is generally used, thereby producing a finer-grained tougher structure. Furthermore, the addition of subsequent passes generally produces a grain refining action which is beneficial, also (Masubuchi *et al.*, 1966).

Another factor often included in a welding procedure is a preheat or postheat treatment. Although these treatments may often provide improvements in some properties of the weldment, they do on occasion produce an embrittling effect. Consequently, they should be used with caution and their effect fully appreciated before being specified. Another after-welding treatment sometimes used is that of peening. This technique

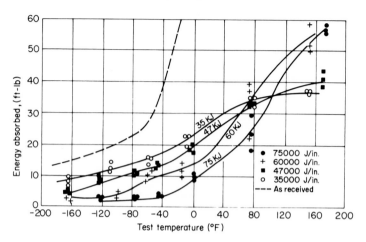

Fig. 37. Notch impact strength of grain-coarsened region as a function of temperature for energy inputs of 35,000, 47,000, 60,000, and 75,000 Joules/inch (Savage and Owczarski, 1966).

produces severe plastic deformation in the weld metal and can be expected to provide a detrimental effect on the notch toughness of the material.

In summary, it is apparent that the details of the welding procedure can produce significant effects on the notch toughness of weldments, depending on the chemical compositions of both the filler metal and the base metal, and also on the welding process. Consequently, care must be exercised in establishing the details of welding procedures used for the broad family of steels now used for steel structures.

Most of the titanium alloys can be welded with the various welding processes, also. However, the TIG, MIG, and resistance welding processes appear to be the most effective processes (Wu, 1966). Notch toughness of the base metals, even in thick sections, of the weld- and heat-affected zone can be made equal to or better than that of the base metal both with the TIG and electron beam welding processes (Monroe *et al.*, 1965). However, to do this may require some sacrifice in the ultimate strength of the materials.

B. Geometry, Flaws, and Stress Concentrations

Low-stress brittle fractures have generally been associated with weld flaws. These may be internal or external flaws, each of which can produce severe stress concentrations. The flaws may be porosity, slag inclusions, hot cracks, cold cracks, microcracks, lack of penetration, underbead cracks, or weld-toe cracks. Thus, a variety of flaws can be encountered in weldments. Ways and means of controlling or excluding such flaws must be provided.

In addition to the defects of weld geometry, the geometry of a member itself may affect its susceptibility to fracturing in a brittle manner. As the size of a test section is increased, the transition temperature is generally increased also. Figure 13, for example, shows the rise in transition temperature of a test specimen afforded by an increase in plate thickness. However, this effect of thickness depends also on other geometrical factors involved in the structure (Agnew and Stout, 1962).

Weld flaws will affect the properties of weldments in different ways. For example, in mild steel, porosity which reduces the cross section of a weldment by as much as 7% will not materially affect the strength of such a weldment (Green *et al.*, 1958). However, weld flaws can be expected to have a significant effect on the notch toughness and brittle behavior of such members. Initially, the catastrophic brittle fractures were considered to be a result of weld flaws. Then as additional information was accumulated, it became evident that residual stresses as well as the material itself play an important role in the fracturing process. Nevertheless, the weld flaw is still an important factor.

Of great significance are the size, shape, and location of the flaws associated with welding. As shown in Fig. 4, and also as demonstrated in the fracture analysis diagram of Fig. 16, the flaw size plays a major role in establishing the stress level at which brittle fractures will initiate; the larger the flaw, the lower the fracture initiation stress. Similarly, the sharper the notch provided by the flaw, the lower the notch toughness of the member. Thus, weld cracks are more severe and cause greater loss in toughness than weld metal porosity.

The exact location of a flaw may be important in terms of its effect on the behavior of a weldment. In the case of the notched-and-welded plates, low-stress fractures resulted when the notch tips were placed in a region of high residual tensile stress. When the notch depth was increased, placing the notch in a region of lower residual stress, higher levels of applied stress were necessary to initiate brittle fractures. Thus, the fracture behavior of the members was a function of the notch, its location, the associated residual and applied stresses, and the toughness of the material at the location of the notch tip.

The stress concentrations associated with weld flaws apparently play an important role in establishing the stress level at which fracture occurs. As shown in Fig. 38, the net fracture stress for weldments decreases as the stress-concentration ratio increases. Residual stresses have an effect on the scatter obtained in such a comparison; nevertheless, consideration of only the stress relieved members shows the marked effect the stress

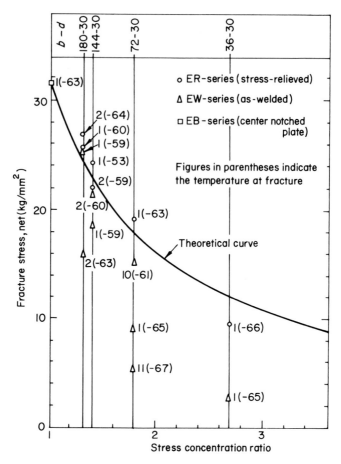

Fig. 38. Relation between brittle fracture stress and stress concentration ratio (Hall *et al.*, 1967).

concentration alone has on the behavior. It is clear that the stress concentrations associated with flaws are important insofar as fracture behavior is concerned.

C. Residual Stresses

On several occasions in this chapter, reference has been made to the important role played by residual stresses in the brittle fracturing of weldments. As long as the material behaves in an elastic manner, residual stresses produce the same effects in materials as do the applied stresses. Consequently, an understanding of the magnitudes and distributions of the stresses becomes extremely important in evaluating the brittle fracture problem.

The general distribution of longitudinal residual stresses in butt-welded specimens has long been known. High peak tensile stresses exist in the weld itself, and compressive stresses exist in the adjacent material to provide equilibrium. The distributions for a mild steel as well as an alloy steel are shown in Fig. 39, where the highest level of residual stress is produced in the higher strength steel.

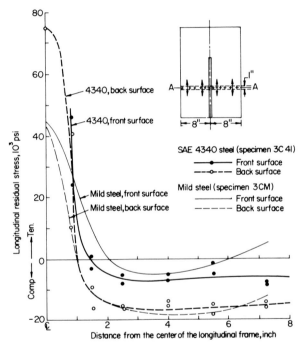

FIG. 39. Distributions of longitudinal residual stresses in welded plate, line AA (Masubuchi and Martin, 1966).

Also of interest is the distribution of residual stresses through the thickness of a weldment. In most instances, investigators have considered the residual stresses in terms of surface stress measurements. However, significant variations in the residual stress are found through the thickness, particularly in the transverse direction (transverse to the axis of the weld); high transverse residual compressive stresses are reported at midthickness (see Fig. 40). The general effect of residual stresses on initiation and propagation was discussed in an earlier section and is shown in Fig. 6. The residual stress distribution associated with the irregular crack velocity in

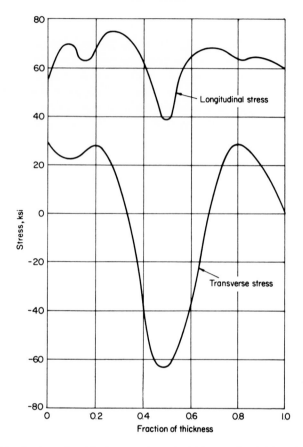

FIG. 40. Distribution of residual stress through thickness of weld in 1-inch-thick as-welded specimen (Nordell and Hall, 1965).

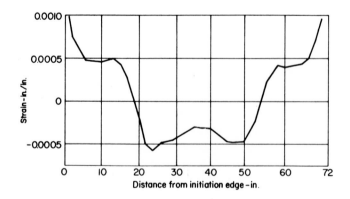

FIG. 41. Distribution of residual strains in prestressed plate (Hall *et al.*, 1967).

Fig. 6 is shown in Fig. 41. A high residual tensile stress existing at the edges of the member greatly increased the ease with which the brittle fracture could be initiated. The high residual compressive stresses in the center of the member tended to arrest the brittle fracture. Thus, without doubt, residual stresses can have a major effect on the ease with which brittle fractures initiate and propagate in welded structures.

Recent studies by Godfrey and Hauser (1967) show that the apparent fracture toughness of titanium alloys, as well as structural steels, is affected by residual welding stresses. The toughness of the stress-free titanium was lowered by a factor of 2 as a result of the residual welding stresses.

D. Weld Treatments

Several means are available to stress relieve weldments. Thermal, mechanical, or low-temperature treatments can be used to alter or reduce the residual stresses. The tests of notched-and-welded plates have exhibited improved low-stress fracture behavior as a result of thermal stress relief (Kihara et al., 1959b; Wells and Burdekin, 1963). This treatment apparently reduces the residual stresses and also restores the ductility to the notched region of the weldments.

The extent to which the residual stresses can be reduced by a thermal treatment is shown in Fig. 42 for two steels and three stress relieving temperatures. With the higher temperature, most of the residual stress was removed within a relatively short period of time.

Although stress relief treatments may improve the notch toughness of some weldments, they do not always provide this benefit. Figure 43, for example, indicates the improvement in toughness in electroslag-deposited welds in carbon steel when the materials have been normalized and stress relieved; however, as shown in Fig. 44, the notch toughness of some weld metals may be decreased as a result of stress relieving treatments.

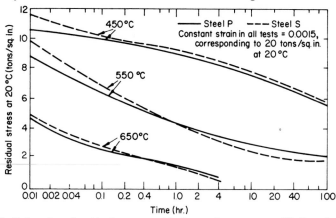

FIG. 42. Relaxation of residual stresses with time and temperature (Hall et al., 1967).

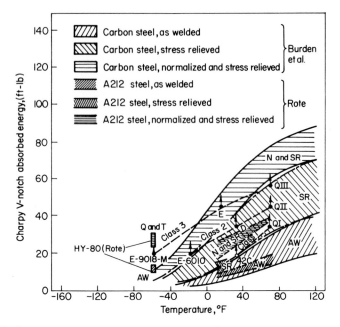

Fig. 43. Improvement through heat treatment of notch toughness of electroslag-deposited metals (Masubuchi et al., 1966).

Preheating is another weld treatment that may also help to improve the properties of a weldment. Flanigan and Micleu (1953), in studies of microcracking, found that preheating some steels provided improved notch toughness. In addition, preheating reduces somewhat the residual stresses and for this reason also may be expected to improve the behavior of a weldment. However, this latter effect is relatively small. Furthermore, in some instances, preheating will produce grain coarsening and a corresponding decrease in toughness.

A third treatment is that of mechanical stress relief. This is achieved by mechanically straining a member or structure plastically to reduce or alter its residual stresses. In laboratory tests of large spheres and in notched-and-welded plates, this type of mechanical treatment, as well as the thermal stress relief treatment, proved beneficial in lessening the possibility of brittle fracture (Kihara et al., 1959a,b). However, care must be exercised in applying the mechanical stress relief treatment so that failure does not occur during the initial straining operation.

Two other means of trying to improve the behavior of weldments are by a low-temperature stress relief treatment and the removal of the weld reinforcement by machining or grinding. The low temperature stress relief treatment is in essence a mechanical treatment in that it attempts to reduce

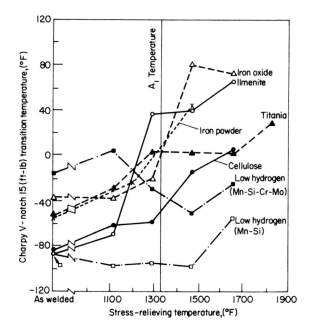

FIG. 44. Effect of stress relieving on the notch toughness of weld metals (Masubuchi *et al.*, 1966).

or possibly reverse the residual stresses that exist in a member by thermally straining the member. This treatment may improve the behavior at one location but be detrimental at another. Removal of the weld reinforcement is also a mechanical treatment and would not, in general, be expected to have a very great effect. However, in some instances (Hartbower, 1954) the reinforcement removal has to some extent improved the notch toughness of a material. The reason for this improved behavior is not readily evident.

E ARRESTERS

Crack arresters have long been of considerable interest to those concerned with the problems of brittle fracture in large structures. Can brittle fractures be stopped and, if so, how can this be achieved? Welded crack arresters for use in mild steel structures were studied by Mosborg (1960). Comparisons have been made also of the effectiveness of welded arresters with the arresting capabilities of a riveted strake. From these studies, it appears that both methods are capable of providing arrest. Details of the test members are presented in Fig. 45 and an indication of the arrest fracture in one of the weldments is shown in Fig. 8. Both the weld metal and the strake of tough material served as arresting material in the specimen of Fig. 8.

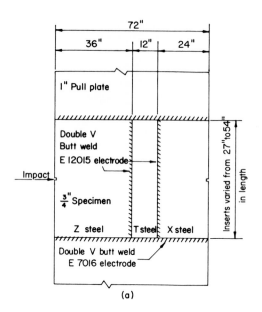

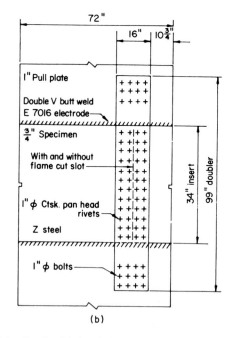

FIG. 45. Typical details of welded and riveted crack arresters (Mosborg *et al.*, 1957).

The data obtained from specimens with welded crack arresters suggest that the propagating brittle cracks are initially arrested or slowed down as they encounter the tough material. However, since a partial fracture then exists in the member, the resulting eccentric load will tend to tear the crack through the remaining material. This makes an analysis of the stress behavior of a crack arrester extremely difficult. Kanazawa *et al.* (1964) have attempted to employ fracture mechanics in the evaluation of the crack arresting characteristics of test members. It appears at this point that such methods may prove suitable for the evaluation of arresters; however, much more study of this matter is needed.

VI. Loading and Environment

Most of the preceding discussion has been concerned with the behavior and fabrication of weldments. However, the question of brittle fracture in weldments cannot be understood fully without considering also the loading conditions and environmental conditions to which weldments may be subjected and the effect that these conditions will have on the behavior of the weldments.

A. STRAIN RATE

The results of laboratory investigations suggest that strain rate and temperature effects in materials and weldments may be quite similar. Thus, both increases in strain rate and decreases in temperature tend to produce an embrittling effect in the materials. An indication of the effect of stress rate on the yield strength of mild steel is shown in Fig. 46. On the basis of these data and the strain rates (100 inches/inch/sec) observed in some of the wide plate studies, it is obvious why extremely high stresses are recorded near high-speed propagating brittle fractures. Once the fracture has been initiated and is propagating at a high velocity, the raised yield strength of the material may be sufficient, in the case of mild steel, for the material to reach the critical fracture stress with the application of only a very small nominal stress. Thus, strain rate plays a particularly important role in the propagation stages of brittle fracture.

B. REPEATED LOADINGS

It is well known that many structures in service have been subjected to repeated loadings before failing catastrophically. Consequently, one might suspect that the repeated loadings have an effect on the susceptibility of the structure to fail in a brittle manner.

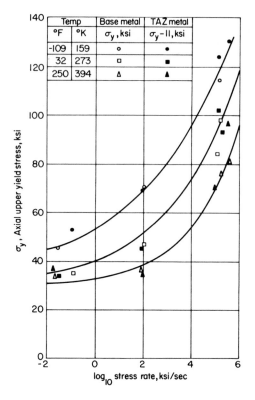

FIG. 46. Increase in upper yield stress produced by increased strain rate (Wright *et al.*, 1965).

In general, repeated loadings on a mild steel structure will change its residual stress fields, and possibly introduce fatigue cracking, but will not reduce its toughness. However, laboratory studies of weldments show that low-stress fractures can occur after repeated loadings and that the question requires a more complete evaluation.

In mild steel weldments (notched-and-welded plates), it has been found that the fracture stresses are greater than the repeated loading stresses to which the members are subjected during any previous loadings. Furthermore, the repeated loadings change the failures from an occasional two-stage low-stress/high-stress fracture to a single-stage low-stress fracture. Such a condition may in general be desirable, but only if the resulting fracture stress of the single-stage fracture is raised to a sufficiently high level (Munse *et al.*, 1967; Kihara *et al.*, 1966). An indication of the fracture stress for members which have previously been cycled is presented in Fig. 47.

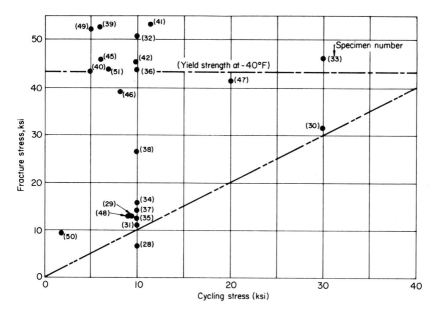

FIG. 47. Effect of repeated cycles of loading on fracture stress of notched-and-welded plates (Munse *et al.*, 1967).

C. LOADS AND RESIDUAL STRESSES

Brittle fractures have been reported to occur at high stresses, at low stresses (those below yield strength of the material) and, in several instances, spontaneous fractures have occurred in members where no applied loads existed. These spontaneous fractures are reported by Osgood (1954) and appear to have occurred because of high residual stresses existing near sharp notches. In general, the failures occurred as the temperature was dropping, thereby causing the material to achieve a lower notch toughness.

In most instances, low-stress brittle fractures have occurred as a result of the superposition of load stresses and residual stresses (Pellini and Puzak, 1963b). When residual stresses are absent or have been removed, applied stresses of yield stress magnitude are generally required for brittle fracturing in mild steel structures. However, in the ultra-high-strength steels or members, the notch itself will usually be sufficient to provide a reduced stress fracture if the material is in a brittle condition.

D. ENVIRONMENT

Several environmental factors are known to be of importance in the brittle fracturing processes. The principal parameter is temperature which, when reduced, generally produces a reduction in notch toughness.

This effect occurs in most metals, has been studied extensively, and is well known.

Stress corrosion and hydrogen-induced cracking are two other "embrittling" processes that often affect the behavior of weldments but have received relatively little attention. These processes are in turn affected by the residual and applied stresses that exist as well as any cracks or other flaws in the weld or its adjacent material. The fractures produced by these processes are characterized by failures that exhibit almost a complete lack of visual evidence of plastic deformation, are either branching or non-branching in nature, and time sensitive (Fletcher *et al.*, 1966; Masubuchi and Martin, 1966). In the case of hydrogen-induced cracking, mild steels provide greater resistance than do the higher strength heat-treated steels. The critical stress levels necessary for this cracking and the time to rupture appear to be directly related to the material strength (see Fig. 48).

Another type of embrittlement observed in laboratory investigations of titanium alloys and their weldments is that of corrosion from a sea water environment. Not all materials are susceptible to this form of corrosion; however, this question, as well as many other questions of environmental effects, are greatly in need of further study (Monroe *et al.*, 1965).

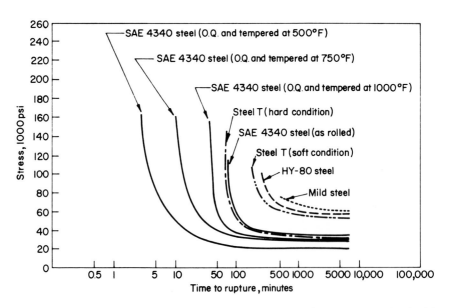

FIG. 48. Hydrogen-induced delayed fracture characteristics of various steels (Masubuchi and Martin, 1966).

VII. Designing against Brittle Fracture

With the existing information on brittle fracture in weldments, the engineering profession must design welded structures in which the probability of brittle catastrophic failures is reduced to a minimum. To do this, the engineer must select the proper materials, specify suitable fabrication processes and procedures, design his structures to minimize stress concentrations, and, finally, require inspection procedures that will ensure adequate quality control.

A. SELECTION OF MATERIALS

Many large welded structures are subject to failure in a brittle manner. Consequently, in the selection of materials for these structures, consideration must be given to the level of toughness required, not only in the base metal of this structure but also in the weld metal and in the adjacent heat-affected and thermally affected zones. In general, engineers have required a weld metal toughness and strength which at least matches that of the base metal. However, in some instances, particularly with ultra-high-strength steels, this may not be possible. In such cases, the weld metal or location with minimum toughness should be considered fully.

B. WELD QUALITY

Since the flaws responsible for brittle fractures in welded structures have been in the welds or produced by the welding, the welding is extremely important in any design where brittle fracture must be eliminated. This requires that consideration be given to the base material, as well as many weld process and procedure parameters. In the ultra-high-strength materials, fracture mechanics can be utilized along with the fracture toughness of the weld and base metal to establish limits of acceptability for flaws. However, when applying this method, the properties of the material at the location of the flaw as well as all stresses must be considered. For mild steels, empirical methods have generally been used to establish the limitations for flaws.

C. DESIGNING WELDMENTS

As noted previously, brittle failures have generally occurred in structures where weld flaws or sharp notches existed in regions of high residual stress and in material that was sufficiently notch sensitive under the service conditions to sustain propagation once a brittle crack had been initiated. Consequently, in design, consideration must be given to all three factors: flaws, stresses, and materials.

The fracture analysis diagram of Fig. 16 has been used by Pellini and Puzak (1963b) for the development of suggested design procedures. The four design criteria they suggest are as follows:

1. NDT temperature criterion. For structures that are not thermally or mechanically stress relieved, or are expected to develop points of local yielding, the lowest service condition must be above the NDT temperature. This is because under these conditions very small flaws serve as crack initiators.

2. NDT + 30° F criterion. This criterion is based on the crack-arrest temperature (CAT) for stresses on the order of one-half the yield stress. If the lowest service temperature is above the NDT + 30° F temperature and the level of stress does not exceed the stated value, flaw size is immaterial, since fractures cannot initiate.

3. NDT + 60° F criterion. This criterion is based on the "fracture transition elastic" (FTE) temperature, which corresponds to a crack-arrest temperature at yield stress.

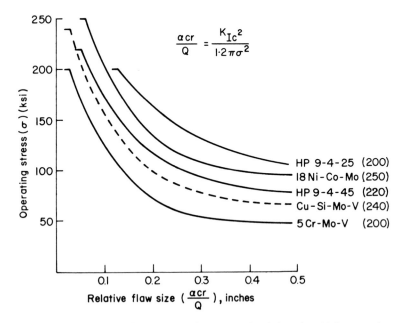

FIG. 49. Effect of flaw size in operating stress level for ultra-high-strength steels (Battelle Memorial Institute, 1964).

4. NDT $+120°$ F criterion. This criterion is based on the "fracture transition plastic" (FTP) temperature, which corresponds to a crack-arrest temperature at stresses approximating the tensile strength of the steel and is intended for service requirements involving plastic overload.

It should be noted, however, that to apply the above criteria, notch toughness information must be available to provide a basis for material and weldments selection.

Another means of designing against fracture involves the application of fracture mechanics and the fracture toughness of the materials (Tiffany and Masters, 1965). In applying this approach, consideration must be given to not only the ultimate strength of the material but also the type of material and the critical flaw size that can be accepted for the stresses at the point of possible fracture initiation. Consideration must be given also to the residual stresses that will exist in the weldment, or structure.

An indication of the importance of the flaw size, in terms of the operating stress for various ultra-high-strength materials, may be seen in Fig. 49. The inclusion of a weld, if it has lower fracture toughness than the materials shown, would provide further limitations which also must be taken into account in design.

D. INSPECTION

Since weld flaws are so important in the brittle fracturing of weldments, quality control over the welds and the adjacent material is extremely important. Such requirements may add greatly to the cost of a structure but provide the only means whereby adequate quality can be guaranteed in the critical locations.

VIII. Recommended Research

Although our understanding of the problem of brittle fracture is gradually improving, new materials and fabrication processes are being added at such a rapid rate that new problems are always being introduced. However, every little change in material and detail of fabrication cannot be studied. The basic relationships between the principal parameters that affect brittle fracture should be studied; then the effects of variations in materials and changes in fabrication processes and procedures can be predicted on the basis of the basic behavior. To provide this basic understanding, however, requires a thorough analysis and evaluation of service failures as well as laboratory studies, and the development of more complete basic failure hypotheses than exist at present.

The goals noted above are indeed noble and in need of pursuit. However, some research must also be directed toward the solution of the more immediate problems. The effects of flaws and embrittling treatments in weldments such as thermal and strain cycling strain aging, irradiation, stress corrosion, and hydrogen embrittlement, have in recent years received increased attention but are little understood. In addition information must be obtained concerning the interrelationship between these parameters and residual stresses, the state of stress, and the stress concentrations in welded structures. Only through a full understanding of these many factors can the initiation of brittle fractures be effectively eliminated.

Another area in which further research is needed is that of fracture analysis. Although the procedure developed by Pellini has been very helpful it must be expanded to include the many factors noted above. In addition, the methods of analysis using fracture mechanics must be further developed to better handle ductile materials. Possibly, a combination of fracture mechanics and Pellini's fracture analysis will serve as the best means for brittle fracture analysis of ductile materials to provide the designer with a means of obtaining fracture-safe design.

Finally, a strong concerted effort should be made to synthesize the results of the volumes of research on the problems in brittle fracture. A deep searching study of the existing information would aid greatly in better defining the problem of brittle fracture and, possibly of more importance, in defining more clearly the areas for which additional information is needed.

IX. Summary

Numerous reports can be found in the literature on low-stress brittle fractures in such welded structures as ships, bridges, pressure vessels, etc. Consequently, there has been much research conducted on the many problems associated with such fractures in welds, weldments, and welded structures.

Most of the catastrophic failures, and particularly those at low stresses, have initiated or been associated with welding. Failures have initiated from flaws or stress concentrations and appear to be affected also by the residual stresses which exist in the structures. Consequently, much of the research on brittle fracture and weldments has been directed toward an evaluation of the geometrical, metallurgical, and stress effects in the brittle fracturing process. Such information has then been applied in various fracture analyses which define the various modes of ductile and brittle fracture or behavior encountered in welded structures.

As the data are examined, it becomes readily evident that several zones exist in a weldment where fracture may initiate; the weld metal, the fusion zone, the heat-affected zone, the thermally affected zone, and the base metal itself. Each of these zones must be considered in evaluating the brittle fracture resistance of a weldment. Furthermore, as the new ultra-high-strength materials have been introduced, along with new welding processes, it has been found that the notch toughness or fracture toughness in the weld and the weld affected zones has become more important. In these areas, the toughness is affected not only by the materials employed but also by the fabrication processes and the details of the fabrication procedures.

Variations in toughness resulting from fabrication, as well as various treatments and conditions to which the materials are subjected in service, may also affect the brittleness of a structure. For example, the thermal and strain cycling to which a weldment is subjected during fabrication operations markedly affects the properties of the material at or near the weld, This, in effect, produces an exhaustion of ductility and thereby provides a region which may be highly susceptible to fracturing in a brittle manner. In addition, such factors as nuclear radiation, stress corrosion, or hydrogen embrittlement are important. Thus, the service conditions must also be considered when evaluating the behavior of a welded structure.

In some weldments, it is possible to improve the toughness by use of special treatments. Stress relieving treatments, for example, appear to greatly improve the resistance of many members to low-stress brittle fracture. However, these same procedures may, in some materials, reduce the toughness and strength of the material. Thus, the many processes and procedures used to treat welds must be carefully examined before being applied.

It is obvious that much has been done to provide the engineering profession with an understanding of the problems associated with brittle fractures in weldments. By properly applying this information for the design of welded structures, it is possible to greatly reduce the probability of brittle fracture in these structures. However, there are still many questions which confront the engineering profession if this probability is to be further reduced.

REFERENCES

Acker, H. G. (1953). "Review of Welded Ship Failures," Report No. SSC-63. Ship Structure Committee, National Academy of Sciences, Washington, D.C.
Agnew, S. A., and Stout, R. D. (1962). *Welding J.* (*N. Y.*) *Res. Suppl.* **41** (4), 154s.
Armenakas, A. E., and Mylanos, C. (1967). *Welding J.* (*N. Y.*) *Res. Suppl.* **46** (11), 570s.
Armstrong, T. N., and Warner, W. L. (1958). *Welding J.* (*N. Y.*) *Res. Suppl.* **37** (1), 27s.

ASME (1964). "A Review of Engineering Approaches to Design against Fracture." Prepared by Subcommittee on Brittle Fracture, Research Committee on Prevention of Fracture in Metals, ASME, New York.

ASTM (1960–1964). ASTM *Bull.* **243**, 29; **244**, 18; *Mater. Res. Std.* **1** (5), 389; **1** (11), 877; **2** (3), 196; **4** (3), 107.

ASTM (1965). "Symposium on Fracture Toughness Testing and Its Applications," STP 381. ASTM, Philadelphia.

Baird, J. D. (1963). *Iron & Steel (London)* **36** (5), 186; **36** (7), 326; **36** (8), 368; **36** (9), 400; **36** (10), 450.

Baker, A. J., Birkle, A. J., Trozzo, P. S., and Wei, R. P. (1965). "Metallographic Examination of Fracture Origin Sites in the 260-SL-1 Motor Case" (Project No. 89.025-027(1)). Applied Research Laboratory, U.S. Steel Corporation, Monroeville, Pennsylvania.

Barton, F. W., and Hall, W. J. (1960). *Welding J. (N. Y.) Res. Suppl.* **39** (9), 379s.

Battelle Memorial Institute (1964). "Problems in the Load-Carrying Application of High-Strength Steels." Report No. 210. Defense Metals Information Center, Battelle Memorial Institute, Columbus, Ohio.

Board of Inquiry (1967). "Report on the Brittle Fracture of a High Pressure Boiler Drum at Cockanzie Power Station," *Welding Research Abroad* **13** (8), 2.

Board of Investigation (1947). "Final Report: The Design and Methods of Construction of Welded Steel Merchant Vessels." U.S. Govt. Printing Office, Washington, D.C.

Boulger, F. W., and Hanson, W. R. (1962). "The Effect of Metallurgical Variables in Ship-Plate Steels on the Transition Temperatures in Drop-Weight in Charpy-V-Notch Tests," Report No. SSC-145. Ship Structure Committee, National Academy of Sciences, Washington, D.C.

Boyd, G. M. (1955). *Welding J. (N. Y.) Res. Suppl.* **34** (5), 217s.

Bradley, J. W., and McCauley, R. B. (1964). *Welding J. (N. Y.) Res. Suppl.* **43** (9), 408s.

British Welding Research Association (1966). "Brittle Fracture of a Thick Walled Pressure Vessel." *BWRA Bulletin* **7** (6), 149.

Brown, W. F., Jr., and Srawley, J. E. (1967). "Plane Strain Crack Toughness Testing of High Strength Metallic Materials," STP 410. ASTM, Philadelphia.

Burdekin, F. M. (1967). *Brit. Welding J.* **14** (2), 81.

Campbell, J. E. (1964). "Current Methods of Fracture Toughness Testing of High-Strength Alloys with Emphasis on Plane Strain," Report No. 207. Defense Metals Information Center, Battelle Memorial Institute, Columbus, Ohio.

Cannon, J. P., and Munse, W. H. (1966). "Evaluation of Flow and Fracture Propensity of Notched Steel Plates by Means of a Photoelastic Model," Structural Research Series Report No. 314. Civil Engineering Studies, University of Illinois, Urbana, Illinois.

Carpenter, S. T., and Linsenmeyer, R. F. (1958). "Weld Flaw Evaluation," Report No. SSC-105. Ship Structure Committee, National Academy of Sciences, Washington, D.C.

Clark, R. E., and Privoznik, L. J. (1965). *Welding J. (N. Y.) Res. Suppl.* **44** (5), 199s.

Daley, D. M., Jr., and Hartbower, C. E. (1956). *Welding J. (N. Y.) Res. Suppl.* **35** (8), 447s.

Davis, S. O., Tupper, N. G., Lagrone, D. C., and Niemi, R. M. (1965). "Center Notch Plane Strain K_{Ic} Fracture Toughness Properties of Several High-Strength Steel Alloys," Technical Report AFML-TR-65-214. Air Force Materials Laboratory, Air Force Systems Command, Wright-Patterson Air Force Base, Dayton, Ohio.

Dekker, P. F. W. (1962). "Some Experiments of the Metallurgical Concomitants of Residual Stress," Document No. IX 329-62. International Institute of Welding.

Dorschu, K. E. (1963). "Influence of Alloying Elements on Mechanical Properties of High Strength Steel MIG Weld Metal." Air Reduction Sales Company, Murray Hill, New Jersey.

Dorschu, K. E., and Stout, R. D. (1961). *Welding J.* (*N. Y.*) *Res. Suppl.* **40** (3), 97s.

Evans, R. M. (1966). "Metals Joining." *Review of Recent Developments*. Defense Metals Information Center, Battelle Memorial Institute, Columbus, Ohio.

Evans, R. M., and Martin, D. C. (1965). "New Developments in Welding Steels with Yield Strengths Greater than 150,000 psi," Memorandum No. 208. Defense Metals Information Center, Battelle Memorial Institute, Columbus, Ohio.

Evans, R. M., and Monroe, R. E. (1963). "The Current Status of the Welding of Maraging Steels," Memorandum No. 182. Defense Metals Information Center, Battelle Memorial Institute, Columbus, Ohio.

Flanigan, A. E., and Micleu, T. (1953). *Welding J.* (*N. Y.*) *Res. Suppl.* **32** (2), 99s.

Fletcher, E. E., Berry, W. E., and Elsea, A. R. (1966). "Stress-Corrosion Cracking and Hydrogen-Stress Cracking of High-Strength Steel," Report No. 232. Defense Metals Information Center, Battelle Memorial Institute, Columbus, Ohio.

Fragetta, W. A., Krysiak, K. F., and Dorschu, K. E. (1964). "Development of HY-180/210 Maraging Steel Filler Metals and Joining Procedures: Part I," Status Report. Air Reduction Sales Company, Murray Hill, New Jersey.

Godfrey, L., and Hauser, H. A. (1967). *Welding J.* (*N. Y.*) *Res. Suppl.* **46** (11), 500s.

Green, William L., Hamad, Mahmoud F., and McCauley, R. B. (1958). *Welding J.* (*N. Y.*) *Res. Suppl.* **37** (5), 206s.

Greene, T. W. (1949). *Welding J.* (*N. Y.*) *Res. Suppl.* **28** (5), 193s.

Hall, W. J. (1968). "Evaluation of Fracture Tests and Specimen Preparation." This volume.

Hall, W. J., and Chamberlain, A. D. (1966). *Welding J.* (*N. Y.*) *Res. Suppl.* **45** (5), 193s.

Hall, W. J., Nordell, W. J., and Munse, W. H. (1962). *Welding J.* (*N. Y.*) *Res. Suppl.* **41** (11), 505s.

Hall, W. J., Kihara, H., Soete, W., and Wells, A. A. (1967). "Brittle Fracture of Welded Plate." Prentice-Hall, Englewood Cliffs, New Jersey.

Hartbower, Carl E. (1954). *Welding J.* (*N. Y.*) *Res. Suppl.* **33** (3), 141s.

International Institute of Welding (1964). "Provisional Report on an International Investigation of Brittle Fractures," Document No. IX-407-64. International Institute of Welding.

Johnson, H. H., and Stout, R. D. (1960). *Welding J.* (*N. Y.*) *Res. Suppl.* **39** (11), 493s.

Johnson, R. E. (1965). "Fracture Mechanics: A Basis for Brittle Fracture Prevention." Westinghouse Atomic Power Division, Pittsburgh, Pennsylvania.

Kammer, P. A., and Martin, D. C. (1966). "Welding High-Strength Steels," Report No. 229. Defense Metals Information Center, Battelle Memorial Institute, Columbus, Ohio.

Kanazawa, T., Machida, S., and Matoba, M. (1964). "Some Basic Considerations on Crack Arresters for Steel Structures," Document No. IX-413-64. International Institute of Welding.

Kiefner, J. F., and Munse, W. H. (1967). "Influence of Thermal and Strain Cycling on Fracture Susceptibility of Mild Steel," Structural Research Series Report No. 319. Civil Engineering Studies, University of Illinois, Urbana, Illinois.

Kies, J. A., Smith, H. L., Romine, H. E., and Bernstein, H. (1965). *In* "Symposium on Fracture Toughness Testing and Its Applications," STP 381, p. 328. ASTM, Philadelphia.

Kihara, H. (1961). "Recent Studies in Japan on Brittle Fracture of Welded Steel Structure under Low Applied Stress Level." Japan Institute of Welding, Tokyo.

Kihara, H., and Masubuchi, K. (1959). *Welding J.* (*N. Y.*) *Res. Suppl.* **38** (4), 159s.

Kihara, H., Masubuchi, K., and Ishii, H. (1959a). *Welding J.* (*N. Y.*) *Res. Suppl.* **38** (11), 451s.

Kihara, H., Masubuchi, K., Iida, K., and Oba, H. (1959b). "Effect of Stress Relieving on Brittle Fracture Strength of Welded Steel Plate," Document No. X-218-59. International Institute of Welding.

Kihara, H., Yoshida, T., and Oba, H. (1959c). "Initiation and Propagation of Brittle Fracture in Welded Steel Plate," Document No. X-217-59. International Institute of Welding.

Kihara, H., Iida, K., and Fujii, E. (1966). "Brittle Fracture Strength of Welded and Notched Wide Plate Subjected to Prior Cyclic Loading," Document No. XIII-460-67. International Institute of Welding.

Knoth, R. J., and Petersen, W. A. (1965). *Welding J.* (*N. Y.*) *Res. Suppl.* **44** (1), 21s.

Masubuchi, K., and Martin, D. C. (1966). "Investigation of Residual Stresses in Steel Weldments," Report No. SSC-174. Ship Structure Committee, National Academy of Sciences, Washington, D.C.

Masubuchi, K., Monroe, R. E., and Martin, D. C. (1966). "Interpretation Report on Weld-Metal Toughness," Bulletin No. 111. Welding Research Council, New York.

Meister, R. P., and Martin, D. C. (1967). "Welding of Aluminum and Aluminum Alloys," Report No. 236. Defense Metals Information Center, Battelle Memorial Institute, Columbus, Ohio.

Meitzner, C. F., and Stout, R. D. (1966). *Welding J.* (*N. Y.*) *Res. Suppl.* **45** (9), 393s.

Mellon Institute (1965). "Large Solid Booster Case Material and Fabrication Process Evaluation with Related Metallurgical Studies," Report. Mellon Institute, Pittsburgh.

Mishler, H. W., and Nichols, H. J. (1961). *Welding J.* (*N. Y.*) *Res. Suppl.* **40** (12), 564s.

Monroe, R. E., Martin, D. C., Wolfe, R. J., and Nagler, N. (1965). "Recent Developments in Welding Thick Titanium Plate," Memorandum No. 211. Defense Metals Information Center, Battelle Memorial Institute, Columbus, Ohio.

Mosborg, R. J. (1960). *Welding J.* (*N. Y.*) *Res. Suppl.* **39** (1), 40s.

Mosborg, R. J., Hall, W. J., and Munse, W. H. (1957). *Welding J.* (*N.Y.*) *Res. Suppl.* **36** (9), 393s.

Munse, W. H., Cannon, J. P., and Kiefner, J. F. (1967). "Effect of Repeated Loads on the Low Temperature Fracture Behaviour of Notched and Welded Plates," Structural Research Series Report No. 329. Civil Engineering Studies, University of Illinois, Urbana, Illinois.

Mylonas, C. (1959). *Welding J.* (*N. Y.*) *Res. Suppl.* **38** (10), 414s.

Mylonas, C., and Beaulieu, R. J. (1965). "Restoration of Ductility of Hot or Cold Strained ABS-B Steel by Heat Treatment at 700 to 1150° F," Report No. SSC-167. Ship Structure Committee, National Academy of Sciences, Washington, D.C.

Nordell, W. J., and Hall, W. J. (1965). *Welding J.* (*N. Y.*) *Res. Suppl.* **44** (3), 124s.

Osgood, W. R. (1954). "Residual Stresses in Metals and Metal Construction." Reinhold, New York.

Parker, E. R. (1957). "Brittle Behaviour of Engineering Structures." Wiley, New York.

Pascover, J. S., Hill, M., and Matas, S. J. (1965). "The Application of Fracture Toughness Testing to the Development of a Family of Alloy Steels." *In* "Symposium on Fracture Toughness Testing and Its Applications," STP 381. ASTM, Philadelphia.

Peck, J. V., and Gerken, J. M. (1966). "Development of Welding Procedures and Filler Materials for Joining High Strength Low Alloy Steels," Technical Report AFML-TDR-64-255, Pt. 3. Air Force Materials Laboratory, Air Force Systems Command, Wright-Patterson Air Force Base, Dayton, Ohio.

Pellini, W. S. (1952). "Performance Evaluation of Structural Steels and Weldments." *In* "Conference on Materials and Design for Low-Temperature Service," p. 129. Engineer Research and Development Laboratories, Department of the Army, The Engneer Center & Fort Belvoir, Virginia.

Pellini, W. S. (1956). *Welding J.* (*N. Y.*) *Res. Suppl.* **35** (5), 217s.

Pellini, W. S., and Puzak, P. P. (1963a). "Fracture Analysis Diagram Procedures for the Fracture-Safe Engineering Design of Steel Structures," Report No. 5920. U.S. Naval Research Laboratory, Washington, D.C.

Pellini, W. S., and Puzak, P. P. (1963b). "Fracture Analysis Diagram Procedures for the Fracture-Safe Engineering Design of Steel Structures," Bulletin No. 88. Welding Research Council, New York.

Pellini, W. S., and Puzak, P. P. (1963c). "Practical Considerations in Applying Laboratory Fracture Test Criteria to the Fracture-Safe Design of Pressure Vessels," Report No. 6030. U.S. Naval Research Laboratory, Washington, D.C.

Pellini, W. S., Steele, L. E., and Hawthorne, J. R. (1962). *Welding J.* (*N. Y.*) *Res. Suppl.* **41** (10), 455s.

Pellini, W. S., Goode, R. J., Puzak, P. P., Lange, E. A., and Huber, R. W. (1965). "Review of Concepts and Status of Procedures for Fracture-Safe Design of Complex Welded Structures Involving Metals of Low to Ultra-High Strength Levels," Report No. 6300. U.S. Naval Research Laboratory, Washington, D.C.

Puzak, P. P., and Pellini, W. S. (1955). *Welding J.* (*N. Y.*) *Res. Suppl.* **34** (12), 577s.

Randall, P. N. (1966), "Severity of Natural Flaws as Fracture Origins," Report No. 4439-6009-R0000. TRW Systems, Redondo Beach, California.

Rockey, K. C., Ludley, J. H. and Mylonas, C. (1962). *Proc. ASTM* **62**, 1120.

Rogers, H. C. (1959). "Hydrogen Embrittlement of Engineering Materials." *In* "Fracture of Engineering Materials," Ch. 9. ASM, Metals Park, Ohio.

Rolfe, S. T., Hall, W. J., and Newmark, N. M. (1959). *Welding J.* (*N. Y.*) *Res. Suppl.* **38** (4), 169s.

Rolnick, J. M. (1964). "Covered-Electrode Coating-Formulation Study," Engineering & Development Report. Air Reduction Sales Company, Murray Hill, New Jersey.

Roper, C. R., Jr., Koschnitzke, K. A., and Stout, R. D. (1967). *Welding J.* (*N. Y.*) *Res. Suppl.* **46** (6) 254s.

Rosenstein, A. H., and Lubahn, J. D. (1967). *Welding J.* (*N. Y.*) *Res. Suppl.* **46** (11), 481s.

Royal Commission (1963). "Report of Royal Commission into the Failure of King's Bridge." Royal Commission, Victoria, Australia.

Savage, W. F., and Owczarski, W. A. (1966). *Welding J.* (*N. Y.*) *Res. Suppl.* **45** (2), 55s.

Shank, M. E. (1954). "A Critical Survey of Brittle Failure in Carbon Plate Steel Structures Other Than Ships," Bulletin No. 17. Welding Research Council, New York.

Shank, M. E. (ed.) (1957). "Control of Steel Construction to Avoid Brittle Fracture." Welding Research Council, New York.

Soete, W. (1960). "Mechanical Aspects of Brittle Fracture," Houdremont Lecture. International Institute of Welding.

Sopher, R. P., Lowe, A. L., Jr., and Rieppel, P. J. (1958). "Evaluation of Weld-Joint Flaws as Initiating Points of Brittle Fracture," Report No. SSC-107. Ship Structure Committee, National Academy of Sciences, Washington, D.C.

Stout, R. D., and Doty, W. D'O. (1953). *In* "Weldability of Steels," Ch. 2. Welding Research Council, New York.

Telford, R. T., and Enis, A. (1965). "MIG Welding 5 Ni-Cr-Mo-V Steel." Newark Laboratories, Linde Division, Union Carbide Corporation, Newark, New Jersey.

Tiffany, C. F., and Masters, J. N. (1965). "Applied Fracture Mechanics." *In* "Symposium on Fracture Toughness Testing and Its Applications," STP 381. ASTM, Philadelphia.

Van Elst, H. C., Buys, E. C. J., Koning, D., and Verbraak, C. A. (1964). "Dynamic Recording of Brittle Fractures in Weldmetal." Stichting Centrum Voor Lastechniek, Rotterdam, Netherlands. (Also available as Document No. IX-425-64. International Institute of Welding.)

Weck, R. (1966). *Brit. Welding J.* **13** (11), 658.

Wei, R. P. (1965). "Fracture Toughness Testing in Alloy Development." *In* "Symposium on Fracture Toughness Testing and Its Applications," STP 381. ASTM, Philadelphia.

Wells, A. A. (1956). *Trans. Inst. Naval Architects (London)* **98**, 296.

Wells, A. A. (1959). "Brittle Fracture Mechanics: A Survey of Published Work," Document No. IX-239-59. International Institute of Welding.

Wells, A. A., and Burdekin, F. M. (1963). *Brit. Welding J.* **10** (5), 270.

Wessel, E. T., and Hays, L. E. (1963). *Welding J. (N. Y.) Res. Suppl.* **42** (11), 512s.

Wessel, E. T., Clark, W. G., and Wilson, W. K. (1966). "Engineering Methods for the Design and Selection of Materials against Fracture." Westinghouse Research Laboratories, Pittsburgh.

Williams, Morgan L. (1954). "Analysis of Brittle Behavior in Ship Plates." *In* "Symposium on Effect of Temperature on the Brittle Behavior of Metals with Particular Reference to Low Temperature," STP 158. ASTM, Philadelphia.

Wright, R. N., Hall, W. J., Terry, S. W., Nordell, W. J., and Erhard, G. R. (1965). "Studies of Some Brittle Fracture Concepts," Report No. SSC-170. Ship Structure Committee, National Academy of Sciences, Washington, D.C.

Wu, K. C. (1966). "Welding of Titanium Alloys." *In* "Titanium—1966." Memorandum No. 215. Defense Metals Information Center, Battelle Memorial Institute, Columbus, Ohio.

Zapffe, C. A., and Worden, C. O. (1949). *Welding J. (N. Y.) Res. Suppl.* **28** (11), 527s.

AUTHOR INDEX

Numbers in italics refer to the pages on which the complete references are listed.

SUBJECT INDEX

Absolute zero, 70, 92
Acoustical failure criteria, 159
Aerospace applications, structural, considerations in, 288
AGARD Handbook, 304–305
Air Force Materials Laboratory, 80, 104
Airframe loading, design criteria for, 286
Albert Canal Bridge failure, 374
Alcoa Research Laboratory, 101
Aluminia, bolted joints in, 323
Aluminum, *see also* Notched columns
  in column tests, 117
  fatigue crack tests in, 117
  as fracture mechanics alloy, 101
  notched tensile strength of, 101
  notch tests on, 117
  plane strain fracture toughness of, 102
  temperature sensitivity in, 72
  weldability of, 102
Aluminum alloy
  cryogenic testing of, 87
  electron fractograph of, 89
  K_{Ic} tests on, 56–57
  temperature effects in, 101–103
Aluminum columns, slenderness ratio in, 138
Aluminum oxide beam, segmented, 199
Aluminum oxide bend bars, 328
Aluminum 2000, 102
Aluminum 7039, 102
Aluminum 7075, 90
Anisotropy, in brittle materials, 331
Arc welding, *see also* Welding
  residual stress and, 346
Arde Portland Co., 92
ASTM specifications 4, 10, 80–83
Atlas ICBM, 80, 90, 98–99
Attachments, experimental evaluations of, 322–329

Axial compressive bending, failure criteria and, 115
Axial compressive stress, equation for, 203

Backbone column, in segmented columns, 228–229
bcc structure, *see* Body-centered cubic materials
Beam(s)
  deflection delta for, 179
  elastic-perfectly plastic, 193
  moment capacity of, 210–211
  with nonflat interfaces, 201
  nonlinear bending theory of, 178–198
  perfect, 178–198, 201
  prestressed and segmented, 178–209
  segmented, *see* Segmented beams or columns
  stress block for, 179
  stress distribution in, 180
Beam analysis
  notched columns and, 127
  in unnotched columns, 124–125
Beam column, eccentrically loaded, 234
Beam-column effect, 209
Beam deflection
  elastic tendons and, 185–186
  tendon stiffness and, 181–182
Bend bars, failure strength and, 327–328
Bend tests
  failure probability and, 306–307
  fixture for, 60–61
  K_{Ic} and, 48
  temperature and, 85–90
  three-point, 48
Bending strength, and statistical strength theory, 213–221
Bending stress, formula for, 308
Body-centered cubic materials, 72